CAVES OF THE NORTH CUMBERLAND PLATEAU

Larry E. Matthews

Featuring Photographs by Bob Biddix

CAVE CONSERVATION

Caves are fragile and extremely easy to damage—including speleothems such as described in this book, mineral deposits, cave flora and fauna, plus archaeological, cultural, and historical artifacts. Breaking or removal of cave formations deprives others of this priceless heritage and is against many state laws.

The conservation ethic of the National Speleological Society—and other speleological associations worldwide—is to enjoy the natural beauty of speleothems and other cave assets in place, without disturbing them in any way. Remember that cave conservation is more a state of mind than a set of rules. Use your common sense and always remember to take the action that will cause the least damage to the cave.

Front Cover: Erica Sughrue by massive formations in Robinson Cave, Overton County Tennessee. Photo by Bob Biddix, November 7, 2014.

Back Cover: Erica Sughrue admiring a large gypsum flower in an unnamed North Cumberland Plateau Cave. Photo by Bob Biddix, February, 2011.

Copyright 2021 Larry E. Matthews
Published by:
National Speleological Society, Inc.
6001 Pulaski Pike NW
Huntsville, Alabama 35810, USA
Phone: (256) 851-1300
http://caves.org

ISBN13: 978-1-68044-016-4
ISBN10: 1-68044-016-0

Printed in the U.S.A.

Contents

Acknowledgements

Caver Bill Mixon used to insist that I am NOT an author, but merely an Editor. Certainly, the list of the MANY cavers who contributed to this book lend credence to his argument. But, in my own defense, I did write portions of the text myself.

Caver *Fred Anderson* provided information on Devil's Dungeon Cave.

Caver *Darlene Anthony* provided information on Billy Deane Anderson's Hideout Cave.

Caver *John Barnes* provided information on Abbott Saltpeter Cave and Wolf River Cave.

As always, *Thomas C. Barr, Jr.'s* classic book, *Caves of Tennessee*, provided a logical starting point for information on many of the caves described in this book. Tom was an inspiration to all of us.

Caver and computer expert *Jody Bailey* provided expert technical assistance and converted many old photographs and slides into a digital format. He kept my computers and printers running! Thanks Jody!

Cave photographer and co-author *Bob Biddix* provided many of the beautiful photographs in this book and consulted on the content of the book.

Caver *Kristen Bobo* provided information and photos on several of the caves in this book.

Caver *Jeff Bowers* provided information on Robinson Cave.

Caver *Todd Bryan* provided the history of the exploration of the Black House Mountain Cave System in Fentress County.

Caver *Joel Buckner* provided information on Alaster Cave, Cornstarch Cave, Redbud Cave, and Three Forks Cave.

Figure Acknowledgements-1. Kristin Bobo in the Enchanted Forest area of Wolf River Cave. Photo by Dave Bunnell, July 1, 2005. (Facing page)

Caver *Dave Bunnell* provided excellent photos of Wolf River Cave, Xanadu Cave, and others.

Caver *Steve Capps* provided excellent photos of the Black House Mountain Cave System and Bunkum Cave.

Caver *Charles Clark* was instrumental in the exploration and survey of Xanadu Cave and the other caves in the Obey River Gorge.

Caver *Martha Clark* was also one of the major explorers and surveyors of the caves of the Obey River Gorge. She provided wonderful stories and photographs on Wolf River Cave.

Local historian **Kay Wood Conatser** provided fascinating information on Billy Dean Anderson's Hideout Cave, Rile Pile Cave, and Russell Caverns.

Caver *Jay Cox* provided information on Brier Cave, Buffalo Cave and Stinging Nettle Cave.

Caver *Bill Deane* provided information on the Great Saltpeter Chasm and Zarathustra's Cave.

Cave historian *Joe Douglas* provided information and photographs on saltpeter mining in the caves in this book.

Caver *Chris Druai* provided important information on the Mountain Eye Cave System.

Cave photographer *Clinton Elmore* provided photos of the Mountain Eye Cave System.

Caver Photographer *Jim Fox* provided photos of the Great Saltpeter Chasm.

Cave Geologist *John Hoffelt* provided a description of the geology of the Obey River Karst.

Caver *Justin Huffman* provided information on Rile Pile Cave.

Caver **David Irving** provided information on Copena Skull Pit and Shiver Well.

Caver *Larry Johnson* contributed information on the exploration of Three Forks Cave and other information.

Caver *Chris Kerr* provided information on Campbell Saltpeter Cave.

Vertebrate Paleontologist *Matthew C. Lamanna* from the Carnegie Museum of Natural History provided valuable information and photographs on the Robinson Cave materials.

Caver *Jerad Ledbetter* provided information on Urodela Cave.

Caver *Ray Lewis* provided information of the discovery and exploration of Xanadu Cave.

Caver *Chuck Mangelsdorf* contributed information about Falling Springs Cave, Mill Hollow Cave, and Three Forks Cave.

Caver *Ray Maslak* provided photos of Wolf River Cave

Caver *Erin McKee* provided a photo of bats in Wolf River Cave.

Caver *Gerald Moni* is the custodian for the Tennessee Cave Survey's files and is a remarkable repository of information on the caves of Tennessee. Gerald answered many questions concerning the caves and pits in this book.

Caver *Joe Morgan* provided information on Devil's Dungeon Cave.

British caver *Rostam Namaghi* provided information on the Mountain Eye Cave system.

Caver *Brad Neff* provided information on Hillham Pit and the Mountain Eye Cave System.

Caver *Ken Oeser* provided a map of Hazard Cave in Pickett County.

Caver *Ken Pasternack* assisted Bob Biddix with the photography of many of the caves in this book.

Caver *Eddie Reasoner* carefully proofread several of the chapters in this book.

Caver *Mike Rogers* provided information on Stinging Nettle Cave.

Graphic artist *Elizabeth Rousseau* provided typography and layout for the book.

TN State Museum Curator of Archaeology *Debbie Shaw* provided help in trying to locate the Robinson Cave materials.

Caver *Barb Shaeffer* provided information on Devil's Dungeon Cave.

Caver *Barb Simpson* provided information on Devil's Dungeon Cave and Wolf River Cave.

Caver *Lou Simpson* was a major explorer and surveyor of several caves, including Abbott Saltpeter Cave, Cornstarch Cave, Devil's Dungeon Cave, Wolf River Cave, and Zarathustra's Cave. Lou also proofread many of the chapters.

Caver **Jeff Sims** provided information on Big Jordan Cave, Bugger Hole, Xanadu Cave, and many other caves in this book.

Cave historian *Marion O. Smith* provided information on Buffalo Cave, Zarathustra's Cave, saltpeter mining, and in general was a great source of information on many of the caves covered in this book.

Caver *David Socky* provided information on Campbell Saltpeter Cave.

Caver *David Stecko* provided information on Wolf River Cave.

Caver *David Stidham* provided information on the Bugger Hole and McDonald Hole.

Cave Model *Erica Sughrue* is featured in many of Bob Biddix's photographs and assisted Bob with the photography.

Cave photographer *Chuck Sutherland* provided excellent photographs of Buffalo Cave, Bunkum Cave, Wolf River Cave, Xanadu Cave, York Cave, and Zarathustra's Cave and a wonderful cave density map of Tennessee.

Caver *Jack Thomison* provided the map of Stinging Nettle Cave.

NSS Librarian *Bill Torode* provided copies of many Grotto Newsletters containing articles about the caves covered in this book.

Caver *Frank Vilcheck* provided information on Buffalo Cave and Fern Camp Cave.

Caver and photographer *Edward M. Yarbrough* provided excellent photographs and information on several caves and pits in this book, including the Bugger Hole, Crabtree Cave, Hellhole, MacDonald Hole, Robinson Cave, and Three Forks Cave.

Caver *Ronald L. Zawislak* provided excellent photos of the Great Saltpeter Chasm.

Rugby, TN Historian **George Zepp** provided fascinating information about a trip to Buffalo Cave by his grandmother, Esther Walton in 1893.

Caver *Bruce Zerr* provided information on Fallen Entrance Cave and Yggdrasil Cave.

Figure Acknowledgements-2. Erica Sughrue admiring a large gypsum flower in an unnamed North Cumberland Plateau Cave. Photo by Bob Biddix, February, 2011.

Figure Introduction-1. Kristen Bobo in the Enchanted Forest of Wolf River Cave. Photo by Dave Bunnell, 2005.

Introduction

The Cumberland Plateau is a major geographic feature that extends from Kentucky, south through Tennessee, and into Alabama. The western edge of this plateau is an escarpment which drops approximately 1,000 feet to the Highland Rim. This escarpment exposes several thick beds of limestone which contain many large and interesting caves. This book will cover the north end of this Cumberland Plateau Escarpment, specifically Fentress, Overton, and Pickett Counties. Currently, there are 1,845 known caves in these three (3) counties and this book features the largest and most interesting of these caves.[1]

This book is the eleventh in a series of books, starting with Cumberland Caverns in 1989, that has chronicled the history of exceptionally large caves (*Big Bone Cave, Blue Spring Cave, Cumberland Caverns, Dunbar Cave,* and *Snail Shell Cave*) or exceptional cave areas (*Caves of Chattanooga, Caves of Grassy Cove, Caves of Fall Creek Falls, Caves of the Highland Rim,* and *Caves of Knoxville and the Great Smoky Mountains*).

Wherever possible, the stories of the caves in this book are told in the words of the original explorers and surveyors. Enjoy.

---

1 Gerald Moni, Personal communication, September 11, 2020.

KUBLA KHAN
By Samuel Taylor Coleridge
In Xanadu did Kubla Khan
A stately pleasure-dome decree:
Where Alph, the sacred river, ran
Through caverns measureless to man
 Down to a sunless sea.
So twice five miles of fertile ground
With walls and towers were girdled round;
And there were gardens bright with sinuous rills,
Where blossomed many an incense-bearing tree;
And here were forests ancient as the hills,
Enfolding sunny spots of greenery.

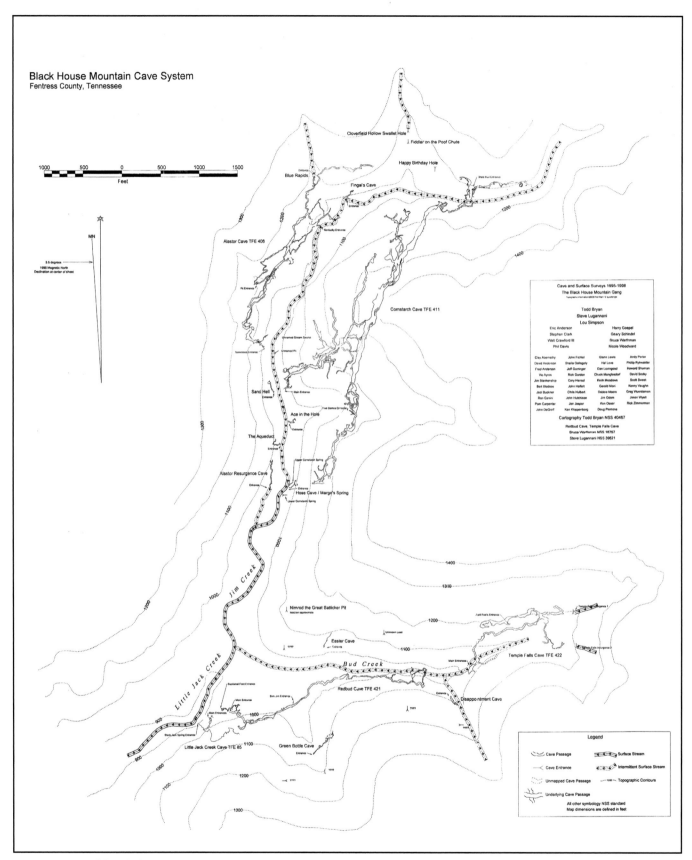

Figure 1.1. Map of the Black House Mountain Cave System, including Cornstarch Cave, Alastor Cave, Temple Falls Cave, and Redbud Cave, drafted by Todd Bryan.

CHAPTER 1
Black House Mountain Cave System

The Black House Mountain Cave System is located in Fentress County, Tennessee. The longest cave in this system, Cornstarch Cave, has a surveyed length of 22,700 feet (4.3 miles) which makes it one of the longer mapped caves in Tennessee. It is one of a cluster of four (4) caves which combined have a surveyed length of 8.5 miles.

Caver Todd Bryan wrote the following, *A Brief History of the Black House Mountain Cave System*, which was published in the 1998 NSS Convention Guidebook:

Big Scoops under Black House Mountain

October 1996. The Fall weather remained warm and bright; sunlight angled against the sharp sandstone cliffs of Black House Mountain. This pleasant and unexpected continuation of summer provided the backdrop for the weekend's activities. A group of cavers from Ohio, Virginia, Kentucky, and Tennessee had gathered here in Fentress County, near the Kentucky line, to continue their investigations within the limestone foundation of the massif. The previous July, two of them, Vic Ayres and Stephen Clark, had followed a cold and wet tunnel upstream from a karst window hidden in the head of a remote valley. After 1,600 feet of low crawl through the chattering stream, they emerged into a cavern of high domes and suspended breakdown floors, full of waterfalls and stream passages. Grateful to reap the reward of many hours spent ridgewalking, the pair dubbed their find Temple Falls Cave. The cave had quickly become the focal point of the group's

exploration and two days had been spent this October weekend mapping and exploring in its beautiful but challenging passages.

Two full days in Temple Falls had tired most of the cavers, and four of them decided to check out some entrance leads found earlier. Lou Simpson of Ohio, who had been instrumental in negotiating caver access to the area, had spent hours walking the valleys of Redman Mountain, a minor ridge of Black House, and had located several pits along its flanks. The group of four, composed of Phil Davis, Steve Lugannani, Geary Schindel, and Todd Bryan, set off to investigate these leads. After a couple of duds, the group began to grow tired, thinking that no discoveries would be made this day. Not even after reaching the bottom of the third pit, a 60-footer, did any of the four think that they had found anything special. This one just looked like any other short cave, a tight canyon which got low fast. In the interest of thoroughness, the team pushed it, expecting to find the end within minutes. It still hasn't been found.

This warm evening in October saw a scoop in what became Alastor Cave. About 5,000 feet of walking borehole were investigated on that first day. Having no survey gear, the initial explorers scooped with some guilt, but the raw excitement of such a major find shattered moral compulsions and they ran over the cobble floors in awe. Ascending out of the cave on Geary's stretchy Sterling rope, the group was mostly silent—unable to believe that what they had done was possible. They had seen giant, virgin passages right here

Figure 1.2. John Baker at the Alastar Spring Resurgence. Photo by Steve Capps. July, 2020.

Figure 1.3. The Entrance Tube to Cornstarch Cave. Photo by Steve Capps. May, 1997.

Figure 1.4. Stephen Capps (Left) and Charlie Capps (Right) in the entrance to Cornstarch Cave. Photo by Steve Capps. July, 2020.

Figure 1.5. The Black House Mountain Gang Hideout, located near Pall Mall, TN. 1998. Photo courtesy of Lou Simpson.

Figure 1.6. Charlie Capps (Front), Karl Niles (Middle), and John Baker (Rear) in a canyon in Cornstarch Cave. Photo by Steve Capps. July, 2020.

Figure 1.7. Charlie Capps (Left) and John Baker (Right) in a stream passage in Cornstarch Cave. Photo by Steve Capps. July, 2020.

in the midst of the United States, in an area settled for 250 years.

The Short History of Black House Mountain Caving

Black House Mountain, in Fentress County, Tennessee, is located near many popular caves and caving areas. Well-known **Jaguar Cave**[1], first mapped by Lou Simpson, is located just across the valley. A short journey down the watershed brings one to the Obey River Gorge, home to such monsters as **Xanadu, Mountain Eye,** and **Zarathustra's**. The stream valleys of Black House, though, were off limits to cavers until a few years ago. While continuing work in **Jaguar Cave**, Lou Simpson negotiated limited access to the BHM area and began ridgewalking in September 1995.

Black House Mountain and its valleys are near the Tennessee-Kentucky border

in Fentress County. The caves themselves are mostly formed in the Mississippian age Monteagle Limestone, of which 250 horizontal feet are exposed. Some Black Mountain caves continue through the overlying Hartselle Formation and into the Bangor Limestone. There is some development within the Bangor formation near the head of Kerrs Creek Valley.

The one area cave listed in the TCS records, **Little Jack Cave**, was quickly found and re-explored by Simpson and a gang of Ohioans and Tennesseans. Soon the group of cavers had found a new cave overlooking Whistle Creek. Mapping began in **Redbud Cave** in November of 1995 when Scott Sweet, Bruce Warthman, and Lou Simpson mapped the 1,000 feet of entrance area they had discovered. Redbud was thought to be worthy of a continued mapping effort and explorations continued with the warmer weather in the Spring of 1996. In June 1996,

---

1 Jaguar Cave is described in this book in Chapter 6 under the preferred name Wolf River Cave.

Figure 1.8. Charlie Capps (Left) and John Baker (Right) in a Trunk Passage in Cornstarch Cave. Photo by Steve Capps. July, 2020.

Figure 1.9. Charlie Capps (Front) and John Baker (Rear) in a Trunk Passage in Cornstarch Cave. Photo by Steve Capps. 1994.

Figure 1.10. The Whole Wheat Way Passage in Cornstarch Cave. Lou Simpson is in the foreground. Photo by Steve Capps, May, 1997.

Figure 1.11. Dave Goodman, Tom Patton, and Jim Blankenship in Cornstarch Cave. Photo by Steve Capps, May, 1997.

Jeff Sells and Keith Unke made a critical discovery, linking the main section of Redbud with **Baptismal Font**, a resurgence cave which fed into Whistle Creek. With this discovery came renewed interest in the potential of the area, and soon more intensive ridgewalking began.

Temple Falls: The First Big Breakthrough
All during the Summer of 1996, the core group of Ohio and Tennessee cavers began checking out some of the 100 or more cave entrances they had located within the Whistle Creek Valley and the two tributary valleys of Kerr and Buffalo Creeks. In early July, 1996 came the aforementioned breakthrough in **Temple Falls Cave**. Finding a large entrance hidden in the folds of the upper Buffalo Creek valley, the group made several attempts to traverse the long and challenging water crawl within. Finally in early July 1996 Stephen

Clark and Vic Ayres succeeded in pushing the entire "Wet Wang" and broke out into large cave. Mapping began in October 1996 but was hampered by the grueling nature of the entrance passage. About 1,600 feet long, the Wet Wang carries the entire drainage of the Buffalo Creek valley. Cavers must battle upstream while the flowing water, low ceiling, and gritty floors conspire against them. Once past this obstacle, however, the cave opens up into grand galleries connected by jagged canyons, forming a complicated maze sure to baffle cavers for years to come.

After two mapping trips in October 1996, Temple Falls Cave and its entrance series lay untouched until April 1997, when Phil Davis and Greg Cotterman discovered a new entrance high in the valley wall. Dry and easily accessible, the Aprils Fool's Entrance was connected into Temple Falls proper by May. After a tight spot, the Butt Crack, was

Figure 1.12. Lou Simpson (closest to camera) in the New York Strip Passage of Cornstarch Cave. Photo by Steve Capps, May, 1997.

Figure 1.13. Randy Paylor in a large passage in Temple Falls Cave. Photo by Steve Capps. 1994.

enlarged by chemical means, easy access to the cave was gained. Quickly the mapped length of the cave grew from 2,100 feet to over 4,000 feet. The vast majority of passages within Temple Falls are still unexplored, however, for the group of Black House Mountain cavers were drawn elsewhere.

Kerrs Creek Giants

With the discovery of Alastor Cave in October 1996 the Black House Mountain Gang began to realize that they had stumbled upon a prime caving area that had somehow totally escaped notice. The landmark weekend in October marked the beginning of a legitimate cave system. In mid-November 1996 came the first surveys in Alastor Cave, which yielded up 4,000 feet of formerly virgin passage on the first day of surveying. The Gang capped off their accomplishment when Bruce Warthman and Phil Davis exited the cave through a horizontal entrance they found while pushing

a lead. This, the Kentucky Entrance of the cave (named after a distinctive rock just inside), provided easy horizontal access to Alastor, but also served as a flood insurgence for Kerr's Creek. The tree trunks wedged inside the entrance served as a notice of the flooding that this cave could experience.

Returning for a second day of surveying in Alastor, a group of four cavers—Vic Ayres, Steven Clark, Earl Bailey, and Lou Simpson were distracted by an entrance they found near the creekbed. While standing near the hole, they felt a cool breeze issuing forth, and the burbling sound of a stream within. Abandoning plans to survey in Alastor, the four instead entered their lead and discovered the most significant cave, by size, in the Whistle Creek Valley. Known as Cornstarch, after its dry, sandy floors, the cave proved huge, full of walking passages and active streamways. Tantalizing airflow seemed to be

Figure 1.14. Erica Sughrue in Redbud Cave beneath a ceiling covered with Indian Petroglyphs. Photo by Bob Biddix, May 24, 2020.

everywhere as the group scooped the tunnels now known as New York Strip and Whole Wheat Way -- God's Holy Hall on a winged Avatar on Whole Wheat Toast. Returning from the trip, Lou Simpson remarked, simply: "We scooped hugely." The Gang seemed to grasp the significance of the find quickly, and the thought formed in several minds that perhaps there was a huge, integrated cave system under Black House Mountain. By the end of 1996 over a mile had been mapped in Cornstarch and 0.8 miles in Alastor.

Birth of a Project

The Black House Mountain Gang approached 1997 with survey tape firmly in hand. By the first anniversary of the discovery of Cornstarch Cave (November 1997), it had been mapped to 3.84 miles. Alastor stood at

1.64 miles, Temple Falls at 0.85 miles, and Redbud Cave at 0.93 miles. So far none of the Big Four have been connected to each other but the continuing survey coupled with a series of dye traces is helping to pinpoint areas of potential. With nearly eight miles of cave passage surveyed so far, the mapping continues, with full exploration of the system as it primary goal and identification of connection passages as a secondary target. As long as virgin passage awaits in the dark tunnels and warrens under Black House Mountain, as long as the cold waters and barren walls hide new secrets, exploration will continue.[2]

2 Todd Bryan, "Scoop! A brief history of the Black House Mountain Cave System", 1998 NSS Convention Guidebook: Journeys through TAG, Edited by Geary M. Schindel and John L. Hickman, pp. 105-108.

The question now remains, what discoveries have been made since the above article was written in 1998?

THE SURVEYS OF ALASTOR CAVE, CORNSTARCH CAVE, REDBUD CAVE, AND TEMPLE FALLS CAVE

The final map of Alastor Cave, Cornstarch Cave, Redbud Cave, and Temple Falls Cave is shown as Figure 1.1. The cartographer for this map was Todd Bryan. It represents the surveying efforts from 1995 to 1998. This excellent map not only shows the four main caves, but several minor caves that undoubtedly make up part of the overall underground drainage system. Clearly, this is a major group of caves with a combined total of 8.5 miles of surveyed passages.

Alastor Cave

Alastor Cave is close to Cornstarch Cave. They lie on opposite sides of Jack Creek. It is certainly possible that both caves were connected at one time, only to be separated by the downward erosion of Jack Creek. The current surveyed length of Alastor Cave is 11,600 feet (2.2 miles).

Cornstarch Cave

The Tennessee Cave Survey says that this cave has a surveyed length of 22,700 feet (4.3 miles) which makes it one of the longer mapped caves in Tennessee. This cave has three entrances. Entrance #1 is the lower entrance. It is 10 feet high and 25 feet wide. The passage becomes a crawlway just inside. This entrance can sump shut in wet weather. Cornstarch Cave is typified by large, dry, and sandy trunk passages. The Whole Wheat Way is a pleasant trunk passage that serves as the cave's main north/south thoroughfare. A room in the New York Strip (inside the Main Entrance) is used as a bat hibernaculum.

Entrance #2, the Shale Hail Entrance, is 4 feet by 3 feet. It is a crawl/climbdown through breakdown to a stoop passage that goes 300 feet to the stream passage in Cornstarch Cave. In this section of the cave, there are a series of upper level passages interconnecting with the stream passage. To go from Entrance #2 to Entrance #1, one must traverse a series of major waterfalls and climb through an unstable breakdown pile.

Entrance #3, the Five Domes Entrance, provides access to the main cave if the main entrance is sumped. This entrance takes water in wet weather.

This information is from the TCS Narrative File for Fentress County, Tennessee, Edited by John W. Stembel and dated November 1997. The Cornstarch Cave narrative is credited to Gerald Moni (1997) and Todd R. Bryan (1998).

Steve Capps reports that this cave got its unusual name from the fine white sand that resembles cornstarch.[3]

Redbud Cave

Redbud Cave is south of Alastor Cave and Cornstarch Cave and is located on Little Jack Creek. The current surveyed length of Redbud Cave is 5,109 feet (1.0 mile). There are two entrances. The main entrance is 30 feet wide and 5 feet high and leads into 500 feet of overflow stream passages and interconnecting upper levels before the main trunk passage is reached. This passage consists of stream crawls and small trunk passages. Another, smaller entrance, the Slim Jim Entrance provides direct access to the main trunk passage.

Redbud Cave is a stream cave and the water in this cave is the same stream as Temple Falls Cave, which is located 400 feet to the northeast.[4]

Temple Falls Cave

Temple Falls Cave is south of Alastor Cave and Cornstarch Cave and is located on Bud Creek. It is the upstream extension of Redbud Cave, which is located 400 feet to the southwest. The current surveyed length of Temple Falls Cave is 5,220 feet (1.0 mile).

Temple Falls Cave is a stream cave and the water flows from northeast to southwest. The first 1,600 feet of the cave has been named the Wet Wang and is a crawl through the stream passage, to where it ends at the base of 30-foot high

---

3 Steve Capps, Personal communication, April 10, 2020.
4 Todd R. Bryan, TCS Narrative Files, 1998.

Figure 1.15. The entrance to Hazard Cave. Photo by Chuck Sutherland, September 27, 2013.

Temple Falls. A short distance away is 25-foot high Cathedral Falls, carrying the larger volume of water. Past here is over 2,000 feet of trunk passage. Based on the results of a 1997 dye trace, this water reappears in Redbud Cave. A wet suit is recommended for the stream crawl and this cave is subject to flash flooding.

Hazard Cave

Hazard Cave is located in Pickett State Park. It is a huge rock shelter 122 feet wide and 18 feet high that extends inward for 100 feet. It is the most popular feature in Pickett State Park and a loop trail leads to the entrance. Hazard Cave is located in Pickett County, but it is included here because it is so close to the other caves covered in this chapter and because it is such a popular local attraction.

Hazard Cave has been surveyed at least two times. Once on May 23, 1992 by John Smyre and Patti Smith and then again on August 12, 2001 by Ken Oeser, Annette Oeser, and Alexandra Oeser. The most recent map is included as Figure 1.17.

Cave Access

All of these caves are located in Pickett State Forest. Please be sure that you have the necessary permission before you enter these caves. No special permission is needed for Hazard Cave.

Pickett State Forest

Pickett State Forest, in which all of the caves described in this chapter are located, originated from a land donation to the State of Tennessee by the Stearns Coal and Lumber Company in 1933. It was not designated a State Forest until 1935. The original tract of land was 19,200 acres and the Forest is now slightly larger with 20,887 acres. In addition to being used as a working forest (i.e. trees are harvested), the area is also used for hunting, hiking, and horseback riding. Many caves are also located within the State Forest in addition to the four described in this chapter.

Pickett State Park

Beginning in 1934, a portion of the Pickett State Forest was developed into a State Park by the

Figure 1.16. Alfred Crabtree inside the entrance to Hazard Cave. Photo by Chuck Sutherland, March 29, 2017.

Figure 1.17. Map of Hazard Cave, Surveyed by Ken Oeser, Annette Oeser, and Alexandra Oeser, August 12, 2001.

Civilian Conservation Corps. This roughly 1,000-acre section of the larger State Forest has a Visitor Center, a Civilian Conservation Corps Museum, campsites, and rental cabins. There is a loop trail that leads to Hazard Cave.

POGUE CREEK CANYON STATE NATURAL AREA

Pogue Creek Canyon State Natural Area lies immediately south of Pickett State Forest and southwest of Pickett State Park. The Tennessee Chapter of The Nature Conservancy acquired 3,000 acres of Pogue Creek Canyon to protect it from development, then sold the tract to the State in 2006. It was then designated as a State Natural Area.

Pogue Creek and its tributaries have cut a deep and spectacular gorge into the side of the Cumberland Plateau at this point. The gorge has abundant, immense, sheer bluffs and cliffs

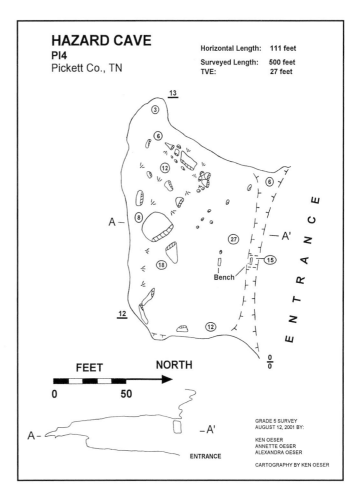

Figure 1.18. Erica Sughrue rappels into the Bugger Hole. Photo by Bob Biddix, September 2, 2018.

Figure 1.19. Erica Sughrue climbing out of Bugger Hole. Photo by Bob Biddix, September 2, 2018.

Figure 1.20. Bill Cuddington, Dan Hale, and Buddy Lane gear up before heading up the hill to Bugger Hole. Photo by Ed Yarbrough, April, 1972.

exposing multi-colored layers of sandstone. There are rockhouses along the hiking trail. Because the sandstone would be damaged and marred by climbing, rock climbing is not allowed.

BUGGER HOLE

Bugger Hole is also located in the same general area of Fentress County, Tennessee and for that reason, it is included in this chapter. Located on Arion Mountain, it is a very deep and impressive pit.

Caver David Stidham gives the following description of the Bugger Hole:

> The Bugger Hole is located on the west slope of Arion Mountain, near the top of Arion Mountain. The entrance narrows to 25 feet in diameter and drops free-fall for 145 feet. The pit bells out into a large chamber over 100 feet in diameter. The entrance is square shaped as viewed from the bottom. The pit is impressive—like Conley Hole.

A 20-foot slope leads to a second drop of 42 feet. The top of this drop is dangerous because of loose rock. The pit is dry and has one horizontal passage less than 100 feet long.[5]

This report was written by David Stidham on November 26, 1973 and submitted to the Tennessee Cave Survey.

Caver Larry Johnson gives the following insight on the origin of the name:

> The name is sometimes spelled "Booger Hole." My family was from Putnam County, nearby, and when I was a kid they often referred to a "booger" as a spook or ghost. So the name "Booger Hole" would be similar to "Spook Hole" or "Devils' Hole". There is a famous ghost story about "Booger Holler" (Booger Hollow) which they used to tell me was located somewhere around Burgess Falls.

5 David Stidham, TCS Narrative File For Fentress Co., TN, Edited by Bruce Zerr, September, 1995, p. 14.

Figure 1.21. Harry White on rope in the entrance to the Bugger Hole. Photo by Ed Yarbrough, December 29, 1971.

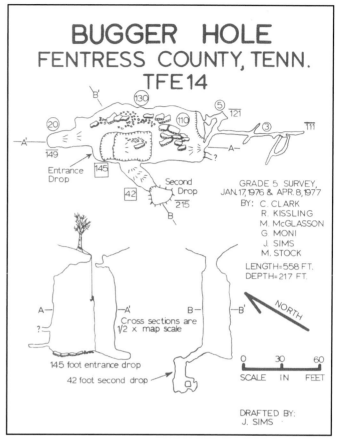

Figure 1.22. Map and Profile of the Bugger Hole, Jeff Sims, 1977.

I don't remember the story exactly, but I remember it was kind of like the Bell Witch story.[6]

It is not clear who was the first caver to explore the Bugger Hole, but Ed Yarbrough reports that Harry White and Charlie Weeks explored the pit on August 21, 1971. Harry White returned with Ed Yarbrough on December 29, 1971.[7] (See Figure 1.21)

THE SURVEY OF THE BUGGER HOLE

The Bugger Hole was surveyed by Charles Clark, Randy Kissling, Martha McGlasson, Gerald Moni, Jeff Sims, and Mark Stock on January 17, 1976

and April 8, 1977. The map shows a total length of 558 feet of horizontal passages and a total depth of 217 feet. The map includes a plan and two profiles and was drafted by Jeff Sims. (See Figure 1.22)

CAVE ACCESS

Current access to this cave is unknown. Please be sure you have the owner's permission before you enter this, or any other cave.

---

6 Larry Johnson, Personal communication, March 30, 2020.

7 Ed Yarbrough, Personal communication, March 30, 2020.

Figure 2.1. Ken Pasternack in a rock floored passage in Briar Cave. Photo by Bob Biddix. May 23, 2020.

CHAPTER 2
Buffalo Cave

Buffalo Cave is located in Fentress County, Tennessee. With 25,000 feet (4.73 miles) of explored passages, it is a major cave and is well-known locally and frequently visited.

EARLY VISITORS TO BUFFALO CAVE

As always, cave historian Marion O. Smith is one of the best sources of information on early visitors to Tennessee caves. Here is some of his information on Buffalo Cave:

Buffalo (Cave) was perhaps the most popular cave in Fentress County during the late nineteenth and early twentieth centuries, even though its main entrance was not as obvious as the resurgence of Wolf River. Tucked away at the eastern end of Buffalo Cove about four miles southwest of Jamestown, it is the longest of over forty caves in that immediate area. It has four entrances and many large and complex, sometimes multi-layered passages. The first white persons to take notice of it are unknown, but it was mined for saltpeter during early frontier times or the War of 1812-15.

For a while after the Civil War, Buffalo Cave was known by the name Cudjo's, probably inspired by J. T. Trowbridge's 1864 book, *Cudjo's Cave*. The earliest known printed reference to it was July 7, 1875 in the *Knoxville Whig and Chronicle*, when the June 25 comments of Benjamin Lodge Brier (b. *c*1813), an Ohio-born former Wisconsin resident and now Jamestown merchant, were published:

Four miles from this place is Cudjo's Cave; it is second to none, except the Mammoth Cave in Kentucky. It has been explored for miles, yet the extent is not known. Some of the apartments in this cave are from twenty to forty feet wide, one hundred to one hundred and fifty feet long, and fifty to seventy feet high.

The majority of the late 1800s and early 1900s graffiti in Buffalo Cave was made by Fentress Countians, but a hefty portion was made by residents of the English colony at Rugby in western Morgan County, and their guests. Visitors from England, Pittsburg, Pennsylvania, Cincinnati, Ohio, Ludlow, Mt. Sterling, and Lexington, Kentucky, Portland, Indiana, Winchester, Massachusetts, Dallas, Texas, and elsewhere participated in excursions to the cave through their association with Rugbeians.

The Rugby newspaper first alluded to Buffalo Cave November 25, 1882, by stating that "under a huge…cliff overhanging Buffalo Cove in Fentress County," there was "a cave of such dimensions to fairly rival "Kentucky's Mammoth Cave." It had been "explored some time ago by two young men for a distance of 5 miles," who indicated that some of the chambers were "very extensive and lofty," with "beautiful stalactites that had been "discolored by ferruginous tints."

Within a fifteen-month period during the mid-1880s the Rugby papers noted or gave details about four outings to Buffalo Cave. The total number of trips taken by Rugby residents, associates, and guests to Buffalo Cave is unknown, but wall graffiti provides dates for a minimum of fifteen to sixteen additional trips.[1]

Below is the first-hand account of one of those trips:

---

[1] Marion O. Smith, "Historic Rubgy and Local Signatures in Buffalo Cave", 2014 Tennessee Caver, pp. 14-23.

AN 1893 TRIP TO BUFFALO COVE AND CAVE

The following is the written story of a trip to Buffalo Cave on September 28, 1893. It was written by a resident of the nearby community of Rugby, Esther Walton Keen. Esther was born on November 16, 1878, so she was only 14 years old at the time of this adventure.

Figure 2.2. Erica Sughrue at the entrance to Buffalo Cave. Photo by Bob Biddix. November 16, 2019.

About eighteen miles from the little village of Rugby, on the Cumberland Plateau of East Tennessee, there is a wonderful cave, named Buffalo Cave, which is a great attraction to all who are fond of natural curiosities. For years it has been visited by parties from Rugby, and this summer as usual, several trips were made there.

The party with which I had the pleasure of going consisted of Dr. Nellie Schenck, the proprietor of the Tabard Inn, Miss Schneck, Mrs. Handman, Miss KcKeown, Fanny Dunlap, Ella May Bassett; Minnie and Addie Hamby, Esther Walton, Ms. Hamby, Oatis Hamby, Daly Alexander and Will Cummins, who went as guide.

We left Rugby at 5:30 A.M. sharp, having risen (at our house) at half past four and breakfasted by lamplight. There were nine of us in the Rugby Road hack, which we had with some difficulty secured for the occasion, and Dr. Schenck and Miss Schenck, Mr. Hamby and Mr. Cummins followed in buggies.

It was quite light when we left the Tabard, and ere we were far on our way, we had the pleasure of witnessing an almost perfect sunrise. First the eastern sky was all flecked with exquisite little pink clouds, which presently faded away and gave place to a pearly gray sky, and shortly after old Sol himself burst over the horizon, and beamed across at us, as if to say "Good morning to you, friends. So you are on your way to Buffalo Cove? Well, I hope you will have a jolly time, and I will do my part by chasing away any black clouds that may threaten to

sprinkle you." But, as we shall see hereafter, his will was better than his deed, for he broke the promise he made us in the morning.

Our road led across the pretty little Clear Fork River, which was then glistening in the morning sunshine, up the long hill on the other side and then right along over a very pleasant woodland road, partially shaded from the sun's rays by the many trees on either side.

It was about seven o'clock when we passed through the little settlement of Armathwaite, which, as far as one can see from the road is composed of a log "church-house" where the country people hold great revivals, a store and post-office combined in one log house and one or two log dwelling houses.

During the conversation, someone remarked on the fact that the party numbered thirteen, that so-called unlucky number, and two of the party, who really believed, by experience, in the unluckiness of the number, declared that they would not go into the cave with a party of thirteen. But, happily, they were spared the disappointment of remaining behind, by the addition to our party, at Allardt, of Dr. Schenck's brother and his wife, who drove over in their own conveyance.

Allardt is a very nice little place, not approaching Rugby in prettiness of location or buildings, but nevertheless, as respectable looking a little town—always excepting

Figure 2.3. "Esther Walton, Rugby, Tenn." scratched on the wall in Buffalo Cave. Photo by Bob Biddix. November 16, 2019.

Figure 2.4. "C. H. Blacklock, 24th Aug., 1888," scratched on the wall in Buffalo Cave. Photo by Bob Biddix. November 16, 2019.

Figure 2.5. Erica Sughrue by the cast of a saltpeter vat in Buffalo Cave. Photo by Bob Biddix. November 16, 2019.

Figure 2.6. Rami Ayoub sticks his head out of a hole in the floor of the Snake Passage of Buffalo Cave while Kristen Bobo stands to the rear. Photo by Chuck Sutherland, January 7, 2012.

Rugby—as I know of in this vicinity.

Passing on through Allardt, we drove a few miles farther, and about half-past eleven came to the end of our journey. We left the conveyances near the road, and made our way through the underbrush, presently coming to a large rock, from which we looked at one of the most beautiful scenes I ever saw. Far,

Figure 2.7. Hannah Crawford, Ken Pasternack, Kristen Bobo, and Sarah Phillips (Left to right) in the Dinosaur Room in Buffalo Cave. Photo by Chuck Sutherland, January 7, 2012.

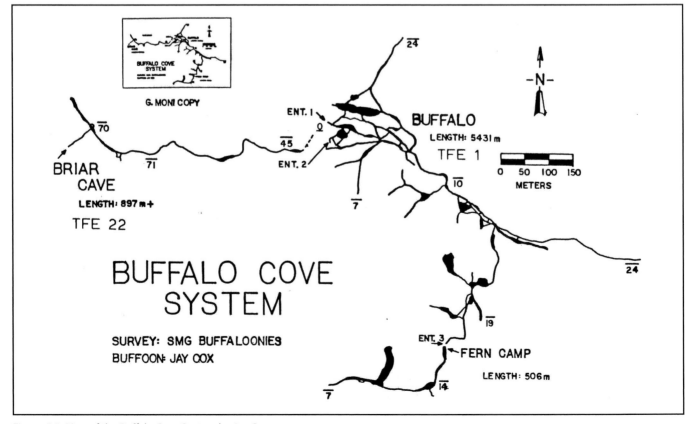

Figure 2.8. Map of the Buffalo Cave System by Jay Cox.

far, below us, some six hundred feet or so, lay Buffalo Cove in all its midsummer beauty. Away-down in the cove, there was a cornfield, and nestled in the midst of the green, waving corn, a little log cabin stands; this one cultivated spot makes a pretty contrast to the mass of trees surrounding it on every side. Presently someone called our attention to the cliffs on the other side of the cove, and pointed out one in particular, which seen at the distance and through the green trees looked exactly like the door of a church. The likeness was so striking that not one of us failed to perceive it.

We ate our ample lunch on this rock, and immediately after we started down to the cave, Mr. Cummins leading the way down the hill. On our way we passed right through the cornfield which we had observed from the rock, and beside the very door of the log-cabin in the middle of it.

Finally some of the party, who were out of sight, but not far away, called to us, "Here we are at the Cave", at which we who were behind, scrambled along every way in our haste to get there. In a few minutes we saw them, resting under a ledge of rock, which seemed to project out from the hillside and was higher than a man's head. On coming closer, we perceived that this cliff was covered, underneath, with the names and initials of all who had visited the cave before us. Concluding this to be the register of Buffalo Cave, we made haste to inscribe our own names and initials thereon, and by the time this was accomplished, we were ready for the cave, having been warned by Dr. Schenck not to go in while we were warm.

We had all heard of the entrance to the cave, so we were not surprised to hear Mr. Cummins say, "Follow me," as he lay down and crawled backward into a hole underneath the cliff. We all obediently began to crawl and slide into the hole, one at a time, until in a few minutes we were all in the cave, where we could look up the slant and see the entrance.

Apropos to this entrance, it is said that an old man in the neighborhood can remember when the entrance to the cave was so large, that a horse and wagon could be driven in with ease, but in course of time, it appears that the earth and rocks have filled up the entrance until it is now a mere hole.

It being as dark as night in the cave, we had three lanterns, four candles and one big torch carried by Mr. Schenck, with which to light our way.

A few steps inside the cave brought us to a couple of wooden troughs full to the brim with clear, cold water, which probably drips off the sides of the cave.

A little further on, we came to what are known as the Saltpetre Vats, where, we were told, some one had made saltpetre during the War of 1812. I hardly credit that, myself, but I do think it possible that some person may have selected this cave as a spot in which to make saltpeter to be used in ammunition in the late war.

As we went on, we found the floor, in some places, to be covered with a clayey sort of mud, so sticky that it was rather unpleasant to walk through. I have since learned, however, that the cave is muddy like this only at times, for other parties have found it perfectly dry.

In one place, there is a curious object, shaped just like an old earthen-ware pitcher, and hanging very high, otherwise I have no doubt, but that curio-seekers would have knocked it off and borne it away in triumph long ago.

This reminds me, that if you turn to the right just as you enter the cave, you will see on the wall what appears like the outline of a man. Unfortunately, none of us knew of this interesting sight until afterwards so we missed seeing it.

Presently, Daly Alexander, who was in front with a lantern, stopped and called to us to "look out", and when we naturally came up and asked why, he showed us a hole in the middle of the path, into which one of us might have fallen. Bending over, and holding his lantern into the hole, he showed us that the rock floor was for a radius of about a foot around the hole, merely a thin crust, which would instantly give way under a person's weight. On dropping a stone down, we could hear it hit bottom, and Daly said, "yes, it was only a few feet deep", some of the boys, who had been there at other times, had descended into the hole to see how deep it really was.

Soon we came to a place where the surface of the walls changed, for whereas it had been, in the first part of the cave of ordinary smoothness, it was now covered with knots or lumps which we girls jokingly called warts. We were able to knock off any quantity of them, and I think we all brought some of them home with us. An in addition to these "warty"

substances, we presently found long pendants, which, as we could write very clearly on the walls with them, we dubbed "pencils."

We had gone in some little distance, when Mr. Cummins told us that he would next take us through the "Snake Passage". Borrowing a candle from one of the ladies, he fastened it firmly in an upright position between a couple of stones that lay on the floor, and then calling out, "Come on", he led the way into the Snake Passage, so called from its many turns, through which nothing except a snake could go through with ease. It is so narrow that it is all a large person can do, to walk through it, and in some places some of our party had to move side-ways. We made several turns and then found the ceiling so low that we had first to bend very low to avoid bumping our heads

Figure 2.9. Erica Sughrue in a large passage in Buffalo Cave. Photo by Bob Biddix. November 16, 2019.

against the uneven ceiling and then to get down on our hands and knees and crawl along until we came to a small chamber. When we were all here, Mr. Cummins told us to look in a certain direction and there what did we see but the candle he had fixed on the floor, shining only a few feet away, but just where we had left it. Then it was evident to us, that there was another way into this chamber, much shorter than the Snake Passage, but Mr. Cummins said that this short path was very rough and rocky, so we went back through the Snake Passage.

Regaining the candle and going on a few steps, we came to a place where we had to descend three or four feet by means of a ladder. As I had never been there before, I did not know how rough the place was, so

I jumped from the top of the ladder, and had a fall over the loose stones below, which afforded no foothold. I was not hurt at all, and they all laughed heartily at me.

Mr. Cummins presently stopped and asked us if we wanted to go in there, indicating a place where the wall of the cave seemed to open, leaving a space of about two feet. On the principle that we might never be there again and had better see all we could while we were there, we decided to go into this place, and Mr. Cummins went first, to show us how to get through it. Lying on his side and holding his lantern carefully, he rolled over and over through the opening. There was really no other way for it, so we all followed in like manner. After rolling down quite a little hill, we were able to walk if we bent

Figure 2.10. Erica Sughrue next to Walltites in Buffalo Cave. Photo by Bob Biddix. November 16, 2019.

Figure 2.11. Erica Sughrue by the cast of a saltpeter vat in Buffalo Cave. Photo by Bob Biddix. November 16, 2019.

very low, which we did til our backs fairly ached. But there is an end to all things and we finally reached the end of this passage (very appropriately called "Fat Man's Misery") and found ourselves in a much larger place than we had been in before, although it was here very rough and rocky. We would have liked to go on, but Mr. Cummins said we had come three quarters of a mile and our lights were burning low, so, thinking discretion the better part of valor, we turned back.

The walls of the cave are everywhere marked with arrowheads pointing to the entrance and with the names of all who have been there, and on our way back, we wrote our names in ever so many places with the 'pencils' before mentioned.

The clear, cold water in the troughs near the entrance was very refreshing, and we all stopped there and took a drink. The light we saw as we looked to the entrance, seemed to us, after being in the dark for two hours (that was the exact time we spent in the cave), as pale as moonlight. Had the sun been shining, it might have looked different, but, as we found when we got outside, it was raining steadily.

This seemed a little unpleasant, and we waited some time to see if the rain would stop, but we finally agreed that it would be better to go on up the hill, than to wait any longer. We therefore set out, and climbed the hill in the rain, which was now quite gentle and only made us warmer without wetting us much.

Figure 2.12. Talley marks scratched on the wall by saltpeter miners in Buffalo Cave. Photo by Bob Biddix. November 16, 2019.

The bushes, however, were not so merciful, for they seemed to be dripping wet, and by the time we reached the top, our skirts were the most be-draggled, muddy looking sight imaginable.

We found Dr. Schenck and Mrs. Schenck in the big hack, where they had precipitately retreated when they saw the rain coming across the cove.

As soon as we could hitch the horse, we drove off and reached Allardt about five o'clock. We had intended to go to the hotel for supper, but Mrs. Schenck said, "No, indeed." She was all ready for us and nothing would do but we must go to her house for supper, which was very kind indeed for it is no light matter to get a hot supper for thirteen hungry persons. Mr. Schenck, too, insisted in such a

way that we could not refuse, but we made a compromise, by which eight went to their house and the other five to the "Commercial House".

About this time it ceased raining and the sky cleared off beautifully, the sun setting in a mass of red clouds. Before long the full moon came up and our drive home was all the way in the clear moonlight.

We left Allardt in fine style and had a delightful drive home. We sang about fifty gospel hymns and all the popular (songs) we could think of. After the Ball, The Bowery, Comrades, and even Annie Rooney, as we drove along in the bright moonlight, and any person who did not feel as gay as we did, would have thought it was surely a case of "making the night hideous".

Figure 2.13. Ken Pasternack at the entrance to Briar Cave. Photo by Bob Biddix, May 23, 2020.

It was about nine o'clock when we reached Rugby, and as we said goodnight, we all declared that we had spent a most delightful day and would remember our trip to Buffalo Cove as one of the pleasantest events of 1893.[2]

Sounds like caving was as much fun in 1893 as it is today. Ken Pasternack and Bob Biddix located Esther Walton's signature with the 1893 date in the cave. (See Figure 2.3)

A DESCRIPTION OF THE CAVE

Buffalo Cave is described by Thomas C. Barr, Jr. in his book, *Caves of Tennessee* (1961):

2 Esther Walton, "The Hermit, the Donkey and Uncle Dempsey: Recollections of a Rugby Girl", With Introduction and Notes by George R. Zepp, Historic Rugby Printing Works, 1993.

Figure 2.14. Ken Pasternack in a round tube passage in Briar Cave. Photo by Bob Biddix. May 23, 2020.

The cave is a complex network of large passages developed under a low spur, capped by Cypress sandstone, which forms the toe of the interfluve between the two forks of the cove. The cave has two mouths, one of which consists of two small holes beneath an overhanging ledge. The other is 10 feet wide and 8 feet high and extends downward steeply for 30 feet.

Buffalo Cave is constructed along joint sets that strike north, east N. 40° W. and N. 40°E., and thus exhibits a complex and confusing pattern. The "main" passage, which one enters from the twin mouths beneath the ledge, trends S. 40°E. and is 600 feet in length. One east-west passage is 100 feet high and 10 feet wide for 200 feet or more. One large room is 70 feet wide, 30 feet high, and 100 feet long. Some of the galleries are narrow and sinuous; one of these is called "Snake Alley." Most of the passages, however, are 30 to 40 feet high and 8 to 10 feet wide. The original network pattern has been greatly modified by silt filling, secondary removal of some of the fill, extensive breakdown, and occasional domepit solution. About 3,500 feet of passages were explored.

Dripstone formations are infrequent and inferior, and all of the more accessible ones have been greatly vandalized. The remains of some old saltpeter vats were noted in the drier passages, and two wooden water troughs and a pine torch were observed. About 12 vats appear to have been used during mining operations.[3]

The following information was provided in the 1986 SERA Cave Carnival Guidebook:

This is a large, dry cave that was once mined for saltpeter. With over three miles mapped, this is a significant and pleasant cave. The cave has a complex, maze-like structure with numerous high and impressive canyon passages. The two crawlway entrances open immediately into large, walking passages. The most extensive area can be found by bearing left at the larger junctions into one of the longer canyons. Traditionally, the most enjoyable way to tour this cave is to wander aimlessly until you are hopelessly lost. The cave can be briefly visited or can be the site of an all-day trip, depending on individual desires.[4]

CONNECTION FEVER

The following story by Frank Vilcheck describes their efforts to connect Buffalo Cave to nearby Fern Camp Cave in 1992:

"Clack, clack, clack." There was no echo as the sound of the hammer hitting the soft rock filtered back to our position. Three of us sat in the dark in the farthest reaches of Buffalo Cave. As we all peered down the narrow belly-craw to the headlamp lit source of the noise, we knew we had already been here for several hours and the chill of the surrounding rock was slowly creeping into our bodies. "Are you tired yet, Wayne?", the three of us would ask, knowing that our turn with the hammer would warm us instantly. The pace of Wayne's hammer blow quickened as he replied, "Not yet." We knew his arm muscles must be burning with pain, but he wouldn't quit now. Not only was he staying warm, but Wayne like the rest of us had "Connection Fever."

The near connection of Buffalo Cave to Fern Camp Cave actually started one year earlier. Mike Russell was giving a tour of the cave to Rick Davis, Lee Gilman, Anita Herold and Frank Vichek. An historic saltpetre cave in the Buffalo Cove area of Fentress County, Tenn., Buffalo had long been a party cave for locals and college students, who used its constant cool temperature as a haven to get away and drink beer on hot summer days and nights. However, only a handful of people knew the key moves and where to find the nearly hidden passages to get into the

3 Thomas C. Barr, Jr., *Caves of Tennessee*, TN Division of Geology, Bulletin 64 (1961), p. 181.

4 1986 SERA Cave Carnival Guidebook.

extensive back part of the cave. Mike gave his usual history and geology lesson as the small group travelled through the cave pointing out unusual and rare cave formations and explaining how the saltpetre mining operation worked. Saltpetre was extracted from caves in this part of the country more than a hundred years ago. It was used to make gun powder. Most of this historic evidence is now gone, destroyed by careless people who entered the cave and had no idea of what they were seeing. There are several miles of known passage in Buffalo Cave and it took more than an hour for Mike, with the aid of a map, to guide the group to his destination. But, upon reaching the rear of the surveyed part of the cavern he explained how Jay Cox and John Smyre had spotted daylight in the area twelve years prior while doing the initial exploration. However, in subsequent survey trips they never again saw the opening. Jay had since then

Figure 2.15. Erica Sughrue in the entrance to Fallen Entrance Cave. Photo by Bob Biddix, May 23, 2020.

disappeared, and John had other cave projects to work on. Now, the five cavers fanned out with the expressed purpose of finding the back entrance to Buffalo Cave. Mike wedged himself farther and farther down a very low-ceilinged squeeze until he was stuck. It took a lot of wiggling, but he finally freed himself without the aid of the others. Meanwhile, Frank was using a tried and true caving technique. The cool damp air in the cave allows one to easily see their breath. Frank simply kept watching the stream coming from his mouth by sitting still and illuminating it with his headlamp. He knew that if there was an entrance nearby, there would most likely be some air movement. This air movement of "breathing" is caused by the air pressure in the cave trying to equalize with the constantly changing atmospheric air pressure outside. As the pressure equalized, air is sucked out or pushed into the cave causing the air currents. Therefore, following the movement of the air in the cave should lead Frank to an entrance. He followed the steam from his breath to a low flowstone ledge and turned off his light. The dim glow of the outside world filtered back to his eyes. This was it. A large slab of flowstone halted any further progress and there was only enough room for two in the area. Lee was close by and came over to help. They figured the slab would have to be moved in order to advance to the until now unknown back entrance to the cave. With no tools, the two dug, pounded, and pushed on the slab with little or no progress. They then decided to maximize their strength by laying on their backs, they pushed up on the bottom of the obstacle with their legs. What makes cave explorers do such things? Digging out a rock with their bare hands and being the first to use a new entrance would bring them no fortune or fame except in their own minds. Perhaps they just did not want to have to retrace their steps back through the cave to get out. Most likely, it is purely the adventure involved in knowing that "you" are the first person on

Earth to be in that spot and achieving that task, no matter how insignificant it may seem to the rest of the world. None of that really mattered, because the slab started to move. After an hour-long struggle, it was finally pulled from the crawlway. Mike told Frank to get moving and see if they could get out, but Frank couldn't help but laugh as he squirmed up the belly-crawl. While he hooked up ahead of him in the passage he could see trees and daylight. The humor was in the fact that the entrance was only big enough for a rabbit. But it did look diggable. Frank retreated and Mike then crawled up to confirm what he thought. When he previously plotted the Buffalo Cave survey on a surface map, this rear entrance should have been somewhere near another cave called Fern Camp. Sure enough, Mike reported he could hear the waterfall which pours into the entrance of Fern Camp Cave. In the early part of their trip through Buffalo Cave, Mike had picked up a plastic pop bottle. He took that bottle out of this pack and shoved it as far as he could reach out of the cave, hoping to find it from the outside near the entrance to Fern Camp. In the coming week, it was never found.[5]

Even though the caves have not yet been physically connected, they are part of the larger drainage system for the cove.

THE SURVEY OF BUFFALO CAVE

Buffalo Cave was first surveyed by the Smoky Mountain Grotto in the 1970s. The survey project was led by Jay Cox. Their survey resulted in a length of 3.68 miles with a vertical extent of 154 feet.[6] The composite map of Briar Cave, Buffalo Cove Cave, and Fern Camp Cave clearly shows that all three (3) caves are part of the same system, with a 200-foot separation between Briar Cave and Buffalo Cave and a 50-foot separation between Fern Camp Cave and Buffalo Cove Cave. The three (3) caves are referred to as the Buffalo Cove Cave System. The total surveyed length of the system is 4.25 miles.

The only available map is at a scale of one-inch equals 400 feet and it shows very little detail and no place names. Marion O. Smith reports: "Within the past several years Bruce Zerr has spearheaded a more thorough resurvey, and as of February 14, 2014, reports a length of 4.13 miles."[7] But, six years later it does not appear that this map has ever been completed.

Despite the name, no buffalo have been observed in Buffalo Cave. Buffalo did, however, live in Tennessee until about 1812, when the last one was shot and killed by a hunter.

SALTPETER MINING IN BUFFALO CAVE

The saltpeter mining operation in Buffalo Cave was relatively large, with twelve (vats) in operation, according to Barr (1961). Local caver Ken Pasternack, who has helped map the cave, thinks there may be as many as twenty-one saltpeter vats. The wood is gone and all that remains are the dirt casts.[8] On her 1893 trip to Buffalo Cave, Esther Walton was told that the saltpeter mining occurred during the War of 1812. It is also Marion O. Smith's conclusion that the cave was mined during "early frontier times or the War of 1812-15.[9]

THE BUFFALO COVE CAVE SYSTEM

Buffalo Cove is located approximately two miles south-southwest of Jamestown. Caves are located up and down the length of Buffalo Cove. Water sinks underground at numerous points and there seems to be a vast underground drainage system which could be described as the Buffalo Cove Cave System. The following caves are all

5 Frank Vilichek, "Connection Fever", Cleve-O-Grotto News, v. 38 (1992), no. 8, pp. 4-5.

6 Marion O. Smith, "Historic Rugby and Local Signatures in Buffalo Cave", 2014 Tennessee Caver, pp. 14-23.

7 Ibid.

8 Ken Pasternack, Personal communication, March 27, 2020.

9 Marion O. Smith , "Historic Rugby and Local Signatures in Buffalo Cave", 2014 Tennessee Caver, pp. 14-23.

important parts of this cave system, in addition to Buffalo Cave.

Annie's Roar Cave

This cave is developed at the Hartselle-Monteagle contact, approximately 1,000 feet northeast of the main entrance to Buffalo Cave. The stream sinking here is the beginning of the Buffalo Cove Cave System which must run the length of Buffalo Cove. According to Jay Cox, this cave drains approximately 2 square kilometers.[10]

According to Bruce Zerr: "The entrance is 6-10 feet tall by 25-30 feet wide. The stream sinks rapidly into a super wet fissure full of swirling water. This is a very picturesque insurgence to

visit just to see and hear the water." Only 300 feet of passages could be explored.[11]

Briar Cave

Briar Cave lies immediately west of Buffalo Cave and is only 200 feet away, according to the survey. Caver Jay Cox provides that description from June 1974:

> The entrance to Briar Cave is in a small sink where a small branch sinks.
>
> Briar Cave twists and drops down as a stoop-walk passage for about 80 feet to a room. A passage from this room leads to a chimney, down to a small crawl. At the bottom of the chimney the crawl starts with average dimensions of 3 feet high and 3 feet wide.

10 Jay Cox, "An Interim Report: Buffalo Cove, Fentress County TN", Speleotype, v. 9 (1974), no. 4, pp. 48-49.

11 Bruce Zerr, TCS Narrative File For Fentress Co., TN, Edited by Bruce Zerr, September, 1995, p. 4.

Figure 2.16. Erica Sughrue at the entrance to Shane Cave. Photo by Bob Biddix, May 23, 2020.

There is usually 6 inches of water standing in the crawl. This crawl trends north 44 degrees east for 150 feet. A belly crawl trends north 70 degrees east and turns back to north 40 degree east for 100 feet to a 3-foot drop into larger passage. This passage curves around for 75 feet to a tight short crawl into a trunk passage! To the west (right) the passage trends 280 degrees for 200 feet to a sump with water. Back at the entrance to the trunk you can go east for about 1,200 feet. The passage trends north 75 degrees east to a waterfall. The waterfall is 15 feet high and there is about 50 feet of passage above it. The passage is full of breakdown. Above the main passage about 100 feet west of the waterfall, an upper level trends west for 800 feet. The passage averages 7 feet high and 15 feet wide and is muddy.

Two major side passages are developed in the trunk. One was explored for 400 feet and didn't end. The other, the most promising, was not explored.[12]

From the sound of this Trip Report, this was the discovery trip.

Fallen Entrance Cave

This cave is located downstream from Oil Well Cave and also receives water during wet weather. According to Jay Cox, this cave drains

approximately 15 square kilometers, including the water it receives from upstream caves. The cave has 3,000 feet of explored passages. Jay Cox provides the following information about this rather large cave:

The entrance was at one time a walk-in, but it has collapsed, and one must crawl through the breakdown to get into the cave. The cave starts as a crawlway for 100 feet. At the end of the crawl you perpendicularly intersect a large room. From the room two passages trend northwest-northeast. One passage continues as a muddy creek passage. After 100 feet you intersect a low stream passage. It continues in both directions.

The northeast passage is an upstream passage averaging 8 to 10 feet high and 5 to 7 feet wide. This passage was followed for 200 feet and kept going with these same dimensions.[13]

Frank Vichek and Mike Russell provided more information in 1989:

The cave is a wet-weather overflow spring entrance. Crawl into the cave and go directly beneath the road into the north slope of Buffalo Cove. The first 60 feet is a crawl. Then a good-sized room is encountered. From there the cave trends east, up Buffalo Cove. This is probably an overflow conduit tube for the normal underground water flow.

This is a great discovery by the Ohio cavers. This cave holds much promise and is probably the down stream section of Briar Cave.[14]

Bruce Zerr gives more information in 1996:

Be warned: Save this cave for a late summer trip, when the weather has been bone dry for a month. The high, upper level passage, seen in the middle of the first room, goes about 500

---

12 Jay Cox, TCS Narrative File For Fentress Co., TN., Edited by Bruce Zerr, September, 1995, pp. 11-12

Figure 2.17. Ken Pasternack at the entrance to Oil Well Cave. Photo by Bob Biddix, May 23, 2020.

13 Jay Cox, TCS Narrative File For Fentress County, TN, Edited by Bruce Zerr, September, 1995, pp. 32-33.

14 Frank Vichek and Mike Russell, TCS Narrative File For Fentress County, TN, Edited by Bruce Zerr, September, 1995, pp. 32-33.

feet. This is the highest part of the whole cave. There were leaves, twigs, and debris in the highest ceiling crevices.

Bring along about 50-60 feet of rope and full vertical gear to get down an undercut 12-foot drop up ahead. You enter high near the top of a large room. Slide down to the floor a further 25 feet below you. There are three more passages off this room. At the low end of the room (south) you can find a low, gravel-floored side passage about 2-3 feet high by 15 feet wide going east up the cove. It goes about 150-200 feet.

Across the other side of the room is the continuation of this passage. This passage stays low, wet, and muddy for about 200 feet before it opens up to dry hands and knees. This passage then makes a 1,000 feet loop back to the second, muddier passage in the northwest corner of the entrance room.

The last passage off the room is a trunk passage that heads up the cove. It goes for

about 500 feet until it hits a low, wide room with a collapsed ceiling. When we plotted this part of the cave out, we found out that we had passed underneath the surface stream that heads north, a half-mile to the east of the cave. The cave passage ended up under the far hillside, underneath Toilet Cave. There is a good air flow here.[15]

At least 3,000 feet of passage has been explored in this cave. **Warning:** This cave is especially prone to flooding. Do not enter when rain is in the forecast.

Fern Camp Cave

Fern Camp Cave lies immediately south of Buffalo Cave and is only 50 feet away, according to the survey. Entrance 3 of Buffalo Cave is on the north side of the sinkhole and the entrance to Fern Camp Cave is on the south side of the sinkhole. According to Jay Cox, this cave is 250 meters long and it drains an area of 1.5 square kilometers.[16]

Note: Gerald Moni reports that Fern Camp Cave has been connected to Buffalo Cave since the above description was written.[17]

Oil Well Cave

Oil Well Cave is another major insurgence cave, draining approximately 1.5 square kilometers. According to Jay Cox the entrance is 4 feet high, 3 feet wide, and a wet-weather stream runs into it. The cave could only be explored for 300 feet because natural gas from the nearby oil well was seeping into the cave.[18]

Shane Cave

Shane Cave is also located in Buffalo Cove. Jay Cox submitted the following description of the cave to the TCS in 1974:

Figure 2.18. Erica Sughrue in Shane Cave by what appears to be the base of an old moonshine still. Photo by Bob Biddix, May 23, 2020.

15 Bruce Zerr, TCS Narrative File For Fentress County, TN, Edited by Bruce Zerr, September, 1995, pp. 32-33.
16 Jay Cox, "An Interim Report: Buffalo Cove, Fentress County, TN", Speleotype, v. 9 (1974), no. 4, pp. 48-49.
17 Gerald Moni, Personal communication, April 15, 2020.
18 Jay Cox, TCS Narrative File For Fentress Co., TN, Edited by Bruce Zerr, September, 1995, p. 65.

Figure 2.19. Kristen Bobo by flowstone columns in Shane Cave. Photo by Chuck Sutherland, January 7, 2012.

The cave entrance is in a sink, with a good-sized stream flowing in. The cave is mainly walking passage for 200 feet in the stream and 200 feet past the place where the stream sinks.[19]

Mike Russell submitted another description in 1986:

The ceiling of Shane Cave is Hartselle Sandstone. The Monteagle Limestone dissolved beneath it. The present entrance to Shane Cave is where a section of the Hartselle ceiling collapsed, producing a small sink and deflecting a surface stream into it. One must stoop to enter the cave, but after that most of it is a short walking passage containing many small flowstone columns and soda straws. Only one crawl was encountered and that is

where the water normally drains. It is about 200 feet long and ends in a small pocket where the water flows through a crack in the chert.[20]

Another, more recent description is by Bruce A. Zerr:

This cave lies halfway between the back end of Fallen Entrance Cave and Briar Cave. The crawl mentioned above really got my attention because of the large amount of water it takes, the strong flow of air down it, and the echo from the room on the other side. I envisioned finding a virgin 130-foot pit, dropping down into a missing mile of trunk passage of the Buffalo Cove Cave System.

Four drill holes later, using my Ryobi Hammer Drill, and a little better caving through chemistry got me into a virgin dome,

19 Jay Cox, TCS Narrative File For Fentress Co., TN, Edited by Bruce Zerr, September, 1995, p. 81.

20 Mike Russell, TCS Narrative File For Fentress Co., TN, Edited by Bruce Zerr, September, 1995, p. 81.

Figure 2.20. Ken Pasternack by a flowstone covered wall in Fallen Entrance Cave. Photo by Bob Biddix, May 23, 2020.

with a tight, low drain hole that is too tight to follow. Better luck next time.

While mapping a very farthest back corner of the cave, we crawled up and saw a sliver of light. Back on the surface, Mike Russell and I used the survey notes to take us to the back end of the cave. We found a very small hole next to a 3-foot high ledge of Hartselle Sandstone. I went back into the cave and was surprised to see the fingers of a hand come down our light hole. We are only 18 inches from the surface—if anyone wants to dig a second entrance to Shane Cave.[21]

Currently, the explored length of Shane Cave is 420 feet.

Whirlpool Flume Cave

This cave is reported to drain six (6) square kilometers. Fern Camp Creek flows into the entrance of Whirlpool Flume Cave. Obviously, it is a vital component of the Buffalo Cove underground drainage system. Jay Cox gives the following description of the cave:

This cave takes a lot of water, so the passage which averages 1.75 meters high and 1 meter wide has about 0.5 meters of water in it. At about 70 meters the stream flows down a cascade. One may climb up into the ceiling and by-pass the falls. From here a climbdown leads to a 40-meter crawl which rejoins the stream. You can follow the stream for about 150 meters to the terminal siphon.[22]

This report is dated April 1974.

CAVE ACCESS

Buffalo Cave and the other caves described in this chapter are located on private property. You must have the owner's permission to explore Buffalo Cave and the other caves described in this chapter.

SUGGESTED READING

Marion O. Smith wrote a fascinating paper, titled: "Historic Rugby and Local Signatures in Buffalo Cave". It was published in the 2014 Issue of the Tennessee Caver on pages 14-23. It is an absolute gold mine of information on early visitors to Buffalo Cave.

---

21 Bruce A. Zerr, TCS Narrative File For Fentress Co., TN, Edited by Bruce Zerr, September, 1995, p. 81.

22 Jay Cox, TCS Narrative File For Fentress Co., TN, Edited by Bruce Zerr, September, 1995, p. 101.

Figure 3.1. Carol Lamers next to a carving on the cave wall of York Cave: "Are You Ready To Meet Jesus?". Photo by Bob Biddix.

CHAPTER 3
Campbell Saltpeter Cave

Campbell Saltpeter Cave is located in Fentress County, Tennessee. With a surveyed length of three (3.01) miles, it is a significantly long cave.

A DESCRIPTION OF THE CAVE

Chris Kerr submitted the following brief description of this cave to the Tennessee Cave Survey on March 8, 1978:

> Campbell Saltpeter Cave is basically a stream passage for 1,500 feet to a point of low ceiling five (5) inches above water. The back passage was thought to proceed N. 40°E. by compass bearing, which would indicate it is draining Carpenter Hollow, not Campbell Hollow, the hollow which has the entrance to Campbell Saltpeter Cave. An upper level abandoned stream passage was encountered for most of the way before pinching out in all directions. The cave is horribly trashed out, garbage everywhere. Hay has been strummed inside the saltpeter area, and the front section of the cave stinks.[1]

In 1985 Gerald Moni added the following information:

> The stream passage was pushed, and an upper level was found. To date (7/85), over 3 miles have been surveyed.[2]

Marion O. Smith visited this cave on August 16, 1987, accompanied by Mike Russell, Mike's girlfriend Libby, and Patricia Anthony. Here are his notes from that visit:

> We drove by the barn and down to the creek, a couple hundred feet from the Spring Entrance. Mike and I went around in circles searching for the Dry Entrance but gave up and entered the Spring. This cave is maybe four miles long, but we only saw perhaps 500 feet—the saltpeter section which was all I was interested in. There were at least eleven (11) vats, all just piles (of dirt) or partial casts of dirt now. There were lots of turn of the century graffiti on the ceiling and walls. We exited the crawl-in, Dry Entrance at 5:58 pm after 1 hour and 18 minutes inside.[3]

Marion returned on December 24, 2011. Based on the large number of saltpeter vats, it is his opinion that this was a small, commercial operation and that it probably was mined in the early 19th Century.[4]

The Survey of Campbell Saltpeter Cave

The Blue Ridge Grotto (Roanoke, Virginia) explored and mapped this cave on a number of trips in 1984 and 1985. Below are their Trip Reports for this project.

> One day last year we were all caving down by the Smith Boys' place. Friday evening we ran into Danny Molter and Floyd Harold of the Cleveland Grotto. They told us about pushing a stream passage in Campbells Cave, which none of us had been to before. At the end of the stream passage Floyd had moved some rocks and gotten through what looked like terminal breakdown. Floyd said it opened back up to walking passage. He had only gone in about 20 feet and turned around because everyone else was cold.
>
> We thought that this Campbells Cave would be a pretty good trip for Saturday even

1 Chris Kerr, TCS Narrative File For Fentress Co., TN, Edited by Bruce Zerr, September, 1995, p. F-14.

2 Gerald Moni, TCS Narrative File For Fentress Co., TN, Edited by Bruce Zerr, September, 1995, p. F-14.

3 Marion O. Smith, Personal communication, June 16, 2020.

4 Ibid.

Figure 3.2. Erica Sughrue by remains of a saltpeter vat in Campbell Saltpeter Cave showing plank impressions in the dirt cast. Photo by Bob Biddix, December 15, 2019.

though it was wet. Danny and Floyd had made other plans so we would have to find the way ourselves.

Rick Miller had been there before, so he was able to show us through the historic section, but he hadn't been down the stream passage, so we were on our own. Actually it was pretty easy because it was only a single passage that we had to follow to the breakdown. We had some trouble finding our way through the breakdown, but by moving some additional rocks we were able to break into the virgin passage. Because the cave was named Campbells and the route through the breakdown was pried open we decided to name the connection "The Can Opener".

It only took us 3 minutes to determine that the walking stream passage went much, much further than the 20 feet that Floyd had seen. The mostly walking stream passage

continued on for 300 meters at which point it degenerated into crawlways. However, we found a route up through the breakdown and discovered a large, dry upper level room which we named the "Soup Kitchen". The route up we named the "Stairway To Heaven". The follow summary documents the trips into Campbells Cave so far:

Easter Weekend 1984 (April 6-8)
Participants: David Socky, Doug Feller, Keith Goggin, Ric Miller.

Friday – Drove up Thursday night and met Ric at Pickett State Park. Next day (Fri.) went over to the Smith Boys and had them drive us up to Umbrella in their pickup truck. Had to move a huge rock out of jeep trail to get by. Danny led the way in Umbrella (Cave) taking us down the ladder drop and into the lower levels. A revolt was precipitated when Danny

Figure 3.3. Ken Pasternack with numerous casts of saltpeter vats in Campbell Saltpeter Cave. Photo by Bob Biddix, December 15, 2019.

"twinkle toed" across a 40-foot pit. Doug and Floyd went ahead and the rest of us exited the cave.

Saturday – Our first trip into Campbells Cave. We went in early Saturday afternoon and found our way down the stream passage and through the breakdown. After this point it was virgin cave. After 300 meters, we found the "Stairway To Heaven" and "The Soup Kitchen" in the upper level. We spent an hour or two to explore the large rooms and many passages in this level without finding an end. We finally got tired and left.

Memorial Day Weekend 1984 (May 26-28)
Participants: Mary Sue Pullano, David Socky, Keith Barnes, Howard Kirkland, Jim Kelly, Dick Graham, Keith Goggin.

Saturday – Keith and Dick put their wet suits on and surveyed the water passage half way to the "Can Opener". The rest of us

surveyed the dry historic section close to the entrances, and a couple of side leads off the water passage (U Survey).

Sunday – Keith's party finished the water passage up to the Can Opener, while the rest of us surveyed through the Can Opener and all the way to the Stairway To Heaven. We also surveyed the large room/passage to the left of the Soup Kitchen. One lead off the end of the passage, the L Survey, was surveyed by the other party.

Summer Time 1984 (July 1-2)
Participants: Keith Goggin, Dave Socky, Doug Feller, Ric Miller.

Saturday – Our first goal was to survey a side lead off of a large room near the water entrance. This accomplished, we started surveying northeast (to the right) of the Soup Kitchen. We had checked this out for about 100 meters before but had turned around with

Figure 3.4. Erica Sughrue by flowstone formations in Campbell Saltpeter Cave. Photo by Bob Biddix, December 15, 2019.

many leads. This time we were able to survey into virgin cave. The large rooms are separated by small holes through very unstable breakdown collapses. But as we surveyed, every little hole broke into another large room. Finally we got into a really large passage with an actual floor (no breakdown). This led to an even larger room with a most beautiful column formation perched on a ledge. This we name the "Son of Sam". Tired of surveying, we did a little pushing, but found that the main passage apparently ended. However, there were many side leads that we had passed by.

Late Summer 1984 (August 18-19)
Participants: Dave Socky, Doug Feller, Ric Miller, Rhonda Ravenhorst.

Saturday – We didn't do any surveying this trip. We pushed the stream passage just

before the Stairway To Heaven and found several very unstable rooms, but they seemed to all end in breakdown. We pushed a small pit at the end of the L Survey, but it ended right away. We then explored the side leads before and at the Son Of Sam. We christened this maze "Doug's Messy Maze". Passages went everywhere and all seemed interconnected. We even found our way back to the dead-end rooms before the Stairway To Heaven. (Doug had checked the one room out the first time and said that there were absolutely no leads!)

Thanksgiving, 1984 (November 22-25)
Participants: Dave Socky, Doug Feller, Keith Goggin, Mary Socky, Ron Simmons, Ric Miller, Dick Graham, Rhonda Ravenhorst, Bob Kelly.

Thursday – Keith, Ron, and Dick went in early and surveyed the "Slot Machine", an

Figure 3.5. Erica Sughrue in a passage in Campbell Saltpeter Cave. Photo by Bob Biddix, December 15, 2019.

interesting canyon right below the Son Of Sam. They also surveyed in Doug's Messy Maze and took plenty of excellent pictures. Meanwhile Dave Socky, Bob Kelly, and Doug Feller discovered the continuation of the main stream passage. After a tight, wet, water crawl the passage opened up into huge dimensions and just kept going for many meters. We finally found the end though, a low, wet, stream crawl with plenty of wind blowing out. We left at this point and caught up with the rest of the party, who had been touring the dry upper levels.

Sunday – Surveyed the newly found stream passage. Too cold to push the stream crawl at the end but did partially push a couple of the side leads.

Sometime in February 1985
Participants: Dan Molter, et al.
(Cleveland Grotto)

From personal conversations: Dan and his group found a continuation past the Son Of Sam. They had dug through breakdown and broke out into more large passage which eventually ended. But there were many side leads which they didn't check.

Winter time 1985 (March 9-10)
Participants: Dave Socky, Doug Feller, Bob Alderson, Ric Miller, Bob Kelly

Saturday – Surveyed the first side lead off the new stream passage. Another maze. We only explored and surveyed a portion of it. Hard to tell the extent of that area. We then

Figure 3.6. Ken Pasterknack (left) and Erica Sughrue (right) in a formation room in Campbell Saltpeter Cave. Photo by Bob Biddix, December 15, 2019.

went and pushed the stream crawl that we had left before. With only about 8 inches of air space, we got totally soaked, with the last part nearly swimming. But the crawl developed a small canyon in the ceiling, then actually opened up into a big, dry room. Surprise! Curses, 10 minutes later we found the only way on was another low, wet stream crawl just like the one before. But, it still goes! We left after that.

Sometime in March 1985
Participants: Dan Molter, et al.
(Cleveland Grotto)

Again by personal conversations: Dan says that they pushed the new stuff beyond the Son Of Sam fairly extensively. Apparently nothing

went. He did say that there seemed to be a lower level but no way to get in.[5]

The story continues in the next issue of the Carbide Dump with the following article by David Socky:

Doug Feller and I drove down to Tennessee on April 28, 1985 (Friday) in Road Kill. We arrived at about 1:30 a.m. with beautiful, clear skies. By morning it was raining. Rick Miller, Rhonda Ravenhorst, Kenny, and Pee (the Dutchman) arrived about 11:30 a.m. While waiting for it to stop raining, we lounged around under a tarp between the cars and discussed the new "Chicken Bob" franchise.

5 Dave Socky, "Fun In the Soup Kitchen - Campbells Cave, Tenn.", The Carbide Dump, v. 20 (1985), no. 4, pp. 29-33.

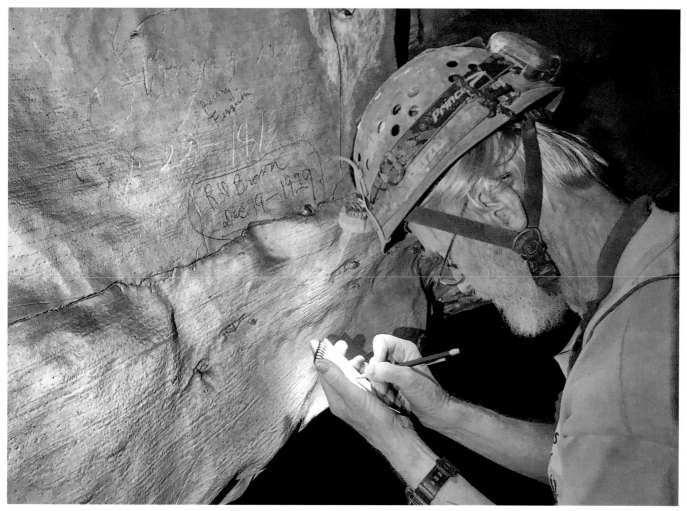

Figure 3.7. Marion O. Smith records old names and dates in York Cave. Photo by Jim Fox, August 30, 2019.

We finally managed to drag our bodies up and get prepared for the great cave trip to the back of Campbells. Our plan was to push the low, wet, stream crawl at the end of the Duncan Trunk Passage (the giant stream passage that was discovered Thanksgiving of '84). As usual, things didn't work out exactly as planned.

We entered the cave about 2:30 p.m. and made a fairly quick trip to the Can Opener, and then on up the nice walking "Victory Passage" (note the new name) to the Soup Kitchen where we took a short rest. A half hour later we were at the beginning of the Duncan Trunk Passage. Just as we were getting ready to surmount the first huge breakdown pile, Pete the Dutchman exclaimed: "Where does that big hole up on the left go to?" Doug, Ric, and I looked up and sure enough there

Figure 3.8. Ken Pasternack stands in an area of York Cave with the casts of many saltpeter vats. Photo by Chuck Sutherland, December 18, 2011.

was a big hole. Nobody knew where it went. It was decided that we might as well take a quick look before heading for our favorite stream crawl.

The hole was about 20 feet above the floor, but still 20 feet below the ceiling. Once we got up, we found passages everywhere. Surprise !!! We ran down the easiest canyons, finding many come arounds and intersecting passages, but we always seemed to end up back at the start. But Pete found an upper lead and went one way, while Doug went another. Meanwhile, Ric found another upper lead which the rest of us decided was the best to follow. I went back to get Doug. Following his trail I soon ran into Ric and the rest, so we all ended up chasing after Doug who had just disappeared. Fifteen minutes later we popped out of the walking canyon into a low, wide passage that went both ways. Doug was waiting there. "There are passages everywhere, and formations, too!", Doug yelled. That's when we started to get excited.

We explored this section of the cave for at least two hours. We found beautiful formations, fantastic sparkling crystal sands, gypsum flowers and lips covering the walls. It was great. We finally found a couple of passages that ended, so we decided we better get to the stream crawl or it would never get done. We did leave a good lower level canyon unexplored, plus any leads we didn't see. We named the first canyon that led to the low, wide passage the "Dutch Extension", with the last part the "Dutch Connection". The first section after that, with the formations, "La La Land", and the part with the gypsum flowers, the "Crystal Palace Passage".

Our trek down the Duncan Trunk Passage was uneventful. We reached the first stream crawl that we had checked in March 1 about a half hour and dived right in. The water wasn't as cold, or as deep, but it was still painful. Through the Room of Hope we went and right back into the water and into the unknown. The wind was blowing, but it was even lower and colder. It finally got to the point that we had to belly crawl in the water. Yeech. Doug was in the lead and was about ready to turn around because it was getting so low, but

he could see that it just might open up, so he went a little further. Good thing he did! Boom, it opened up into a huge room, at least 40 feet high, 40 feet wide, and extending off into the distance. Even better, it had a flat, sandy floor with no breakdown!

But alas, after 200 feet it closed down again, but this time it wasn't into another lousy stream crawl. It was back into smaller breakdown passage that went up and down, into and out of the water. Pete poked down the passage for about 50 feet, indicating that it went. It was getting late, and we were tired, so we decided to leave further exploration and mapping for another trip. At least we know that there is more, and possibly much more![6]

There were other trips to Campbell Saltpeter Cave, which David Socky summarizes as follows:

June 29, 1985 – The Q, Z and BS surveys were conducted. The Q and E surveys essentially pushed the end of the stream passage—the northeast end of the cave. I remember that it was a wide, but very low crawlway of cobbles. It was pretty tight. We surveyed until we couldn't fit anymore. But it didn't end and if you really wanted to work, it could possibly be dug out. There was still air flow.

The BS survey is the section of the cave past Son Of Sam. The Z survey was La La Land and the Crystal Passage.

November 29, 1985 – The E survey was conducted.

David Socky concludes with: "There are still leads left in the cave. We never pushed the Dutch Connection-La La Land-Crystal Passage section that hard, plus there is still stuff in the Psycho Ward.

The final surveyed length of Campbell Saltpeter Cave is 15,881 feet long (3.01 miles) with a vertical extent of 113 feet. The map by the Blue Ridge Grotto of the NSS was drafted by David

───────────
6 David Socky, "More Adventures In The Soup Kitchen (Campbells, Tenn.)", The Carbide Dump, v. 20 (1985), no. 5, pp. 43-44.

Socky in 1985 and is shown as Figure 3.17. There are still leads in the cave that have not been surveyed.[7]"

SALTPETER MINING IN CAMPBELL SALTPETER CAVE

The survey of the cave labels the first 500 feet of the cave as the Historic Saltpeter Section. Both Chris Kerr (1978) and Marion O. Smith (1987 and 2011) note the remains of saltpeter vats. Apparently most saltpeter caves in this area were mined in the early 19th Century (War of 1812 era), but there is no historical data to place the time that this cave was mined.

PLACE NAMES IN CAMPBELL SALTPETER CAVE

Can Opener
Crystal Palace Passage
Doug's Messy Maze
Dry Entrance
Duncan Trunk Passage
Dutch Connection
Dutch Extension
Historic Section
La La Land
Psycho Ward
Room of Hope
Son of Sam
Soup Kitchen
Spring Entrance
Stairway To Heaven
Stream Passage
Victory Passage

YORK CAVE

York Cave was another major saltpeter mine in this general area. Barr give the following description of the cave:

York Cave was mined extensively for niter during the Civil War.[8] Entrance to the cave is

Figure 3.9. Rusty Hix at the entrance to Campbell Saltpeter Cave. Photo by Bob Biddix, December 15, 2019.

Figure 3.10. Erica Sughrue rappels into the Entrance of York Cave. Photo by Bob Biddix.

---

7 David Socky, Personal communication, July 1, 2020.

8 Marion O. Smith is confident that this is incorrect, and that York Cave was mined during the War of 1812.

Figure 3.11. Erica Sughrue in the large Main Passage of York Cave. Photo by Bob Biddix.

by a 35-foot vertical drop. The entrance room is 35 feet high, 150 feet long, and 120 feet wide, and is filled with breakdown, dripstone formations, and saltpeter vats. A number of stalagmites, which average 6 feet high and 3 feet in diameter, are present in the entrance room, but farther into the cave very few formations are developed. The cave trends generally northwest and has two branches, both of which end in pits. These branches are about 25 feet in diameter and 50 feet in diameter, respectively. Five pits, which average about 20 feet in depth, were noted. At the bottom of three of these pits are huge niter hoppers 20 feet square. About 25 of these vats were operated in the cave during the mining period. The total length of the cave is 1,500 feet.[9]

According to the TN Cave Survey, the current surveyed length of York Cave is 2,249 feet, somewhat longer than the 1,500 feet reported by Barr in 1961.

The Survey of York Cave

The original survey of York Cave was made by B. C. Stewart in 1956 and that map is shown in Barr's *Caves of Tennessee* (1961). A somewhat more detailed map was made by Jay Cox and others, but it is undated. It shows a total length of 2,249 feet. (See Figure 3.18)

9 Thomas C. Barr, Jr., *Caves of Tennessee*, TN Division of Geology, Bulletin 64 (1961), pp. 186-187.

Figure 3.12. Kristen Bobo next to two large casts of saltpeter vats in York Cave. Photo by Chuck Sutherland, December 18, 2011.

Figure 3.13. Ken Pasternack by a column in York Cave. Photo by Chuck Sutherland, December 18, 2011.

SALTPETER MINING IN YORK CAVE

York Cave was a large, industrial-style saltpeter mine. Barr states what there were twenty-five saltpeter vats. Due to the high humidity in the cave, most of the wood has rotted away and only the dirt casts remain. Cave historian and saltpeter mining expert Marion O. Smith has visited York Cave several times and gives the following information:

> It (York Cave) has a great deal of saltpeter mining evidence, including casts of large rectangular leching vats (with the wood rotted away). On October 4, 1997 I went there with Dr. Jan F. Simek, Alan Cressler, Jay Franklin, Joann Bennett, Gerald Moni, Sarah Sherwood, and Debby Johnson. Everyone except Sarah rappelled the 29-foot entrance pit. During the trip I copied a few names:
>
> > J. J. Pile (No date)
> > James Hill, 1863

Figure 3.14. Erica Sughrue beneath a massive flowstone formation in York Cave. Photo by Bob Biddix.

John W. Frogge, March 18, 1862
C. O. Wallace, June, 1863
A. Hount, 1809
Sam Sparks, April 16, 1942
Ineta Hoss, 1932
Gale York (No date)
Roy Wright, September 24, 1934
R. W. Wolfe, 4/11/35
W. A Garrett, June 18, 1877

Marion returned on August 30, 2019 and copied more names:

> J. M. Y., 1929
> W. A. Garrett, 1877
> R. D. B., 1929 (Reverend R. D. Brown?)
> W. T. Caudin, June 16
> R. D. Brown, December 19, 1929
> C. H. Hatfield, 1929
> Henry Ferguson, 1/23/1813

Marion goes on to add, "I have not tried to research the 1863 names, but for the most part the Confederates did not conduct Nitre Bureau operations in Fentress County—none that I know of. The mining most likely was a commercial operation in 1812-13, or thereabouts. The whole area which became Fentress and Pickett Counties had a great deal of saltpeter mining during the early 19th Century years.[10]

A CHURCH SERVICE HELD IN YORK CAVE

Marion O. Smith located this interesting article written by Richard Hilten about a church service that was held inside York Cave in 1931:

> Conversations with several of the oldest area natives revealed a story even more interesting than I had guessed.
> The cave (York Cave) had been used in 1931 for holding a church service inspired by the Reverend R. D. Brown of the Pilgrim Holiness Church. A large ladder had been constructed by lowering two green saplings

10 Marion O. Smith, Personal communication, June 10, 2020.

Figure 3.15. Kristen Bobo next to several stalagmites in York Cave. Photo by Chuck Sutherland, December 18, 2011.

into the hole and nailing planks across for rungs as the builders descended from the top.

At noon that midsummer Sunday around fifty people—mostly families of mixed ages—went down into the cave. Some were quite jittery, as this was their first underground experience. Their way was lit by several kerosene lanterns, and the unusual procession continued to the large round room.

O. D. Abston, who had sculptured the figure of Christ, helped the Reverend Brown in the two-hour ceremony of preaching and singing which followed. Both were musicians; Brown played the guitar and Abston played the mandolin. That unique, standing service went on until all the favorite hymns had been sung and all the favorite scriptures had been expounded. The service was never repeated, but it was always remembered by those present.[11]

The photo of the inscription "Are You Ready To Meet Jesus ?" and the adjacent carving of the head of Jesus (See Figure 3.1) apparently date from this period. The name R. W. Wolfe and the date 4-11-35 are next to this carving, but were added at a later date.

CAVE ACCESS

Campbell Saltpeter Cave and York Cave were open at the time this chapter was being prepared, but like all caves, but sure you have the owner's permission before you go.

---

11 Richard Hilten, "Once Upon A Cave (but not your ordinary fairy tale)", TN Conservationist, v. 41 (1975), no. 6 (July), pp. 8-9.

Figure 3.16. Carol Lamers in a large, well-decorated section of York Cave. Photo by Bob Biddix.

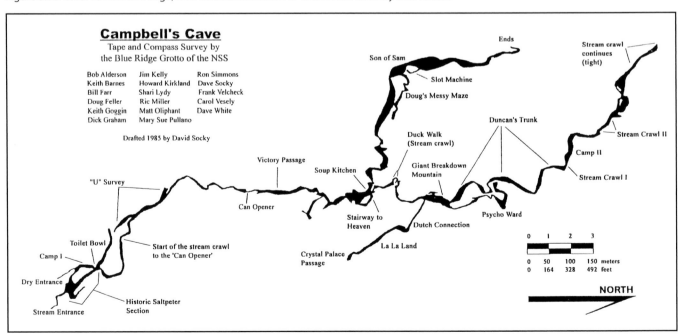

Figure 3.17. Map of Campbell Saltpeter Cave by the Blue Ridge Grotto of the NSS, 1985.

Figure 3.18. Map of York Cave by Jay Cox and others. (Facing page)

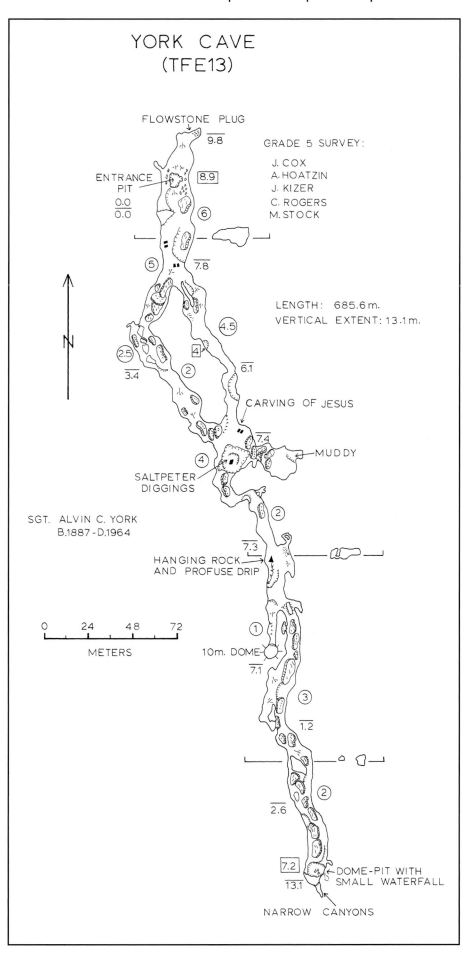

YORK CAVE
(TFE13)

FLOWSTONE PLUG
9.8

GRADE 5 SURVEY:
J. COX
A. HOATZIN
J. KIZER
C. ROGERS
M. STOCK

ENTRANCE PIT
8.9
0.0
0.0
6

5
7.8

N

LENGTH: 685.6 m.
VERTICAL EXTENT: 13.1 m.

4.5

2.5
4
3.4
2
6.1

CARVING OF JESUS

SGT. ALVIN C. YORK
B.1887 - D.1964

7.4

MUDDY

4
SALTPETER DIGGINGS

2

HANGING ROCK
AND PROFUSE DRIP
7.3

0   24   48   72

METERS

1
10m. DOME
7.1

3

1.2

2
2.6

7.2
13.1
DOME-PIT WITH
SMALL WATERFALL

NARROW CANYONS

Figure 4.1. Erica Sughrue by the remains of a saltpeter vat in Cobb Creek Saltpeter Cave. Photo by Bob Biddix, December 19, 2020.

CHAPTER 4
Mountain Eye Cave System

The Mountain Eye Cave System is located in Fentress County, Tennessee. It has a surveyed length of 82,300 feet (15.6 miles).[1] Currently it ranks as the fifth longest cave in Tennessee.

A DESCRIPTION OF THE CAVE

This exceptionally large cave system has nine (9) known entrances. Before all these cave entrances were connected, several different entrances were given their own cave names, including Cobb Creek Saltpeter Cave and Lott Deane Cave. The following description of the cave is by caver Brad Neff:

> There are nine entrances known so far to the Mountain Eye Cave system, of which Cobb Creek Saltpeter Cave is a significant part. There are seven (7) entrances to Cobb Creek Saltpeter Cave and two (2) entrances to Lott Deane Cave. Once the two caves were connected, they were named the Mountain Eye Cave System. The nine entrances to the cave are:
>
> Entrance 1: Cobb Creek Saltpeter Cave Entrance
> Entrance 2: East Eye Entrance
> Entrance 3: West Eye Entrance
> Entrance 4: Lott Deane Entrance
> Entrance 5: Spring Entrance
> Entrance 6: Sorcerers Grotto Entrance
> Entrance 7: Nargathrond Entrance
> Entrance 8: Nightshade Entrance
> Entrance 9: Equulei Crack
>
> Cobb Creek Cave is divided into at least two distinct levels. The upper level consists of the two upper entrances and several hundred feet of mostly walking passage. The floor of this passage is full of pits which drop about 35 feet into the lower level. The lower level consists of at least one major walking passage several thousand feet long, which tends to parallel Cobb Creek, a medium-sized room mined for saltpeter, and numerous side passages. The lower entrance connects directly to this lower level.
>
> Lott Dean Cave was connected to Cobb Creek Saltpeter Cave, creating the Mountain Eye Cave System. Lott Deane Cave has two entrances, a spring entrance, and a higher crawl entrance. The Spring Entrance is usually flooded or requires swimming through deep water. The Dry Entrance begins as a 20-foot crawl that leads to a 12-foot climbable drop. The 20 by 30-foot passage at the bottom leads around breakdown to a room with a 10-foot high dirt cliff. At the top of the cliff a brief crawl opens into a large passage. Abut 50 feet ahead on the right wall at floor level is a crawlway/stoopway passage that leads to over two (2) miles of master trunk passage. This master trunk passage averages 20 feet by 25 feet and runs parallel to the Obey River.[2]

For a cave with nearly 16 miles of known passages, this is not a very adequate description.

A 1979 SURVEY UPDATE

The following brief notice appeared in the June, 1979 NSS News:

> Surveys in late April by Smoky Mountain Grotto members Chris Kerr, Darlene Carter, Greg Brown, and Kevin Smith had increased the length of Tennessee's Lott Dean Cave by 3,800 feet bringing the surveyed total to more than 13,000 feet. However, Lott Dean's total has only been scratched; over two miles of cave remain to be mapped, with both

1 Gerald Moni, Personal communication, May 30, 2019.

2 From the 1978 SERA Cave Carnival Guidebook with additions by Brad Neff in 1984.

upstream and downstream still going. The main passage alone, now surveyed at 8,100 feet, is expected to exceed two miles.

Winter and spring floods have obliterated much of the past year's footprints and have even placed boulders and leaves five feet off the floor. Of unusual interest is a survey tape recovered by Kerr. He found it's orange handle protruding from silt under two and a half feet of water. The tape had been lost upstream from that point in deep water in October, 1978.[3]

MY FIRST VISIT TO THE CAVE

Sometime in early 1979 I made a trip to Cobb Creek Saltpeter Cave to photograph the saltpeter mining artifacts. I was dreading the hike into the Gorge and out, but it was not as bad as I had feared.

Despite the fact that this cave had only recently been discovered by cavers, the locals had already located it and trashed the entrance area with empty beer cans and had pulled apart and destroyed some of the saltpeter vats. Apparently they had followed the trail to the cave left by the explorers and surveyors. Despite the damage, I did get some good photos of the saltpeter mining area.

SALTPETER MINING IN COBB CREEK SALTPETER CAVE

The saltpeter vats in Cobb Creek Saltpeter Cave were in a particularly good state of preservation when the cave was located by cavers in the 1970s. However, locals were apparently curious as to where the cavers were going and tracked them to the Cobb Creek Saltpeter Cave entrance where they vandalized several of the saltpeter vats and left their empty beer cans.

3 Anonymous, "Lott Dean Still Going", NSS News, v. 37 (1979), no. 6, p. 141.

A 2020 TRIP TO MOUNTAIN EYE CAVE SYSTEM

The Nashville Grotto made a trip to the Mountain Eye Cave System on June 20, 2020. The trip was attended by Rachel Saker, Clinton Elmore, Hailey Jackson, Ashley Irons, Chris Durai, Michael Ketzner, Corey Ellis, and Clint Bowe. Chris Durai wrote the following Trip Report:

All parties met at our designated meet up point at 10:00 AM with the exception of two who arrived about half an hour late. This extra time was useful as it gave party members who had not previously met a chance to get to know each other.

Once all assembled, we caravanned to the parking spot along the East Fork of the Obey River. We suited up in our wet suits and began the journey around 11:30 AM. The river bed was dry, so we were able to easily bound over the smooth river rocks for the half mile hike to the cave entrance. At high noon we entered the cave.

The Lott Dean Entrance to the Mountain Eye Cave System is rather unassuming in comparison to the expansive borehole passage inside the cave. Right from the beginning, we were up to our necks in cold mountain water. Any doubts we had about wearing wetsuits were immediately dispelled.

After climbing out of the water into the Warm Reception Room, a nice little spot with a trickle waterfall in the ceiling, we waited for our navigator who mysteriously was not showing up. During our wait we practiced our map reading skills and explored a side passage. Finally we met back up with our navigator who we discovered had been stalled due to settling up his carbide lamp. Oh, that amazing carbide lamp! There is no LED in the world that can match the warm and cozy campfire feel of caving with a carbide flame emitting from a helmet. And the smell of it is strangely addicting. Anyway, now that we were all together it was off to see the system.

Pretty early in there is a canyon that must be navigated by climbing up into it and traversing with a drop beneath you, Kublai Canyon. As far as that sort of stuff goes, it was not particularly challenging, but you would not want to fall in. Then there is a nasty little hole in the floor that must be crossed with nothing but a piece of webbing to hold on to and scant handholds. Hardcore test #2. I found myself wishing I could clip into a traverse line. But everyone made it across fine with us all spotting each other. After that, the going was relatively easy.

Soon we emerged into glorious borehole passage the likes of Mammoth Cave's Grand Avenue. We decided to first go upstream just to take it all in. It just keeps going and going. It is easy to feel like you are walking outside at night until you look up and see the flat ceiling high above you. The walls in places are colored in variations of oranges and browns and the floor at times takes on spectacular variations. There are ruts that resemble wagon wheel tracks, areas of intricate floor scalloping, and wavy impressions filled with brown pebbles that uncannily resemble rattlesnakes. Many of the small pools were homes to white crayfish.

After our first lunch break and my first time seeing someone pull an entire order of chicken nuggets out of their cave pack, we headed northeast into Buff River. Apparently when "the Brits" were surveying this section of the cave, the gnats were so bad in the river that they all needed neck gaiters, or "buffs" to keep them out of their nose and mouth. Hence, Buff River. On our trip the gnats were not that bad, but again we were all thankful for having wetsuits. It is hard to describe the amount of breakdown that is present in sections of this cave. Along the western bank of the Buff River, the breakdown just

Figure 4.2. Bill Cannon stands next to the remains of a V-Shaped Saltpeter Vat in Cobb Creek Saltpeter Cave. Note the piles of dirt left by the saltpeter mining activity. Photo by Larry E. Matthews, 1979.

Figure 4.3. The remains of a V-Shaped Saltpeter Vat in Cobb Creek Saltpeter Cave. Photo by Bob Biddix, December 19, 2020.

Figure 4.4. Will Whalley with aragonite clusters in a side passage in Mountain Eye. Photo by Paul Fairman.

Figure 4.5. Erica Sughrue near the East Eye Entrance of the Mountain Eye Cave System. Photo by Bob Biddix, October 17, 2020.

climbs up and up until it disappears into an enormous rift in the ceiling that is completely choked with it. There is quite an amount of scrambling over broken sideways boulders and unstable shifty paths before lunging back into the water again. Finally you emerge once more into enormous borehole passage.

The Junction Room. If we had brought our vertical gear we could have ascended the rope anchored above in an upper passage to the northwest. But we were headed up the hill of sandy mud across from it. This is a particular section of the cave that could use a good handline and some more foot holds dug into it. Some of the members of our party scrambled up without any trouble at all. I, being last for taking pictures, found this section nerve-wracking. There was

Figure 4.6. Erica Sughrue at East Eye Entrance of the Mountain Eye Cave System. Photo by Bob Biddix, October 17, 2020.

nothing to hold onto up the slippery slope which descended sharply to a steep drop off. However, the reward for crossing this challenge was well worth the effort.

Entering into Clapham Junction one is immediately taken by the vastness of it. The ceiling towers over 100 feet above you. The walls, having a few overhangs near the bottom, eventually shoot straight up revealing all of the layers of rock between you and the enormous sandstone ceiling. And at the far end is the breathtaking dome, Victoria Falls. We could not help but linger in the magic of this place. And then we found the Queen. She was a full-sized frog straight out of a fairy tale book. While we had observed a white frog earlier in the trip, the Queen was still green with those golden frog eyes. How in the world did she get down here? We were determined to save her from slowly becoming an amphibious Gollum, but first we would explore more. On the way back then.

Onward we travelled until we came to Tabletop Mountain, which is quite literally a mountain of loose breakdown. As we all climbed the mountain, we were able to see the vastness of the space. Each individual became like dots of light against the impossibly large subterranean scene. At the top of the mountain we all gathered, enjoyed another lunch and laid out the laminated panels of the map our trip leader had carried in. We connected the panels and it just kept going and going, panel after panel. We decided we would come back and collect the map on our way out.

It was always our goal to make it to the Wanker Yanker, and by God we made it.

Figure 4.7. Erica Sughrue near the East Eye Entrance of the Mountain Eye Cave System. Note pile of bat guano on floor. Photo by Bob Biddix, October 17, 2020.

This is a section of the cave where over time a ravine in the mountain above cut into the borehole and collapsed it. The enormity of the passage shrinks into a sharp, squiggly crack so small one can barely wiggle through without getting their most private of parts yanked by the protruding rock. Once you start down this road, there is no going back. We all grunted our way through and into a tiny little room with just enough space for us all to squeeze into and turn around. As usual, I was last in line. When I finally made it into the room and found a suitable spot to have a short rest, it was observed by one of the party that at that very second was occurring the summer solstice of 2020. It is one I will never forget inside that glorious cave with these wonderful people, all of whom I feel lucky to know.

As far as Covid-19 is concerned, this was the only portion of the trip where I felt that any of us were potentially at risk. Crammed together in a small room with little airflow. Our exposure time in this area was short and we quickly headed back out. Anecdotally on this topic, here is an observation I have made in this cave. Over time, you could see each other's breath with your headlamp, as many cavers are familiar with. Based on visually seeing these clouds of droplets one can observe how they behave. I saw in this cave that these droplet clouds did not linger long but quickly rose towards the ceiling. To my knowledge, everyone on this trip took care not to "hang out" in other people's droplet clouds. I also noticed that on the occasions I wore my doubled-over neck gaiter as a face covering, it reduced the size of my droplet

Figure 4.8. Steph Petri in a scalloped passageway in the Lott Deane Section. Photo by Bob Biddix, July 2, 2016.

cloud substantially, although it was not the most comfortable thing in the world.

It was on our way back to retrieve the map that the only close call of the trip happened. It is because of my proximity to the event that I feels confident to report on it accurately. Because the Table Top Mountain room is so giant, all the members of the party naturally spread out. Some members of the group climbed back to the top of the mountain in order to pack up the map, while others, myself included decided to try and avoid the physically exerting climb by going around the highest part of the mountain. Neither group was particularly aware of their positioning in regard to the other group and at one point a rock fell from on top of the mountain and caused a small but very scary cascade of rocks tumbling down directly in front of the group below. I had a moment

of fright watching the member in front of me narrowly missed by the crashing rocks. Fortunately no one was hit, and we were all OK, but it was an oh-shit moment that brought the dangers of caving into stark focus. After some discussion with those involved as well as the trip leader, we have come to the conclusion that we likely should have had a brief group safety-huddle before ascending the loose breakdown mountain, emphasizing the nature of loose breakdown, the dangers of rock slides, and a reminder to be aware of where everyone is. This is something we only realized in hindsight. That being said, at every other potentially dangerous area, both before and after this occurrence, our trip leader took special care to make sure we were watching out for each other by doing things like spotting one another during climb downs and tricky areas, making sure no one was

Figure 4.9. The climb up to Victoria Falls at Clapham Junction. Photo by Chris Durai, June 20, 2020.

Figure 4.10. Rostam Namaghi sketching near the Wanker Yanker in Lott Deane Cave. Photo by Clinton Elmore.

Figure 4.11. Cavers in a large room upstream in the Lott Deane Section. Cavers, left to right: Rachel Saker, Ashley Adkins, Corey Ellis, Chris Durai, Clinton Elmore, and Michael Ketzner. Photo by Hailey Jackson, June 20, 2020.

Figure 4.13 Adrian, Alice & Rachel at Euston Station looking back towards Mind the Gap in the Mountain Eye system (passage is 150 feet tall). Photo by Paul Fairman.

Figure 4.12. Steph Petri chimneying in a passage in the Lott Deane Section. Photo by Bob Biddix, July 2, 2016.

Figure 4.14. Erica Sughrue in a large stream passage in the Lott Deane Section. Photo by Bob Biddix, July 2, 2016.

Figure 4.15. Tabletop Mountain. Photo by Ashley Adkins Irons, June 20, 2020.

Figure 4.16. Borehole passage north of Tabletop Mountain. Photo by Corey Ellis, June 20, 2020.

Figure 4.17. Erica Sughrue in a joint-controlled passage in the Lott Deane Section. Photo by Bob Biddix, July 2, 2016.

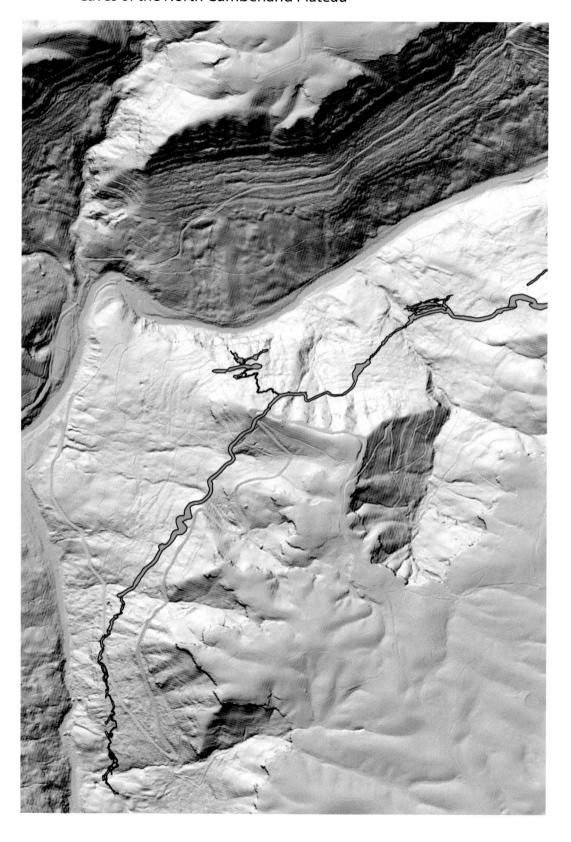

Figure 4.18. Overlay map of the Mountain Eye Cave System, by Rostam Namaghi.

getting too cold, and ensuring we were taking sufficient hydration breaks.

Our next objective was to relocate the Queen and assist in her liberation. Having had such a hard time with the sand hill, I opted to forgo the glory of revisiting Victoria Dome and waited at the junction. When our trip leader returned holding up a yellow dry bag with the biggest smile on her face, I knew that the Queen had been saved. Bets were proposed on whether or not the frog would hop right back into the cave after being released, but none were taken.

It was not until making our way back through Buff River that I realized how tired I had become. Navigating through the cave takes a lot of focus and at times becomes pretty technical. Just in time we all took another rest and had more water and snacks. Several members commented that they had never eaten so much on a cave trip. I for one felt that I needed every calorie I ate and next time I am totally doing chicken nuggets.

Finally we emerged at 7 PM into the hot Tennessee June. With a proper "Ah Zebenya" the Queen was released into her natural above-ground habitat (she did not hop back into the cave—just for the record) and we were off for the obligatory Mexican Feast.[4]

Clearly a wonderful trip that was enjoyed by all. The Nashville Grotto—Caving Since 1953.

THE SURVEY OF MOUNTAIN EYE CAVE SYSTEM

According to Gerald Moni, caver Chris Kerr mapped 15.9 miles of the Mountain Eye System,

but never produced a finished map. The British cavers have nearly finished their survey. A copy of their map has been included as Figure 4.18. According to Rostam Namaghi, 12.84 miles have been mapped and there is a link left between the Hyperborean and the Mountain Eye System that was unsafe to map due to the water level. When that is mapped, it will add another mile, or so, to the survey.[5]

CAVE ACCESS

The Mountain Eye Cave System is located within the newly created Skinner Mountain Wildlife Management Area. Like all caves, be sure that you have the owner's permission.

PLACE NAMES IN MOUNTAIN EYE CAVE SYSTEM

Buff River
Clapham Junction
Cobb Creek Saltpeter Cave Entrance
East Eye Entrance
Equulei Crack Entrance
Junction Room
Kublai Canyon
Lott Deane Entrance
Nargathrond Entrance
Nightshade Entrance
Sorcerers Grotto Entrance
Spring Entrance
Table Top Mountain
Victoria Falls
Wanker Yanker
West Eye Entrance

---

4 Chris Durai, "Mountain Eye System Trip Report", Nashville Grotto Google Group, June 20, 2020.

5 Dr. Rostem Ali Namaghi, Personal communication, February 22, 2021. It is interesting to note that this projected 14 miles of caves is less that the 15.6 miles reported in 1979 by the Knoxville cavers.

Figure 4.19 Carol Vesely in the Lott Dean entrance section to Mountain Eye. Photo by Dave Bunnell, 1980.

Figure 5.1. Erica Sughrue in a breakdown-floored passage in Stinging Nettle Cave. Photo by Bob Biddix, September 5, 2020.

CHAPTER 5
Stinging Nettle Cave

Stinging Nettle Cave is located in Fentress County, Tennessee. According to the Tennessee Cave Survey's Long Cave List this cave has a surveyed length of 17,927 feet (3.4 miles).

Stinging nettle, for which the cave is named, is a plant that has many hollow, stinging hairs called trichomes on the leaves and stems, which act like hypodermic needles, injecting histamine and other chemicals that produce a painful, stinging sensation upon contact. The plant is rather non-descript looking and it is easy to wander into a patch. The best protection is thick pants and boots. The unpleasant stinging sensation lasts for many hours.

A DESCRIPTION OF THE CAVE

Stinging Nettle Cave is located in the west end of a large sink in Bill Creek Hollow. The cave's entrance is in the center of an amphitheater formed by 100-foot cliffs.[1]

The entrance of Stinging Nettle is located in a large sinkhole that drains much of the upper end of the valley. One can either duck through the spray of the waterfall or go through the crack to the right of the falls.

Follow the tight breakdown crawlway through several squeezes to where it opens up in a small room. Bear left here. Follow the passage down several unstable breakdown mounds to the Rain Dome Room. Beyond the Rain Dome is the register and from here a major junction is met. To the left is much stream canyon passage and to the right are several big rooms, a few stream intersections, and lots of canyon passages. Many short drops are encountered throughout the cave, so a 30-foot handline might prove handy in some places. At one point a major stream intersection is met. Upstream goes 200 feet to several rain dome rooms that have been explored for more

than 1,000 feet. Downstream leads to about 3,000-5,000 feet of dry canyon passage (the stream disappears at one point), and several long crawls extending for several hundred feet.[2]

Caver Mike Rogers provides more information about the history of this cave:

> Stinging Nettle Cave was one of the many great Obey River Gorge cave discoveries by Ray Lewis in the mid-1970s. I suspect Ray and his companions explored perhaps a mile or so of passages in the cave. I doubt they conducted any survey—if they did it has certainly been lost. The cave itself is located several miles up Bill's Creek and (at the time) required either a long hike or an arduous 4X4 journey through vehicle-sucking mud holes. It is a very remote cave and was little visited compared to the other major Obey River Gorge caves (Mountain Eye, Xanadu, Zarathustra, etc.)
>
> Members of the Cleveland Grotto learned of the cave and began taking trips there along with the Russells (Mike and Gether of Jamestown, TN) in the early to mid-1980s. I *think* the Ohio cavers were also mapping in the cave. Jay Cox and Jeff Sims explored several of the longer passages as well.
>
> My first interaction with the cave was at the Gether Russell rescue in the summer of 1986 or 1987 (can't quite remember which). He was on a trip with his son Mike and several others. Gether had fallen deep in the cave and landed on his femur/hip. He was able to make it under his own power to the base of the breakdown pile near the entrance of the cave but felt he could not continue. A late-night rescue was called out and members of the Knoxville Volunteer Rescue

1 Ray Lewis, August 2, 1975, TCS Cave Files.

2 1988 SERA Guidebook.

Figure 5.2. Erica Sughrue at the Amphitheater Sinkhole where the entrance to Stinging Nettle Cave is located. Photo by Bob Biddix, February 23, 2020.

Squad and the East Tennessee Cave Rescue assisted in the extraction. Gether suffered significant bruising as a result of the accident but fortunately did not break anything. As I understand it, he essentially quit caving as a result. Gary and Trish Daugherty of Knoxville coordinated the rescue. Jack and Nancy Thomison were there, along with Jim Richards and some Fentress County cavers who were with the Russells when Gether fell.

Shortly after that, Jack Thomison and I returned to the cave. We were both impressed with how nice and dry it was along with the seemingly endless possibilities for leads. Jay Cox had started a survey project on May 21, 1988 and several trips were taken that year, primarily by Jay, Jeff Sims, Jack Thomison, Chris Kerr, me, etc. The project died down

however due to a number of circumstances. However, in November 1993 Jack got the old notes from Jay and took on the task of restarting the survey project. For the next two years we had many, many trips in the cave after this including a few weekend campouts at the entrance sink. Jack persevered with the survey and pushed us all to keep at it. Jack deserves significant credit as the one who spurred on the survey trips, coordinated the teams mapping in the cave, and finally completed a very fine map detailing almost 18,000 feet of the cave passages. Forty-two different surveyors participated in the project. The entrance sink is a beautiful place to camp and the camaraderie around a fire after a long survey trip was especially memorable. However, with a number of new

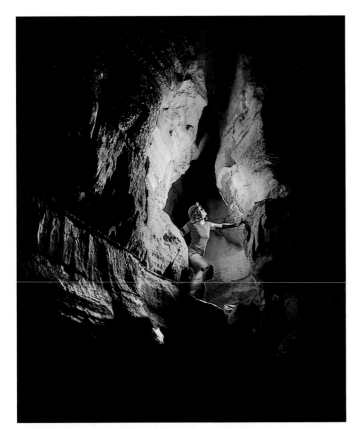

Figure 5.3. Erica Sughrue in a canyon in Stinging Nettle Cave. Photo by Bob Biddix, September 5, 2020.

Figure 5.4. Surveyors after trip in Stinging Nettle Cave. Left to right: Jay Cox, Brian Smith, Gerald Moni, Michele Sims, and Jeff Sims. Photo by Jeff Sims, June 18, 1988.

Figure 5.5. A fossil horn coral exposed on the wall in Stinging Nettle Cave. Photo by Bob Biddix, September 5, 2020.

Figure 5.6. Erica Sughrue by water flowing into the entrance of Stinging Nettle Cave. Photo by Bob Biddix, February 23, 2020.

cave discoveries and other projects all over the state, and a waning interest in pushing leads far from the entrance, interest in the Stinging Nettle survey faded.

There are two distinct "branches" to this cave, starting at the M-1 survey station just beyond the steep entrance breakdown series: the Left Branch and the Right Branch. Multiple passages and side leads take off from each of these and the cave has a bit

Figure 5.7. Erica Sughrue in a large passage in Stinging Nettle Cave. Photo by Bob Biddix, September 5, 2020.

Figure 5.8. Ken Pasternack in a passage in Stinging Nettle Cave. Photo by Bob Biddix, September 5, 2020.

of everything: nice canyons, dry crawls, large breakdown rooms, pits, waterfalls, domes, etc. It is a real caver's cave. Jack's note on the TCS map alludes to the fact that the cave is not fully surveyed, and most likely is not fully explored. With that many surveyors, the survey and sketching quality is understandably quite varied. A number of leads remained unsurveyed and could lead to extensive passages. The Right Branch of the cave generally trends west from the entrance, and the Left Branch trends mostly south. Throughout the cave are several climbdowns and a number of shorter pits in the 15- to 30-foot depth range. We rigged ropes at many of these, but several were left undescended. The total depth is surveyed at 281 feet deep but is likely to be greater than 300 feet due to some

undescended pits in the deeper areas. To my knowledge, none of the domepits were bolted. This was back in the late 80s-early 90s when cavers just weren't climbing domes like they do now. There is only one known entrance to the cave and so every trip had to go in and out that one way.

My most memorable trip in Stinging Nettle Cave occurred on a survey trip with Jack Thomison. The two of us logged a full day of survey and likely were using carbide lights. The dry, dusty canyons and crawls were punctuated with occasional waterfall domes and mysterious high leads we could not access. Late in the day we were mapping a nice, tall 20-foot canyon that looked great and had airflow. Suddenly, we encountered a pit! On the other side we could see continuing

Figure 5.9. Erica Sughrue by scallops on the wall in Stinging Nettle Cave. Photo by Bob Biddix, September 5, 2020.

passage. We looked for a way to free climb the pit or chimney across, but it was just too dangerous with only the two of us and no rope. It would be a long way to haul vertical and bolting gear but certainly had great potential. We reluctantly left and have never been back.[3]

Sounds like a good cave to find new passages and continue the survey.

THE SURVEY OF STINGING NETTLE CAVE

Stinging Nettle Cave was surveyed between 5-21-88 and 7-1-95. The original survey was begun by Jay Cox then finished by Jack Thomison. The

finished map is dated May 14, 2002. (See Figure 5.11) Forty-two (42) cavers assisted in the survey of this cave.

This cave has a significant vertical component and dips 281 feet from the entrance to the southern end of the cave.

CAVE ACCESS

This cave was open at the time this chapter was being written. Like all caves, be sure you have the owner's permission before entering this cave. According to Mike Rogers, this cave is located on a small island (101 acres) of privately owned property surrounded by a huge tract of state land (5,000+ acres).[4]

3 Mike Rogers, Personal communication, April 24 and 25, 2020.

4 Mike Rogers, Personal communication, April 26, 2020.

Figure 5.10. Erica Sughrue in a joint-controlled passage in Stinging Nettle Cave. Photo by Bob Biddix, September 5, 2020.

TFE - 64
FENTRESS CO. TENNESSEE

HORIZONTAL LENGTH SHOWN: 17,927 ft.
VERTICAL EXTENT SHOWN: 281 ft.

Compass, Tape and Clinometer Survey
5/21/1988 - 7/1/1995 by:

Brian Adams	Mark Eisenbies	Andy Porter
Darlene Anthony	Mike Greene	Mike Rogers
Carl Anderson	Robert Hamm	Mike Russell
Harold Anderson	Tonn Haskell	Frank Shires
Jay Arnold	Rosie Hawkins	Jeff Sims
Brent Aulenbach	Chris Hudson	Michelle Sims
Danny Britton	Jack Hutchins	Brian Smith
Art Cathers	Matt Jaeger	B Stickney
Jay Cox	Chris Kerr	Doug Strait
Alan Cressler	Janet A. Kerr	Jack Thomison
Bill Currey	Jerell Killian	Nancy Thomison
Bill Deane	Dylan Little	Bill Walter
Seamus Decker	Gerald Moni	Michael Wilson
Elliot Easterly	Joe Parrot	Bruce Zerr

CARTOGRAPHER'S NOTE:
This cave is not fully surveyed and, most likely, not fully
explored. This survey project has been conducted by many
people over an extended period of time. It was originally
initiated and coordinated by Jay Cox on May 21, 1988.
After a flurry of trips that year, work was discontinued. It
was reactivated on November 20, 1993 when the
cartographer got the old notes from Jay. The last data
shown here is from July 1, 1995. The survey notes are of
various levels of quality reflecting many different sketching
styles, thus the map is not as detailed as most modern
maps. There are many remaining unsurveyed and possibly
unexplored leads. The cartographer feels that it is best to
publish the map using the existing data and showing all known
leads. Any additional data on areas not shown can be
added since the map is in electronic media. Please forward
any new survey data for inclusion to the cartographer.

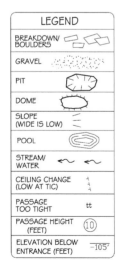

AutoCAD map © 5/14/2002 by Jack Thomison
Scale: 1" = 160' for B-size (11"x17")

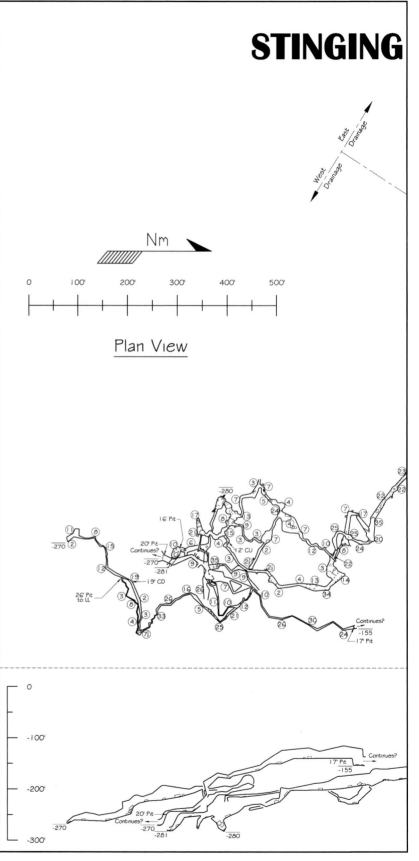

STINGING

Plan View

Figure 5.11. Map of Stinging Nettle Cave by Jack Thomison, May 14, 2002.

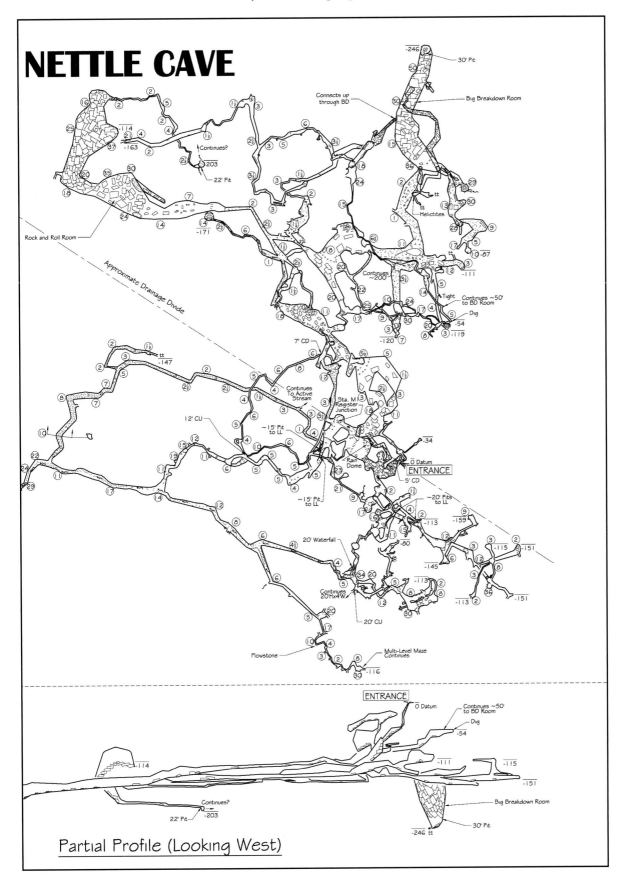

NETTLE CAVE

Connects up through BD

Big Breakdown Room

30' Pit

-246

Helictites

tt

tt

Continues ~50' to BD Room

Dig

-87

-111

Continues ~200

Tight

-54

-119

-120

7' CD

Continues To Active Stream

Sta. M Register Junction

tt

-147

12' CU

~15' Pit to LL

Rain Dome

-34

Ō Datum

ENTRANCE

5' CD

~20' Pits to LL

-113

-159

-80

-115

-151

20' Waterfall

~15' Pit to LL

-145

-113

-113

-151

Continues 20'h x 4'w

20' CU

Flowstone

Multi-Level Maze Continues

-116

Rock and Roll Room

Approximate Drainage Divide

Continues?

-203

22' Pit

-171

-163

-114

ENTRANCE

Ō Datum

Continues ~50' to BD Room

Dig

-54

-111

-115

-151

-114

Continues?

22' Pit

-203

Big Breakdown Room

30' Pit

-246 tt

Partial Profile (Looking West)

Figure 6.1. Toni Sullivan in the Enchanted Forest in Wolf River Cave. Photo by Chuck Sutherland, August 19, 2016.

CHAPTER 6
Wolf River Cave

Wolf River Cave is located in Fentress County, Tennessee. It currently has a surveyed length of 41,659 feet (7.9 miles) and is one of the largest known caves in Tennessee. It has been the site of significant vertebrate fossil discoveries and was explored extensively by prehistoric Indians 4,500 years ago.

The cave is well known by the local people as Blowing Cave. The cool breeze that blows from the cave during the summer has made it a favorite gathering spot for the past 150 years. The area to the right of the entrance was at one time a clearing used for parties by school children.

The first known resident in the area was Conrad Pile. He is credited with the initial exploration as well as giving the valley its name. The legend goes that during his first night in the valley while on a hunting trip he heads wolves howling, hence the name.[1]

A DESCRIPTION OF THE CAVE

Wolf River Cave is described by Thomas C. Barr, Jr. in his book, *Caves of Tennessee* (1961):

> This is a large and rather complex stream cavern. It consists of two large, parallel galleries formed during an earlier stage of development, and a secondary, meandering stream which cuts across both galleries and emerges at the mouth.
>
> The entrance is 35 feet wide and 8 feet high. In the summer a strong breeze blows from it and gives rise to the local name, "Blowing Cave." For 150 feet the entrance passage remains 6 to 8 feet high, but farther beyond it intersects the first of the two galleries at a large breakdown. The floor of this gallery is about 10 feet above the present level

of the stream. The stream crosses it in a wide, incised trench, loops back across the gallery a second time, and finally parallels the gallery and undercuts its wall. About 1,000 feet from the mouth a passage connects the main passage with a parallel avenue. The stream flows below the floor and appears again on the far side of its second avenue.

> By following the parallel gallery, one soon comes to a large collapse dome 100 feet high on the left side of the avenue; beyond it the cave continues for 400 feet and ends in breakdown. By climbing up over the talus cone in the collapse dome, one can enter a narrow stream passage, which is penetrable for 330 feet.
>
> The two large galleries strike S. 60° E., and the total length of the major passages of the cave is 2,200 feet. Virtually no dripstone formations are developed.[2]

Considering that the cave is now mapped at 7.9 miles long, Barr cleared missed most of the cave.

PREHISTORIC VISITORS TO WOLF RIVER CAVE

Wolf River Cave is noted for its evidence of use by Prehistoric Indians. One passage, named Aborigine Avenue, contains well-preserved footprints left by Indians. Charcoal from cane torches has allowed the date of these visits to be dated to approximately 4,500 years ago. Based on this evidence, the archaeologists concluded:

> More than 4,500 years ago, a group of prehistoric cavers negotiated complicated cave passages and discovered a side passage approximately two hours' journey from the

1 Doug Stecko, "A History of Wolf River Valley, Fentress County, Tennessee", Cave Cricket Gazette, v. 13 (1988), no. 5, p. 55.

2 Thomas C. Barr, Jr., *Caves of Tennessee*, TN Division of Geology, Bulletin 64 (1961), pp. 185-186.

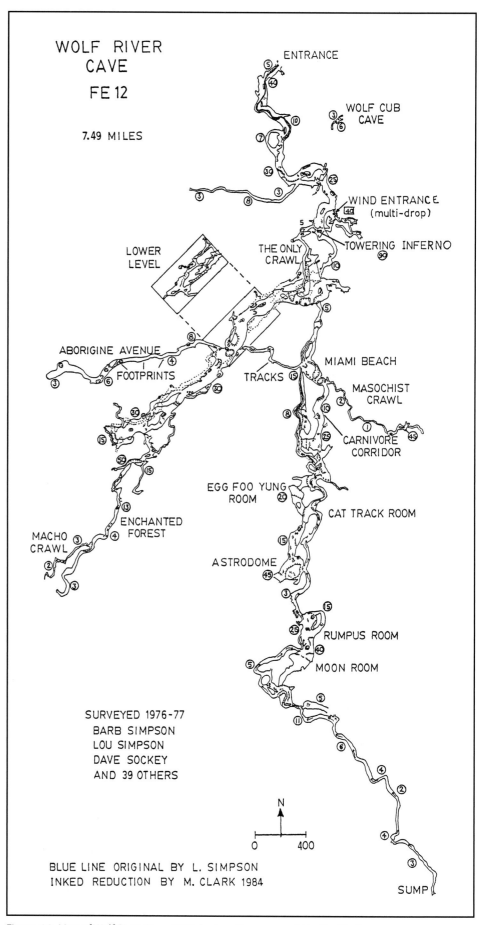

Figure 6.2. Map of Wolf River Cave, 1984, by Lou Simpson and Martha Clark.

Figure 6.3. French cavers in the entrance to Wolf River Cave. Philippe Crochet is the person on the left. Photo by Dave Bunnell, 1981.

Figure 6.4. Footprints left in Aborigine Avenue by Prehistoric Indians. Photo by Ray Maslek, May 5, 2018.

Figure 6.5. Patty Jo Watson (Left) studies jaguar footprints in Carnivore Corridor in Wolf River Cave. 1977. Photo courtesy of Lou Simpson.

Figure 6.6. Mark Hobbs (left) and Erica Sughrue (right) in a huge breakdown chamber in Wolf River Cave. Photo by Bob Biddix, May 24, 2014.

cave's entrance. They explored the passage toward its end, came to the termination of the easily traveled portion, turned around and exited the same way they entered, leaving footprints and torch material in the cave mud. Their remarkable journey is the earliest evidence of human cave use in the eastern United States.

A total of 274 relatively complete footprints remained in the passage's moist substrate when the passage was re-discovered approximately 30 years ago. The malleable deposits were pliable then and remain so today. This pliability made the prints' preservation vulnerable to subsequent events, agents and processes.[3]

The archaeologists concluded that the footprints were made by at least five men, two women, and a child.[4]

The cave is also the site of jaguar bones and footprints (tracks). One large passage in the cave is named Carnivore Corridor. Another location is named the Cat Track Room.

Bill Deane describes the discovery of the Indian footprints and the first jaguar skeleton:

It was Jay Arnold and I that found the upper levels of Wolf River Cave in the early 1970s. We went to the end of the stream passage and started exploring leads on the way back out. In the Dome Room, we climbed up to the top of a rock pile and then climbed into a rather nice tube that yielded access to several thousand feet of what we assumed was virgin borehole. Jay had been leading, but the walking passage

3 P. Willey, Judy Stolen, George Crothers, and Patty Jo Watson, "Preservation Of Prehistoric Footprints in Jaguar Cave, Tennessee", Journal of Cave and Karst Studies, April, 2005, pp. 61-68.

4 New York Times, October 2, 1983.

Figure 6.7. Erica Sughrue (right) and Jessica Preston (left) in the main river passage of Wolf River Cave. Photo by Bob Biddix, May 24, 2014.

turned into a stoop. I ran around Jay to take the lead. I looked down as I stooped and found the footprints, which were associated with cane charcoal. Surprise, surprise, it was not virgin. We also found the first jaguar. I thought it was a bear. Borehole, jaguar, footprints. A rather fine cave trip.[5]

The first jaguar skeleton was removed from the cave by Bill Deane from Knoxville and Ron Wilson from the Carnegie Museum in Pittsburgh in 1976. The skeleton was remote from the current known entrances to the cave, but it was near the breakdown collapse that terminates two levels of the cave. There is large sinkhole on the surface above this breakdown area. In all likelihood, there was an entrance in this sinkhole during prehistoric times.[6]

Lou Simpson describes the discovery of the second Jaguar skeleton:

A party of six—Andy Karolin, John Agnew, Dave Socky, Dave Voelker, and Barb and Lou Simpson—returned to Wolf River Cave in Fentress Co., Tennessee, on September 18 to continue mapping the newly discovered "Horrendous Trunk". This impressive passage, discovered September 4 by Joe Martin, Tom Ramsey, and Lou Simpson, features a roaring 6-foot high main-stream waterfall and a long stream passage with an upper level trunk intersecting the meandering stream passage. The two Daves went ahead to photograph the passage. After several trips back and forth through one particular passage, they chanced to see what looked like bones sticking out from under a flat slab of breakdown! The entire group considered what to do and decided to mark the two breakdown slabs over the skeleton, photograph their

5 Bill Deane, Personal communication, May 4, 2020.

6 Barb and Lou Simpson, "Wolf River Cave", C.O.G. Squeaks, Vol. 19, No. 9 (September, 1976), p. 71.

Figure 6.8. Sarah Cline in the Enchanted Forest in Wolf River Cave. Photo by Chuck Sutherland, August 19, 2016.

position, and then carefully set them aside to expose the rest of the skeleton. Further study will be left to the paleontologists.

In a low crawlway very near this skeleton, Lou and Dave Socky discovered several well-preserved examples of animal tracks.[7]

Another significant bone find was visited on January 13, 1979. This site was located near Survey Station 1409 at the north end of Tremendous Trunk. On that trip Ron Wilson and Mike Mezmar collected bones and teeth that were laying on the surface. They included a tooth from an extinct horse (*Equus sp.*), a dire wolf (*Canis dirus*), a long-nosed peccary (*Mylohyus nasutus*), and the American Mastodon (*Mammut americanum*).[8]

7 Louis Simpson, "Second Skeleton Found In Wolf River Cave", C.O.G. Squeaks, Vol. 19, No. 11 (November, 1976), p. 91.

8 Ron Wilson, "Recent Paleontological Research in Wolf River Cave", Cave Cricket Gazette, Vol. 4, No. 3 (April, 1979), p. 23.

THE SURVEY OF WOLF RIVER CAVE

Wolf River Cave was surveyed by Lou Simpson and 41 other cavers between 1976 and 1977. That map netted 7.49 miles of cave passages. This was during the Golden Age of Cave Mapping in Tennessee. These and other pioneer surveyors put Tennessee on the map with their many long, mapped caves. Below are highlights of some of the survey trips into Wolf River Cave:

July 3-4, 1976

Wolf River Cave, in Fentress County, Tennessee, is considerably easier to get to than Zarathustra's Cave, as just as interesting. Barb and I first went there on July 3, with Dave Socky and Tom Patterson. We began mapping at the entrance, while Tom and Dave mapped toward us from a point farther in the cave. It was soon apparent that one could not map the huge passages quickly, and we tried to put in enough stations to aid sketching so that no great distances remained unmeasured. Leapfrogging the other survey team, mapping a loop or two, we finally came to a black void where the only reasonable thing to do was to map around the edges. We finished our first day's surveying with 3,336 feet mapped, allowing for radial shots. Near where we stopped the stream passage continued upstream on a lower level, and we climbed up into upper levels into hot fog. How about the name for the place being "Towering Inferno?"

Mary and Greg Kalmbach returned with the three of us on Independence Day (Bicentennial Day), and we continued the survey to the sump on the lower level, mapped a short lead to a dome and a long crawl that finally got low. Except for some minor clean-up, the lower level was now complete. Our total for the second day was 1,363 feet.[9]

July 17, 1976

Barb and I returned on July 17 with Joe Martin, and we mapped into the beginning of the second level, through "The Only Crawl", stopping at the beginning of a nice walking passage that leads to the rest of the cave. Several side leads that we did not expect to go, did. Our total for the day was 1,463 feet, which put us over a mile (6,161 feet).[10]

July 20-22, 1976

We finally got to see the rest of the cave on July 20, when Bill Deane and Mark Stock took us on the grand tour. After an exciting eight hours of walking, Barb and I attempted to map some short leads farther out that wouldn't end, and Mark and Bill scooped an entrance near the Towering inferno. We should have realized that the hot air meant an entrance.

Barb and I returned two days later and mapped 1,469 feet, quitting in frustration when the side leads kept opening into virgin cave.[11]

July 23-25, 1976

We drove all the way to the cave from the SERA Cave Carnival, following Dave Socky, and mapped 853 more feet on the second level. What Bill Deane told us was a couple hundred more feet beyond our survey turned out to be another full day's survey, so we left it for another day.

Trips to Wolf River from the fieldhouse in Pulaski County, Kentucky, involve a grueling 55-mile drive over secondary roads. Therefore, we only went to the cave every other day. We returned three more times that week, mapping 1,249 feet Tuesday in the third level, the big trunk. Sometimes the hundred-foot tape was inadequate to measure the width of the room in one shot. We zig-zagged to more accurately define the rooms, and I triangulated on the lights of the other two for additional points. One room was 150 feet wide and 50 feet high, with a deep lake in a lower level at the bottom of the room.[12]

July 29, 1976

We finished the survey in the second level (except for about a mile of loops and clean-up) and mapped 772 feet to the wet breakdown. After this we went to the third level to explore. Touring the already known huge passage, we chanced to push a crawl on the way out and emerged eventually in virgin trunk. On and on it went, finally to many fine formations, often difficult to get past. We also found a room with large gypsum crystals. We were so dumbfounded we didn't want to leave, so we just sat there for an hour. We named our discoveries the "Enchanted Forest" and "Treasure Chamber."

We were so excited we called Greg Kalmbach on Friday and he and Mary came down that night, arriving at 3 a.m. We mapped to the wet breakdown in the big third level for a total of 2,053 feet for that day, or a grand total of 12,697 feet (2.40 miles).[13]

---

9 Lou Simpson, "Mapping Wolf River Cave", C.O.G. Squeaks, Vol. 19, No. 8 (August, 1976), p. 67.

10 Ibid.

11 Ibid.

12 Ibid.

13 Ibid.

August 23, 1976

On August 23 Barb and I went with Greg and Mary Kalmbach, Mike and Susie Warshauer, Tom Patterson, and Roger Sperka to survey the new formation area found in late July. Mary and Barb mapped the hands-and-knees crawl by which we first discovered the area. Warshauers and I mapped the beginning of the larger passages, including the Treasure Chamber, which features large, transparent gypsum crystals. Roger, Tom, and Greg mapped the main formation area, the Enchanted Forest passage, which ends in fill. Bill Deane and Kris Kerr, from Knoxville, pushed leads off the Enchanted Forest and found only a tortuous lower parallel level that offered only a couple of difficult possibilities. There was considerable airflow, however. It is hoped that this lead will open up and reconnect with a section of trunk beyond the breakdown that terminated the main passage of the cave. Total survey for the day was 3,452 feet, making the cave length 16,150 feet (just over three miles).[14]

September 4, 1976

Returning September 4 with a party of thirteen, we knew this would be our lucky day. Barb surveyed north in the big passage (Tremendous Trunk) with Dan Hickman and Carolyn Herel. They found several routes back to the route we had followed on the way in. My party, including Tom Ramsey and Joe Martin, began mapping beyond Barb's party, surveying mostly a huge room 200 feet in diameter. As we were finishing up our loop around the room, we found a virgin walking passage hidden in a breakdown hole along the wall. This went to a breakdown room with a deep pool in a hole and the sound of running water beyond. By the time we mapped two stations past the pool, it was apparent that a major waterfall was responsible for the now roaring torrent we heard. Excited, we abandoned our survey and rushed forward. The passage dimensions grew larger. We found ourselves chimneying along a clean, gray, rock-floored

channel. Then we saw the falls. Five feet high and eight feet wide. Its thunder filled the air and echoed in the mammoth virgin room beyond!

Dazzled by the beautiful waterfall, we entered a dry-floored trunk 100 feet wide and 30 feet high. Our feet crunched through the virgin crust. We walked, passing side leads 50 feet wide and 10 feet high. Some were larger. Climbing a small breakdown hill, we searched for a continuation. Along the right corner was a dark hole leading down into a pool of water. We were back to the river. We followed the edges and finally decided to get wet. After another 700 feet, or so, we decided we'd seen enough for one day. More big, attractive leads were left unexplored. The stream passage continued.

The current survey length is 3.59 miles. The new extension has much potential, to put it mildly. There remains much to survey that is already known, probably over two miles, not including the new passage.

Bill Deane and Ron Wilson, the latter from the Carnegie Museum in Pittsburgh, removed the bones of what Ron believes to be an extinct subspecies of jaguar (*Panthera onca*). The site of the remains is remote from the known entrances. It is near the breakdown collapse that terminates two levels of the cave. There is a large sinkhole on the surface above the breakdown area.[15]

September 18, 1976

A party of six—Andy Karolin, John Agnew, Dave Socky, Dave Voelker, and Barb and Lou Simpson—returned to Wolf River Cave in Fentress Co., Tennessee, on September 18 to continue mapping the newly discovered "Horrendous Trunk." This impressive passage, discovered Sept. 4 by Joe Martin, Tom Ramsey, and Lou Simpson, features a roaring 6-foot high main stream waterfall and a long stream passage with an upper level trunk intersecting the meandering stream passage. The two Daves went ahead to photograph the passage. After several trips back and forth through one particular passage, they chanced to see what looked like

14 Barb and Lou Simpson, "Wolf River Cave", C.O.G. Squeaks, Vol. 19 (1976), No. 9, p. 71.

15 Ibid.

Figure 6.9. Ken Pasternack by formations in the Enchanted Forest. Photo by Chuck Sutherland, August 19, 2016.

bones sticking out from under a flat slab of breakdown! The entire group considered what to do and decided to mark the two breakdown slabs over the skeleton, photograph their position, and then carefully set them aside to expose the rest of the skeleton. Further study will be left to the paleontologists.

In a low crawlway very near this skeleton, Lou and Dave Socky discovered several well-preserved examples of animal tracks.

After mapping a portion of Horrendous Trunk, all six began exploring the upper level trunks together. In the second segment we were able to see a path of animal tracks in soft sand in a room below an overlook.

Climbing up a precarious breakdown pile, we emerged into a big room, 100 feet wide and 400 feet long. A black opening at the far end beckoned, so we passed up possible leads on the lower right and headed for it.

At the threshold of the black void, even John Agnew's Coleman lantern failed to illuminate the room so we could see it. We climbed down into a canyon and saw that this was but the edge of an even larger room with a huge domed ceiling! Climbing up breakdown, we found ourselves in a huge, domed chamber which will probably be all of 300 feet in diameter! An appropriate name for this super-room is "Astrodome". The ceiling above the circular part of the room is about 30 feet high, and one can climb down an additional 20 feet along the edges. We sat in silence in the glow of John's lantern while he wandered over to the far side.

Several obvious possibilities for extending the cave beyond this room were checked, but only a steep breakdown re-connection to the stream passage continued. We explored a series of big rooms for another hour and left the cave, not wanting to push too much farther because we were somewhat sated with the thrill of discovery.

Many obvious leads remain. The survey of 1,301 feet brought the total to 3.83 miles.[16]

October 2, 1976

We entered the cave again on October 2 with vague plans to extend the survey beyond the second skeleton in Horrendous Trunk. With a party of six—Barb and Lou Simpson, Tom Cottrell, Bruce Warthman, Carolyn Herel, and Joe Martin—as well as another party from Knoxville—Bill Deane, Chris Kerr, and Jim Nicholls—we were able to map almost 4,000 feet. Tom, Joe, and Bruce began mapping the main stream passage upstream. Bill's party mapped several large come arounds which connect with the stream passage. They built rock barriers near the cat tracks and slide marks in the Cat Track Room to protect them from being stepped on. Carolyn, Barb, and I mapped upstream from the Cat Track Room until reaching the breakdown rooms beyond the Astrodome. Then we mapped in the Astrodome itself. Cottrell's party, and later

Bill's, also joined us in the Astrodome to help map it.

As in many previous large rooms, we thought it best to map around the edges of this largest room of all. We also put stations along the edge of the breakdown plateau to define it for the sketch and tied in two loops to test our accuracy. The Astrodome is impressive because of its circular shape, rather than any spectacular dimensions. Here you can stand at the top of the room, Station 1618, and see 150 feet in any direction for 120 degrees. Also, the tension dome ceiling is fascinating.

The total survey is now 4.6 miles. It goes!![17]

October 16, 1976

Dave Taylor, Barb, and I mapped 1,500 feet in Indian Trail. A virgin pit, over 40-feet deep, remains the most promising lead in this passage. Darwin Horn, Harold Molter, and Don Pollack helped Ron Wilson remove the bones of another animal from the Carnivore Corridor section of Horrendous Trunk. Ron believes this animal,

16 Louis Simpson, C.O.G. Squeaks, "Second Skeleton Found in Wolf River Cave", Vol 19, No. 11 (November, 1976), p. 91.

17 Louis Simpson, "Mapping The Astrodome", C.O.G. Squeaks, Vol. 19, No. 11, p. 92.

Figure 6.10. Jan Jones is a scalloped crawlway in Wolf River Cave. Photo by Chuck Sutherland, July 7, 2012.

like the other specimen recovered in September from the lower level of Tremendous Trunk, was a jaguar—a female—or it could be a large mountain lion.

Dave Socky, Dan Molter, Jake Elberfeld, and Paul Kruger mapped part of a large, confusing breakdown room farther south in Horrendous Trunk: the Rumpus Room. The day's survey brought the total length surveyed to just under 5 miles.[18]

November 5, 1976

We drove to the cave in only two vehicles to minimize calling attention to our continued visitation to the cave. During the trip to the south end of Horrendous Trunk, over a mile of walking into the cave, a serious hazard was pointed out when several persons slipped on the unstable breakdown at the beginning of Horrendous

18 Lou Simpson, "Tales From The Fieldhouse, Wolf River Cave", C.O.G. Squeaks, Vol. 19 (1976), no. 11, pp. 94-95.

Trunk. On the return trip, we all traversed this section one at a time.

The group essentially mapped all the explored unmapped rooms and passages beyond the Rumpus Room, for a total of 0.67 mile for the day. A party attempted to pursue the survey into the deep water upstream but decided to leave exploration and mapping for a party equipped with wetsuits and inner tubes. The mileage on the map now totals 5.67 miles.

The stream was higher than usual, and water was standing in a come around on the entrance level which had dried up for the past two months. The 6-foot falls in the Horrendous Trunk was more impressive this time. Bruce and Dave Socky took pictures of it.[19]

November 26 – 27, 1976

Barb Simpson and I arrived first to rendezvous with the five from CRF. Alter a discussion with the owner, we proceeded to Horrendous Trunk

19 Ibid.

Figure 6.11. Clinton Elmore by cascades in Wolf River Cave. Photo by Chuck Sutherland, July 7, 2012.

Figure 6.12. Erica Sughrue in the Enchanted Forest. Photo by Bob Biddix, May 25, 2012.

Figure 6.13. Carol Lamers in the Enchanted Forest. Photo by Bob Biddix, May 25, 2012.

where the scientists began their investigation of animal tracks in three places. I heard indirectly later that they found some "fossil regurgitation" from an animal. This had fish bones in it.

Barb and I mapped a short loop with animal tracks and named it Leopard Ledge.[20] Then we began mapping Maso Crawl. This began as a stoop-walk, but it degenerated into a gravely water belly-crawl. Actually, it is usually possible to avoid the water. An air flow is present. We aborted the survey after the twentieth station and left the cave. The crawl continues.

A nearby lead in Carnivore Corridor with animal tracks in it could possibly connect to an upper level of Maso Crawl because the two passages are quite close. Perhaps the animal, probably a female jaguar, came in an entrance from that direction.

Bob Wood rigged the pit in Indian Trail. The pit turned out to be 70 feet deep, but the narrow drain was too difficult for Bob to explore alone.

The total survey in Wolf River for the weekend was 1,214 feet. The current cave length in now 5.89 miles. At least a mile is known and unsurveyed at this time.[21]

February 2-4, 1977

We were surveying by 9 a.m. Thursday morning. First we finished the loop to station 450 that we had found in December. At station 2705 I climbed up a chimney, explored some breakdown a bit, and soon emerged in Tremendous Trunk. Yet another connection. We mapped this and found quite a bit more in the process. We had planned to go to Horrendous Trunk later that day to map a thousand-foot section of the main stream passage

---

20 These later turned out to be footprints left by a Pleistocene age jaguar.

21 Lou Simpson, "Wolf River Cave", C.O.G. Squeaks, Vol 19, No. 12 (December, 1976), pp. 100-102.

just above the falls, but this seemed like too much work. So instead we undertook to map some side passages of Tremendous Trunk beginning at station 802. There turned out to be much more cave here, too, than we realized, and it took the rest of the afternoon and some of the evening to survey it. We found a virgin 20-foot chimney with a tight, blowing crack at the bottom, a virgin breakdown room with a 15-foot pit, and a connection with the Mountain Room near the pit at station 912.

We left the next morning. Our total additional footage was 856.3 feet, making the cave length 34,448.7 feet, of 6.52 miles.[22]

October 1, 1977

Just two weeks after the last trip we made another assault on Maso Crawl of Wolf River Cave, Fentress Co., Tenn. Our group consisted of Scott Morris, Dave Sholar, Steve Scott, Bob Szabo and me (Dave Socky). At the cave we met Lou and Barb Simpson, Bill Thoman, and John Barnes.

Maso Crawl was as low and wet as it was reputed to be. Fortunately we all had wetsuits, although some of us forgot to bring spare clothes to wear out.

The first 100 feet is stoop-walk and hands-and-knees in a nice dry passage. The water shows up in the next hundred feet where knees-and-elbows crawling is required, although the water is just a small trickle. Then come 400 feet of alternating belly-crawl and near-hands-and-knees; sometimes in cold pools and sometimes dry. John Barnes and I surveyed the last 150 feet where the passage height got no higher than 12 inches and we had to cross bathtub pools. But at the end was walking passage. The other four intrepid cavers had gone up the dry 200-foot walking passage to where it was blocked by breakdown. Scott was at the bottom of this huge pile of loose rock diligently trying to pull out the keystone which was also blocking further progress.

After nearly an hour we all managed to get through the small hole and found our way up

steep slopes of dirt until we came out into what looked at first like a huge upper level trunk passage! After we all changed carbide we saw both ends of the 20-foot wide, 60-foot high passage were blocked by high steep walls. We couldn't see (or climb) to the top of the north wall. I almost got up the south wall where I could see a narrow canyon taking off. But I slipped back down the steep slope and then an easier lead was found. This turned out to be a 200-foot long hands-and-knees crawl (dusty dry) that led to a huge breakdown collapse. It is possible to crawl around on each side of this unstable breakdown collapse and maybe even get through, but we didn't try. We decided to leave this lead, the two high leads and about three other leads to the next trip (and this would assure this find would be surveyed).[23]

October 22, 1977

Pat Harrett, Hartley Mays, Lou and Barb Simpson, and I (John Barnes) went to Wolf River Cave to survey. We entered the cave at 12:50 PM and reached the beginning of Masochist Crawl two hours later. There we split up—Barb, Pat, and Hartley heading for Leopard Ledge to survey Scott Morris and Dave Socky's dig, Lou and I to survey the cave past Masochist Crawl.

We put on our wetsuits and headed down the 600-foot water crawl. At the end of the crawl we mapped 200 feet of walking passage, including come-arounds, about 100 feet in two breakdown-floored rooms, and about 300 feet in a narrow crawlway through breakdown. After assuring ourselves that no significant leads remained, we started out. We met Barb's party at Station 409 and headed out as a group.[24]

January 13, 1979

Mike Mezmar and I visited Wolf River Cave to map the station 1409 paleontological site. The area of bony breakdown covers approximately 100 square meters. We didn't do any excavation, but just collected only those bones or teeth we

22 Louis Simpson, "Wolf River Cave", C.O.G. Squeaks, Vol 20, No. 5 (May, 1977), p. 37.

23 David Socky, "Follow-Up Wolf River Trip Of Oct. 1st", Cleve-O-Grotto News, v. 23 (1977), no. 8, p. 64.

24 John Barnes, "Trip Reports", Cave Cricket Gazette, v. 2 (1977), no. 7, pp. 25-26.

Figure 6.14. Jenny Whitby in the Enchanted Forest in Wolf River Cave. Photo by Dave Bunnell, 2005.

happened to see on the surface. This included a tooth from an extinct horse (*Equus sp.*). Other extinct animals from this deposit include dire wolf (*Canis dirus*), long-nosed peccary (*Mylohyus nasutus*), mastodon (*Mammut americanum*), and passenger pigeon (*Ectopistes migratorius*).[25]

July 29, 1995

On July 29, Bruce Warthman and I dug another three feet at the end of the Enchanted Forest in Wolf River, Fentress County, TN. We used a dirt bag to haul the dirt to a point twelve feet back where the tunnel is wider. By digging deep enough to turn over on our backs, we could hammer upward to break the layer of rocks and flowstone that occurs two inches below the

ceiling. We could easily hear the roar of air or a distant waterfall, and it looks like the ceiling and floor rise after just two more feet. The space ahead looks like a "T" intersection. We mapped the dig and learned that it heads west, perpendicular to the Enchanted Forest Passage.[26]

CAVE ACCESS

The Southeastern Cave Conservancy, Inc., in partnership with the Nature Conservancy of Tennessee and Bat Conservation International purchased Wolf River Cave and 33 acres of surrounding karst land on August 15, 2002. Permission is required to enter the cave, which is open from May through August. The cave is closed during bat hibernation season. At the

25 Ron Wilson, "Recent Paleontological Research in Wolf River Cave", Cave Cricket Gazette, v. 4 (1979), no. 3, p. 23.

26 Lou Simpson, "Wolf River Dig Near Breakthrough", C.O.G. Squeaks, August, 1995, p. 2.

time the cave was purchased it contained the second largest hibernation colony of the rarest endangered bat species in the Southeast: the Indiana Bat. The colony numbered between 2,400 and 2,500 bats at that time. The cave also contained a small number of endangered Gray Bats in the summer, as well as a few Rafinesque's Big-Eared Bats.

The current Cave Management Plan allows two (2) permits per day with a maximum of eight (8) persons per permit. Permits are available at no cost at: permits.scci.org. Mr. Ken Pasternack is the current property manager of the Wolf River Cave Preserve. The cave is securely gated.[27]

WARNING

Wolf River Cave is an active stream cave. The entrance is subject to flooding shut during heavy rains. Read below:

A group of six Indiana cavers were trapped inside Wolf River Cave on December 4, 1993 by high water. The group entered the cave for a tourist trip on a day when continuing heavy rain had been forecast for central Tennessee. The entrance is a large stream resurgence which opens directly on the Wolf River. The entrance passage which discharges the stream is 30 feet wide and 7 feet high.

After exploring deep inside the cave for several hours, the group returned towards the entrance. Signs of rising water were encountered as they retraced their route along the cave stream. Upon reaching the entrance, they found the stream sumped, with no way out. The group settled in for a 12-hour wait. Finally, the stream level dropped enough to allow the trapped cavers to exit. Wolf River was in flood, and the cavers found their vehicles had been underwater during the ordeal.

The biggest danger in a situation like this is trying to exit too soon and being swept away by the stream. Drowning is a real possibility.

PLACE NAMES IN WOLF RIVER CAVE

Aborigine Avenue
Astrodome
Carnivore Corridor
Cat Track Room
Egg Foo Yung Room
Enchanted Forest
Horrendous Hallway
Indian Trail
Leopard Ledge
Macho Crawl
Masochist Crawl
Miami Beach Room
Milk and Butter Room
Moon Room
Only Crawl
Panther Ridge
Pit Entrance
Rumpus Room
Towering Inferno
Treasure Chamber
Tremendous Trunk
Wind Entrance

SUGGESTED READING

P. Willey, Judy Stolen, George Crothers, and Patty Jo Watson published *Preservation of Prehistoric Footprints In Jaguar Cave, Tennessee* in the April 2005 issue of the *Journal of Cave and Karst Studies*, pages 61-68. The paper includes excellent photographs of several footprints and three C-14 dates for cane torch material found in the cave. Archaeologists referred to Wolf River Cave as Jaguar Cave in a naive attempt to hide the cave's true name and location.

---

27 Ken Pasternack, Personal communication, August 12, 2019.

Figure 6.15. Jim Fox by flowstone formations in the Enchanted Forest. Photo by Chuck Sutherland, August 19, 2016.

Figure 7.1. Erica Sughrue by formations in Xanadu Cave. Photo by Bob Biddix, September 5, 2011.

CHAPTER 7
Xanadu Cave

Xanadu Cave is located in Fentress County, Tennessee. With a surveyed length of slightly over 24 miles, it is currently the third longest known cave in Tennessee.

THE DISCOVERY OF XANADU CAVE

Caver Ray Lewis and his caving companions recall their adventures in 1977:

Part I

Late in March of 1977 I found myself flying above the wilderness gorge of the East Fork of the Obey River. A friend of mine had taken me up so I could photograph some areas of the gorge which we hadn't checked for caves. It was quite exciting hanging out of the tiny plane's window and being buffeted by the icy prop blast as I took my pictures. As we flew over the central part of the gorge I spotted a disturbance in the river 1,000 feet below. We couldn't fly much lower, because we were just above the walls at the top of the gorge and crosswinds made even flying where we were difficult. We made another pass at a different angle, and I could see a dark hole with water rushing out into the river. The river was high at that time, but this spring was putting out enough nasty orange water to discolor the green river and turn it the color of fall leaves.

The weekend after the plane ride I journeyed to the gorge again. This time Sid Jones joined me, and we even talked Pat Sullivan into the trip by promising to find over a mile of new cave. I figured we could take him to Zarathustra's Cave and rediscover it if we couldn't find anything else. Saturday morning found us hiking into the gorge as the sun came up. We planned to hike downstream from the usual turnoff to Z's Cave and go

about half a mile to the spring. As we strolled along we noticed a huge bluff on the east side of the gorge and several interesting holes at its base. We thought we ought to at least check them out then since we would probably be tired after exploring miles of cave behind the spring resurgence. We found a group of four holes close together. One was low and half full of water with a strong breeze coming out of it while the other three were dry. So wisely we took the dry ones first. They all connected and led up a steep breakdown slope to a low winding passage. This led to a small hole which dropped into larger passage below. This got us excited, we started wondering if this was another Zarathustra's. We couldn't get down the hole without a rope, so we went back to the wet entrance. Sid went in first. He reported his progress as Pat and I started into the water.

The water seemed unusually cold and I hoped it wouldn't get very deep, but it did, well over our waists. Sid yelled that it got shallower and kept going, so we pushed on. We joined Sid as he pointed out a large "white rock" he had found. On examination this proved to be a huge block of ice. No wonder that water was cold. The passage opened up and continued a few hundred feet until we entered a large room. This is where we started hollering and swearing and doing all the things you do when you find a neat new cave. The room was 30 feet high and 100 feet in diameter with leads going off in all directions. We climbed up to a ledge 10 feet above the floor and found nice passage leading off north, down the river. We ran down this one, it had a nice smooth floor and high ceiling. We passed up all the side passages since our main tunnel was going so well. It continued for about a half

Figure 7.2. View into the Obey River Gorge from Hood Town Road Overlook. Photo by Chuck Sutherland.

mile until it broke up into several different passages. We wandered around in them for a while and found more and more leads and maze passage. This was nothing like some of the side passages we had seen off the main trunk, so we backtracked out of the maze.

The first side passage in the main trunk led into a whole new series of passages which also deteriorated into small maze passage. We decided to head out and leave this obviously big cave to another trip since we still had our main objective to reach.

After wading out of the cave entrance, we had to cross the river three times while going downstream. Then we worked our way back up the west bank to the spring. It was visible from the river, but we couldn't see the hole it came out of. Our first view of a cave there was of a huge hole in the bluff, half hidden by the mist from the warm air it was blowing out. It was pouring forth a tremendous

volume of water which seemed to pool up at the entrance. It looked deep so we waded in cautiously only to find it only a little over waist deep. This led to muddy passage which ended when it became too small after only a few hundred feet. It was a nice entrance to be such a crummy cave. We named this one Dragon's Breath Cave, because of the volume of air coming out of it. The water in the cave came out of a pile of breakdown on one side of the cave, while the air came from a different location. There was another cave next to this one. It had a smaller entrance and no air flow, but it put out a lot more water. I couldn't even get inside this entrance, because the velocity of the water swept my feet out from under me. It was a promising looking cave, even though it had no air current. We planned to return in the summer when it dries up. We named this cave the Enchanted River Cave. I believe these two entrances to be the main resurgence for

Figure 7.3. Jonathan Griffith at the Alph Resurgence of Xanadu Cave. Photo by Bob Biddix, July 16, 2011.

the Obey River after it goes underground a mile above the Wilder Bridge.

From the spring we hiked downstream about a mile and found one very small cave in the east bank. This ended our trip in the gorge, except for the inevitable climb out. No matter how many times we do it, I'm always dead when I reach the top.

We decided to name our new big cave Zoroaster's Cave, since it looked like it might be as big as Zarathustra's. We haven't been back to go in that entrance since the first time. Once we tried when the Deanes and Art Bosnak joined us for a tour of the cave, but because of heavy rains we found the entrance flooded. Even though we never went in that entrance again, we visited the same cave many times.[1]

1 Ray Lewis, "The Discovery and Exploration of Xanadu Cave—Part I", Speleotype, Vol. 11, No. 3 (November, 1977), pp. 60-61.

Part II

After our first trip into what we then called Zoroaster's Cave, we headed back the next weekend to further explore out, find and to check for other entrances. We headed up Lints Cove to take the dry streambed to the Hartselle contact. On the way we found a small cave, Lints Cove Cave, which contained lots of small cave pearls. We hiked a long way up the cove until we heard the noise of falling water. As we topped a rise we saw a really beautiful waterfall descending into a deep blue pool and disappearing. On either side of the water were cave entrances. The cave on the southern side had a tremendous entrance, and it seemed to be heading south and west. The possibility of this being an upper level entrance to Zarathustra's Cave was incredible. We started into the cave joking that we might walk out the Saltpeter entrance of Zarathustra's Cave.

We were disappointed as fast as we ran down the large passage. It ended completely. It was exciting while it lasted. On the way out we found a side passage leading into smooth walled tunnel with air coming into it. We found a terrible lead crawling through rotting organic debris and over chert nodules in the rock. Sid pushed it to where it got even worse and came back. Then on the way out I made a wrong turn and ended up in a passage we hadn't seen. Sid and I walked down it and after the bend in the passage we heard a thundering sound that was vibrating the walls. Pat had apparently continued out, so Sid and I pushed on. The noise grew louder. It was spooky, I imagined coming on a huge void with a roaring waterfall dropping into the depth. We found the waterfall alright, but no pit. The water, apparently from the surface pool, dropped into this room, formed a deep pool and poured down a small passage. We went out to get Pat. This was going to go, possibly down a pit. We warmed up outside a little and considered the extent of our finds. Our water cave might connect to Zarathustra, or even our new cave, Zoroaster, and what about that little hole over the pit on the north side of the waterfall?

We went back into the waterfall room and Pat started down the water filled passage. It was waist deep and cold. We all ducked under the curtain of water and waded around a bend and then out into wider passage with a fast-flowing stream. The water cascaded down over the rocks to a drop. At first we thought we'd need a rope but after looking around, Pat and I climbed down a 20-foot chimney and pushed on down the stream passage. It dropped almost immediately off a 40-foot pit into a large room. We really needed a rope here. After a few moments of throwing rocks into the hall and speculating, we hurried outside to warm up.

Once outside we were all tired and considered leaving, but we figured we should check the small cave entrance too. We knew it would probably end quickly. This was to be another in an already long line of faulty conjectures. We scrambled over the loose rock at the entrances and then found ourselves in a 7-foot high, 20-foot wide passage heading northeast. We couldn't believe it; we had lucked up again. We wandered down the passage, wondering what we would find. The passage kept going and we started seeing footprints, two pairs of footprints going into the cave, but none coming out. They were well preserved in the dry sandy floor so we couldn't tell how old they were. We half expected to find an operating still or else two skeletons. The passage led to the edge of a huge hole in the floor that dropped at least 50 feet into an even larger passage. We started wondering if we were in a dream. This cave was going to be incredible. We couldn't get safely down the drop, so we went around the hole. We found several nice areas of stalactites and columns just past the hole. The passage got smaller, but it had a sandy floor, so the crawling was almost pleasant. At a constriction in the

Figure 7.4. Jeri Kizer, Charles Clark, and Martha Clark get ready to hike down the plateau to Xanadu Cave. Photo by Jeff Sims, October 23, 1977.

Figure 7.5. Charles Clark and Randy Kissling surveying in Lower Alph. Photo by Martha Clark, July 3, 1981.

passage we found some writing on two flat rocks. The words were: This is as far as we got. –Pat Stevens 1927. We had seen this name before. He was one of Sid's relatives who roamed the gorge and poked into every big cave which we had found. We wondered what he used as a light and who his companion was when they left their tracks fifty years ago. We wondered what they thought as they explored the same passage we were in. Did they wonder if <u>they</u> were the first ones to see this cave? Did they consider who would follow in their footsteps? Unlike these earlier explorers we didn't leave any marks of our exploration other than our tracks. It would be neat though

Figure 7.6. Cavers in Cumberland Avenue in Xanadu Cave. Photo by Dave Bunnell, July, 1981.

Figure 7.7. The Big Three: Charles Clark, Jeff Sims, and Martha Clark. Photo by Martha Clark, November 20, 1982.

Figure 7.8. Charles Clark, Martha Clark, and Michele Sims at the Upper Camp in Stephens Avenue. Photo by Martha Clark, December 26, 1982.

if we had written something alongside Pat Sevens' note. Then people fifty years from now could find our names and maybe wonder about us.

We pushed past the constriction and crawled over a rough floor and a flaky ceiling until it didn't look like it was going to end. We were low on water and carbide anyway, so we turned back. Going to the entrance we found a side passage. This one led downward and opened into a large passage. Forgetting about our poor light situation we explored into this giant cavern. It was unbelievable! It kept going and getting bigger. We joked about it going through the plateau to Wartburg. We hit a series of very large mountains of loose rock and sand. It was a lot of work going up them, and dangerous too. We stopped at the foot of the biggest mountain while Pat scrambled up it. At the top he reported that it kept going, but we decided to stop for the day and turn back. It was sort of close getting out with only the light of a flashlight after our carbide ran out. The sun was going down when we left the cave. As we hauled ourselves up the mountain to my car in the dark, we could hear the soft roar of the river below us in the gorge. It was beautiful. This gorge was an amazing collection of wilderness. We felt it ought to be protected, but it is probably already condemned by the coal under the caps of the mountains and by the gas the earth holds. That was the most beautiful trip I had ever been on. We were dead tired as we headed home, but it was a good feeling.

We named our new cave, Xanadu Cave, and the waterfall cave became Alph Caverns. Both named for the Coleridge poem, Kubla Khan.[2]

Part III

We returned to the gorge on April 17, 1977. We had tried to keep our find somewhat secret, but it was difficult. This trip was to push each cave as far as we could. We were a rough looking crew going into the gorge that Sunday morning. Jim Matthews had been added to our discovery crew since he had been on a lot of our previous trips finding and exploring Zarathustra's Cave. We carried a foolish 450 feet of rope, (I expected multiple drops in Alph), lots of carbide, food, and warm clothes. I even had my wet suit. It was a real expedition. I almost died carrying all my gear plus 300 feet of rope and camera equipment down the mountain. I couldn't

imagine carrying it out. We finally got to the cave and started into Alph. We rigged the first drop and started down. The water disappeared almost immediately after it dropped into the passage. We found a high, wide hall leading off from the pit and explored it through a dry maze. We finally hit the water again, but it only appeared long enough to disappear again into loose rock. This really ended my hopes. I expected this cave to take us to the river. We hauled all our useless rope up the 40-foot drop and exited the cave. We had seen over a mile of cave, but it was still disappointing.

We were now ready to tackle Xanadu. We left all our rope outside and started to our monster passage. Before we even got to Pat's mountain of the previous trip, we made a discovery. We found a lot of gypsum flowers. They were growing out of the walls in all sorts of shapes and sizes. We all climbed up Pat's mountain to find a long stretch of almost level passage. After a couple hundred feet we got to a 100-foot drop as steep as the one we had just climbed. We slid down on the sand of this one and repeated the process several times on several other mountains before we finally got to a very, very large chamber. We couldn't see the roof or the other side from where we were. The room was 100 feet wide, but the other side proved to be the end of our big passage. We found a side passage which led to the top of a canyon-like drop. We hoped that it dropped into Zoroaster's Cave, but we couldn't be sure. We had left all our rope a couple of miles away at the entrance. We couldn't do anything more, so we left.

Our next trip was our connection trip. We connected Xanadu Cave with Zoroaster's Cave and named the whole system Xanadu Cave. We also found several nice fields of angel's hair in the monster passage and some nice white formations in the lower cave. This was the climax to our explorations. We had connected over six miles of cave (*estimated*), and it hadn't been completely explored. The connection put

2 Ray Lewis, "The Discovery and Exploration of Xanadu Cave—Part II", Speleotype, Vol. 11, No. 3 (November, 1977), pp. 62-63.

Xanadu in the top five longest caves in the state.

We had made a lot of trips and spent a lot of time on Xanadu Cave, and we were tired of it. We had explored most of the main passage, photographed it, named it, and all the remained was the mapping. I don't like to map so we asked the half-crazed map-oriented cavers in Knoxville to take it over.[3]

This is truly one of the great stories of cave discovery and exploration in Tennessee. The next section, as told by the surveyors repeats some of Ray Lewis's story, but after a few pages it is all new material.

THE SURVEY AND FURTHER EXPLORATION OF XANADU CAVE

The discovery and exploration of Xanadu Cave were documented in the August, 1981 News by Charles Clark, Martha Clark, Randy Kissling, Ray Lewis, and Jeff Sims. Here is their exciting story of discovery and exploration:

Chapter One: 1975-1977: Ray Lewis and the Obey River Gorge. By Charles Clark.

In the northern recesses of Tennessee's Cumberland Plateau lies the East Fork of the Obey River. For better than seven miles the river twists and turns in its 1000-foot-deep gorge through Fentress County's wilderness with but one road piercing its solitude where Highway 84 crosses the gorge at Wilder. The river finally flows out from between its towering walls of rock and forest to unite with the West Fork of the Obey River just west of Jamestown, Tenn.

It was a sunny May morning in 1975. Ray Lewis, Jim Matthews, and Sid Jones pulled over and parked on the wide shoulder of Highway 84 just before it crossed the bridge over the then dry East Fork of the Obey River. Two weeks earlier Ray had driven to

the same bridge to size up the river as a canoe stream. The absence of water had quickly decided the issue of floating the river, but it immediately raised the possibility of walking it. Tennessee rivers normally run free in springtime, but this one had disappeared. Ray knew it resurged somewhere downstream before joining the West Fork. Dreams of giant caverns beckoned him on.

The day was hot, and footing was treacherous as the three cavers hiked down the dry riverbed. They had traveled hardly half a mile when an opening in a bluff to the right lured them in out of the heat. They fired up their carbide lamps and explored just enough to see that it kept going. Then it was back to the surface to continue their wilderness odyssey. For five miles they marched. Dozens of entrances opened in the picturesque bluffs along the river. Then probing the wooded coves spilling into the gorge, waterfalls, bluffs, and more caves greeted them. It was a caver's fantasy come true. Names from ancient literature and mythology came to mind and each of the newly discovered netherworlds was honored with one …Yggdrasil, Dragon's Breath, Zarathustra, Mountain Eye Cave, Zoroaster, Alph Caverns, Xanadu….

If I had the power to create a speleo-legend I would combine Ray Lewis's three years of hard and enterprising work into the ultimate fantasy of discovery I have just written. But that would truly be an injustice to Ray Lewis, Jim Matthews, Pat Sullivan, Sid Jones and all the others who slaved in numerous ridge-walks over this challenging wilderness. If the discovery of countless big caverns totaling over 50 miles and more in extent seems a fantasy to the reader then the fantasy is true. However, on the particular May morning I described, Ray had to settle for just one huge cavern, seven-mile-long Zarathustra's. Over the next three years, however, more were to follow.

---

3 Ray Lewis, "The Discovery and Exploration of Xanadu Cave—Part III", Speleotype, Vol. 11, No. 3 (November, 1977), p. 64.

March 26, 1977, Ray Lewis, Pat Sullivan, and Sid Jones proceeded farther downstream in yet another effort to discover that illusive resurgence. Time and time again they had been foiled by discovering some other cave to distract them. This day was fated to be yet another failure.

A mile north of Zarathustra's the three spotted four openings at the base of a large bluff. Upon closer investigation the lowest entrance was found to be blowing with gale force. Wading through the icy river water that half submerged the entrance, the trio walked down a sizeable trunk 15 feet high by 20 feet wide. The trunk proved to be the central artery of a network of branching, cobble-floored side passages. Upon entering any one of these the cave would branch yet again and again. It was a cold, vast maze of dark, rock-strewn cave passage. The newly found giant was christened Zoroaster's Cave.

Ray, Pat, and Sid returned a week later utilizing the old logging road that placed them at the Zoroaster bluff immediately after descending the gorge. Instead of exploring further in Zoroaster the pair hiked up Lints Cove. Lints Cove recedes from the wall of the Obey Gorge so close to the Zoroaster entrances that those entrances open practically at the "corner" formed by the side of Lints Cove and the wall of the main gorge itself.

Lints Cove was a major hollow and drained a large area, but it had no stream flowing out of it. Imaginations went to work as they anticipated a small river falling into a deep pit at the head of the hollow. As the pair neared the contact of the Hartselle Sandstone and the Monteagle Limestone the roar of a waterfall was heard.

Topping a small rise provided an unbelievable spectacle. A large stream fell over

Figure 7.9. Frédéric Langlois in a phreatic tube in the Zoroaster section. Photo by Philippe Crochet, July 1981.

a 30-foot sandstone bluff into a deep pool. To the right of the pool was a very large entrance and on the left was a small hole in the bluff. The large entrance on the right came to be known as Alph Caverns, the "small hole," Xanadu.[4]

Chapter Two: April 2, 1977 – Xanadu Connects to Zoroaster. By Ray Lewis.

We rested awhile outside before we poked into the little hole on the other side of the falls. We were sure it would end quickly so we didn't take all our gear. The small entrance opened into a breakdown passage that led to a smooth-walled tunnel about 10 feet in diameter. It had a sandy floor and headed into the mountain. As we started down the passage, we noticed a trail of footprints preceding us into the darkness. There were two pairs of tracks; both headed into the tunnel and none came out.

We were very alert as we followed the tracks up the passage. The prints continued several hundred feet past a side passage that we saved until later. After a long hands and knees crawl, we finally came to a hole in the floor. It was 20 feet in diameter and dropped almost 40 feet into a large room below us. That room looked like a huge trunk passage running perpendicular to our upper passage. A ledge around the hole led on down the tunnel following the phantom footprints. We crawled through a jungle of columns and stalactites to finally reach a constriction in the passage. There we found out about the footprints. A flat rock had a message on it saying, "This is as far as we got, Pat Stevens, 1927."

On the way out, while discussing our incredible luck, we poked into the only side passage we had seen. It popped out into a large passage. Even our imaginations hadn't gone this far. The passage was more than 50 feet

wide and high and went into the mountain over a floor of boulders and sand.

We were running low on carbide and worked our way down the monster passage. We passed under the hole in the upper passage and kept going. The passage consisted of one breakdown mountain after another. This made our progress pretty slow. The sandy mountains were fun to descend, but impossible to climb. They just kept getting bigger and bigger and the passage kept going. We were all in a daze. This was impossible, the biggest passage in the state! We came to the top of one mountain and looked off. We couldn't see the bottom or the other side. The passage was more than 100 feet high! We slid down this hill to a wide, level floor and rested while Pat scrambled up the next mountain. He got to the top and reported that it continued, but we had to call him back and start out before our light failed. It was very late when we got outside. We were tired but didn't care because of the excitement of our discovery.

The next weekend we returned for a major assault. In Xanadu we made a discovery before we even got to our previous stopping place in the monster trunk. We found a garden of gypsum flowers. Lots of nice flowers and crystals. Finally we reached the monster mountains. Those things just kept going and getting better. They became more dangerous as we progressed. Vertical sand walls made for tough climbing. Finally after what seemed like thousands of feet, the passage leveled out. Then we hit the biggest room we had seen yet. We couldn't see the ceiling and the room was more than 100 feet wide. This was the terminal room. The opposite slope rose to the ceiling.

The monster had died, but the cave kept going. A passage at the bottom of the room led to a deep canyon. We couldn't find a way into this canyon but there was a passage going off the top. It led into a wide, dry, walking passage, but we had to turn back without

---

4 Charles Clark, "Xanadu", NSS News, Vol. 39, No. 8 (August, 1981), pp. 168-169.

Figure 7.10. Erica Sughrue (left) and Carol Lavender (right) in the Sand Hills Passage in Xanadu Cave. Photo by Bob Biddix, February 26, 2011.

Figure 7.11. Only at the top of the largest sand hills does one approach ceiling level in the Sandhill Passage. Photo by Dave Bunnell and Philippe Crochet, July 1981.

checking it. On the way out we discussed our find. We hoped that the canyon drop would lead to more low-level cave and maybe finally connect to Zoroaster's Cave.

The next weekend Sid, Pat and I came back with rope. We repeated the journey through the deserts of Xanadu Cave and made another discovery. We found fields of Angel Hair. Unreal! This cave just kept getting better. Finally we got to the drop. We were hoping this would be the connection trip because the trip over the mountains was becoming a chore.

The drop was about 40 feet to a breakdown slope. I didn't recognize it, but Pat and Sid did. We went a little further and were sure. This was Zoroaster's Cave. We had finally made the connection.

The sun was going down as we started up the mountain to my car. We had not completely explored the cave, but we were ready to turn it in to the Tennessee Cave Survey. There were many leads left to check and mapping needed to get started, but I didn't want to do it. We turned the mapping and future explorations over to the Smoky Mountain Grotto. I felt the urge to look into some other unspoiled portion of the gorge, so we left Lints Cove to the mappers.[5]

Chapter Three: July 4, 1977 – The Xanadu Survey Begins. By Jeff Sims.

It was paranoia! The Ohio cavers had already raped Wolf River Cave and Zarathustra's Cave. They weren't about to get the next one. Luckily, Ray Lewis felt the same way. After connecting Xanadu to Zoroaster's Cave, Ray decided Xanadu needed mapping. Thus, he turned it over to the "crazed" Smoky Mountain Grotto mappers."

5 Ray Lewis, NSS News, v. 39, no. 8 (August, 1981), p. 169.

Figure 7.12. Ken Pasternack by large gypsum flowers in Xanadu Cave. Photo by Chuck Sutherland, November 18, 2012.

Figure 7.13. Angel's Hair in Xanadu Cave. Photo by Chuck Sutherland, July 16, 2011.

Few people had been to Xanadu before July 1977. I had heard reports of a number of unsuccessful ventures to cross the sand-hills. Grotto members who had been to the cave had not, as yet, completed that journey. Ray Lewis's fine, new cave was a big mystery.

The survey started on Independence Day 1977. As our party of mappers descended the old logging road into the gorge we encountered a familiar trio encumbered by backpacks and gear sweating their way back up it. Fellow grottoites Chris Kerr, John Yust, and Jim Nicholls were returning from their own first encounter with Xanadu. Their story of all-night rambles through the cave whetted our appetites for the giant cavern below. The three had successfully crossed the sandhills. But instead of descending the Zoroaster Canyon they had continued on the ledges at the top of the canyon. When the canyon had disappeared, their passage had not. An enormous chamber they had dubbed Fort Sanders and dozens of leads had rewarded their efforts. What awaited us, we wondered, as we hurried down to the cave?

Charles and Martha Clark and I surveyed from the Xanadu entrance. Stuart McGlasson, Chart Guthrie, and Brian Smith tagged along and explored. We quickly mapped down the entrance passage. It was my idea of a

Figure 7.14. Carol Lamers by stalactites in Xanadu Cave. Photo by Bob Biddix, September 5, 2011.

Chapter Four: August 27-31, 1977 – The Expedition. By Martha Clark.

The taller trees at the head of Lints Cove were just beginning to shine in the morning light. I filled the canteens from a trickle of water dripping off the thick mat of moss in the waterfall recess near the entrance of Xanadu. It was the last morning of our five-day expedition. Charles and I had accomplished much during our stay, but not without the help of our friends.

We had begun our trip with Jeff Sims by backpacking large loads, including four gallons of water, down the rough road into the Obey River gorge. At the bottom the trail leading through the seven-foot-tall weeds was faint, but soon gave way to a small, dry wash that served as a path up into Lints Cove. Lowering our packs we paused beside the whispering 20-foot waterfall that divides the entrance to Alph Caverns from the bluff that contains the Xanadu entrance. A short portage with our gear brought us 1,000 feet through the entrance passage to the intersection with the Monster Trunk connector. Here, the cave floor was wide, sandy and flat. This we chose as our base camp.

Being 60 to 70 pounds lighter, we scampered like rabbits over the 14 sandhills, carrying along with us only the survey gear. Locating our last mapping station beyond the Zoroaster Canyon, we continued the survey, following a strong breeze. In no more than a dozen stations a mushrooming expanse opened above our heads where the ceiling and upper walls had been before. We climbed up on a shelf of loose and crumbling dirt and stood facing the 30-foot-wide, 15-foot-high "entrance" to Fort Sanders. The opening gave the appearance of emerging from a cave into the dark of night. Being surveyors, we continued on to our objective and surveyed the perimeter of Fort Sanders (later, Jeff calculated that this room covered an area of three acres). Several leads were left open as we came back around to our starting point.

perfect passage, about 20-30 feet wide and 8-12 feet high, with a sandy floor and the nice, undulating curves of a phreatic tube. About 1,000 feet into the cave the ceiling lowered, forcing us to continue in a wide, sandy crawl. A small walkway to the right was the only lead we had seen so far. Suddenly, the floor vanished, and beneath us we could see a huge, lower level trunk, the sandhill passage! A catwalk around the right led to the continuation of the sandy avenue. At 3,000 feet the ceiling finally lowered to slab breakdown.

The sinuous walkway we had already noted soon popped out into the start of the Monster Trunk. Hundred-foot shots were easy. We made it to the second sandhill before running out of time. Where the survey stopped we stopped, not wishing to spoil the anticipation of our next trip.[6]

6 Jeff Sims, "Xanadu", NSS News, Vol. 39, No. 8 (August, 1981), pp. 169-170.

We prepared to take the survey into a wide side passage Jeff had noticed as he had entered Fort Sanders. We wondered how Chris Kerr and crew could have missed it. No footprints were visible on the smooth sandy floor that gently rolled upward to each side of the 70-foot-wide passage. The ceiling was even smoother than the floor with occasional calcite streaks running parallel to each other down the length of the passage.

Being on point I began pulling out the tape. Realizing that I was the one to permanently mar this picturesque floor with the mark of Vibram, I walked forward carefully. I felt that the serenity of this passage should never have been disturbed.

Setting a point 100 feet from Charles (on compass) I recalled the tale about Roy Davis and company racing down Virgin Avenue in Cumberland Caverns, throwing tackles on each other in their excitement of discovery. Here was our opportunity to literally run down virgin borehole screaming our delight. But it was not as I had imagined. Instead, I was overcome with humbleness. Regretfully disturbing the stillness, I called out each distance.

Jeff was the one who casually crossed the beautiful, unmarked passage to check beneath an overhang. I then discovered that he and Charles had not been aware of my care to make as few steps as possible, for they had been roaming around checking for leads and scuffling the sand at each station. My contemplation and reverie were totally shattered on the stroll back; Jeff and Charles broke into a dead run throwing tackles on each other right down the center of my dream.

With the canteens filled, we broke camp and carried our packs out to the jeep road. Charles brought along the machete to begin chopping a trail to the Zoroaster's entrance. We took the old road to the river and then began to bushwhack through the heaviest honeysuckle and blackberry growth of the year. The August heat completed the tropical atmosphere. At last we dropped down into the dry stream bed and felt the cold air flowing from the cave's lower entrance. I could really appreciate this entrance now for it led to the heart of the cave with only a moderate expenditure of time and energy.

The second morning of our expedition found Charles, Jeff, and I dragging ourselves over those energy-draining sandhills again to continue mapping. This time we mapped away from the wide and beautiful passage we had named Cumberland Avenue. Cumberland Avenue runs past Fort Sanders in Knoxville, Tenn., and evolves into Kingston Pike. So our passage too became Kingston Pike as it quickly narrowed and became lower. After several hundred feet of low crawls in dirt and dried rat droppings we came to a short series of small rooms. Naming these for various small towns along Highway 70 (Kingston Pike) we were stopped by breakdown. Jeff found a small opening blowing air that he was able to enlarge. We dropped through it into a room resonating with the sound of dripping water. L-shaped and 40 feet by 300 feet, the room easily was the second largest in the cave.

Our day ended in time for Jeff to hike out in daylight for work the next day. After two long days of caving and two round trips across the sandhills we were too tired to use the calculator we had brought along to reduce mapping data. Instead, we turned in early.

We awoke the next morning not knowing who if anyone, would arrive to assist us for the next three days. Leisurely doing our morning preparations we had given up hope that someone else was coming. We had just pulled the tarp over the gear when we heard a faint clanking and thump, thump of a pack with dangling canteen. In the distance could be seen a faint glow through the heavy mist as someone followed the turns and twists of the long winding passageway.

With John Smyre as our first tourist Charles and I proudly showed off Cumberland Avenue. We then returned to business and mapped a 40 by 30-foot side lead off the Fort Sanders Room. We found another large dripping chamber whose floor was a funnel filled with large boulders and gravel. Short ventures into other complex leads off Cumberland Avenue consumed most of the day.

After dinner at camp John expressed a desire to look into Alph Caverns. We took the short trip to the back of Alph's entrance passage. John began poking along the south wall. Soon he and Charles had dug open a tunnel leading to a low room, 40 by 200 feet containing several thin stalagmites two to three feet tall. This final discovery topped off a long day.

I sat with closed eyes, bundled on a rock, my feet in the water. Lazily, I enjoyed the sun soaking into my tired, bare back. The large blue-green pool in the otherwise dry riverbed was the last of the swimming holes in late summer (and the best). I sat all alone surrounded by the orange-red river rocks, the towering walls of the gorge, the hot silence of late afternoon and articles of mud-covered caving attire. Knowing no one was around for miles I plunged into the water.

The fourth morning of our expedition found us groggy after a night of tossing inside wet sleeping bags on hard-packed sand. Another morning of instant oatmeal for breakfast didn't liven us up any. We pulled out vertical gear and a 120-foot line and resignedly headed in the direction of the sandhills.

We rigged the rope at the end of the Monster Trunk and rappelled into the 60-foot canyon. Knowing of no other way to enter the Zoroaster level, we continued the survey. Our goal was to map out to the lower entrance. My job as point-setter and pathfinder was made easier by a very strong current of air flowing past us toward that entrance.

The new section was quite different. The 20-foot wide passage was bordered by scalloped walls and carpeted with dark variegated stream cobbles. Occasionally, we passed through narrower channels. My job was complicated by numerous intersections and side leads. This being the backbone of the lower level survey, permanent points had to be distinct and above the winter flood level. Little did we imagine just how complex the survey of the area was to become as we were blown out the lower entrance.

Being very chilled by the cave wind against damp clothes I opted for going to the river. Charles and John re-entered the cave to survey some side leads. After donning my now dry, mud-caked clothes I imagined how nice it would be to have a dry sleeping bag as well. I trekked through the heavy humidity up Lint's Cove to the Xanadu entrance, figuring to spread the sleeping bags in the sun. I abruptly halted at the sight of a machete and felt hat in the entrance. So I hadn't been alone in the gorge!

Cautiously, I went on to camp where I found a note scrawled on the sandy shelf by our packs. "We will find you. Came to survey. RK BP." Reinforcements had arrived in the form of Randy Kissling and Bob Pratt, but Xanadu was a big cave and I wondered if we would ever see the new arrivals.

I re-entered the lower cave via the Zoroaster's entrance to tell John and Charles about Randy and Bob. I was really surprised to hear the loud bantering and laughter of several voices. Each group had found the other on different ends of the dangling rope.

During the last night in the cave, John made a discovery. He had heard a rustling among the dirty dinner dishes. A well-aimed beam from his flashlight revealed two bats lapping spaghetti sauce and leaving an almost clean plate. Rabies can be spread via saliva, but I think the bats are safe. John had not displayed unusual signs before dinner that night.

The morning was hot as we hoisted up our backpacks. The long hike out of the gorge

Figure 7.15. Daniel Wright in a section of the Sand Hills Passage with an unusually large, flat ceiling. Photo by Bob Biddix, November 27, 2004.

seemed easier than scrambling over the sand hills. The jouncing car ride from the top of the gorge out to the highway seemed anti-climactic after spending four days within the vastness of Xanadu. The much-anticipated expedition was over. We had surveyed 8,300 feet to push the cave to 3.2 miles—but we had hardly scratched the surface.[7]

Chapter Five: The Survey of Alph Caverns Begins. By Randy Kissling.

The first thing a caver notices as he or she approaches the Xanadu entrance is not the Xanadu entrance. It is, rather, the gaping entrance of Alph Caverns because of its size and beauty. More than a few parties of cavers have been known to stumble through the entranceways of Alph wondering where the large trunk passages and sandhills are!

The survey of Alph began in September 1977. Thinking that it would be a nice, easy cave to survey, I took this project on to keep myself occupied when I wasn't mapping in Xanadu. It didn't take long before I realized what I had gotten involved in.

In late September Chris Kerr, John Yust, and I began mapping into Alph, following the route water obviously takes in times of flood. We soon heard a distant rumbling and came upon a small waterfall spraying out of the ceiling and disappearing into the floor. After surveying down a 15-foot climbdown we came out at the ceiling of a 30-foot high trunk passage. We rigged a rope and continued mapping to the base of the 30-foot drop (which is a roaring waterfall in wetter periods of the year). To the left the trunk abruptly ended in breakdown and crawlways. To the right it continued into the blackness, so without any discussion we surveyed in that direction. This was going to be a fun survey!

The passage soon doubled back on itself and began to rapidly deteriorate. We mapped into a maze of passages with mud and cobblestone floors, walls and occasionally even cobblestone ceilings. Several times we intersected water filtering its way down. Every other survey station would find another two or three leads at various levels.

"Here's another lead going down and two off to the right," said John.

"Okay, call that point BACB2 and when we survey this passage it will be BACC1 or maybe BACBA1, and when we survey…," I said. Chris just laughed as he read instrument.

While the others slept that morning under the rock shelter I laid awake wondering how I could sucker Jeff or Charles into taking over the survey. I thought of all of our previously unsuccessful attempts to make obvious connection in the Grassy Cove and Lost Creek areas. I could only hope it would be different this time.

As November rolled around I began to get desperate for a connection to be made. Martha Clark, Jeri Kizer, and I came close, but we wimped out and turned back after surveying in a small crawlway for several hours. This became the now famous "Forget it" connection after it was surveyed into from Xanadu. An unofficial connection was made using the "Polish Method." This involved negotiating a small crawlway that leads from the Alph entrance and pops out behind the surface waterfall in Lints Cove. From here the astute caver would continue to crawl the few feet into Xanadu, "never realizing" that he had been outside. The project remained mine, however.

Nonetheless, I decided that as soon as the connection was made the map and notes of Alph would be in the mail to Jeff Sims.[8]

Chapter Six: January 7-8, 1978 – Alph Connection! By Jeff Sims.

Any number of open leads along the entrance passage or the Monster Trunk could be the one. Randy and I had mapped the left-hand

---

7 Martha Clark, "Xanadu", NSS News, Vol. 39, No. 8 (August, 1981), pp. 170-171.

8 Randy Kissling, "Xanadu", NSS News, Vol. 39, No. 8 (August, 1981), pp. 171-172.

Figure 7.16. Rami Ayoub by stalagmites in Xanadu Cave. Photo by Chuck Sutherland, July 16, 2011.

terminus of the entrance passage where half a dozen leads led off. Along the left wall of the Monster Trunk I had noted a number of blowing leads. Charles also had such a favorite crawl. One of these dozens of leads was bound to lead to Alph. Once the connection was made, Charles and I intended to dump the whole damn mess on Randy and his Alph survey.

A convention of cavers gathered for this trip. Regular surveyors Charles, Martha, Randy Kissling, Jeri Kizer, Will Chamberlin, and I were accompanied by Lin Guy, Andrey Duncan, David Young, Chris Kerr, John Yust, John Reid, and Marilyn Hall. We split into only two groups due to the lack of survey instruments. Charles took Martha, Will, Chris, the two Johns and Marilyn to the lower level near the Zoroaster Entrance. I, with the

Figure 7.17. Erica Sughrue in a canyon passage in Xanadu Cave. Photo by Bob Biddix, September 5, 2011.

Figure 7.18. Ken Pasternack by stalagmites in Xanadu Cave. Photo by Chuck Sutherland, November 18, 2012.

remainder began mapping at the bottom of the connection canyon in the Zoroaster level.

At first we mapped muddy crawls, then progressed up to dry, virgin canyons. But I soon discovered six people on a survey crew is just too many. I finally blew my top about the fourth time rocks were dislodged onto Randy, my instrument man. In an ill-concealed rage I led the way up out of the lower level to the Monster Trunk. I intended to go somewhere where it would be impossible to cripple my mappers with rocks and boulders; we'd go map a crawl.

The crawl I decided on was no ordinary crawl! It was located in the side of the Monster Trunk at the base of one of the sandhills and had quite a bit of air movement. Before, we had been surveying virgin walking passage. By switching to crawlways, I nearly ditched two of my clan, Jeri and Lin. This crawl not only blew air, it headed toward the south and Alph

Caverns. I knew the wind must be related to either the Alph Entrance or to the 40-foot waterfall in Alph Caverns.

Randy, Audrey, Dave, and I mapped through the small three by three-foot tube. At every intersection we did the Xanadu breath test to determine which route to follow. Our passage seemed to be a lower level overflow passage: debris clung to ceiling and walls. Several belly crawls and a couple thousand feet later the wind picked up and really came howling through a canyon crack clogged with logs.

Randy and I forged ahead and popped out into walking stream passage. We must be close, I thought. Following the water upstream, I heard the roar of a waterfall. Soon it came into sight. I waited for Randy's announcement, since I had never been below Alph's waterfall before.

"We did it!" Randy exclaimed. I congratulated him on being the new head of the Xanadu survey. He declined so we unanimously gave it to Charles.[9]

Chapter Seven: December 16-17, 1978 – Sunday City. By Charles Clark.

It was satisfying, at last, to finish at least some leads in this nightmare of openings, cracks, chimneys, and chasms that only seemed to multiply. Jeri Kizer, Jeff, and I were finding that some do eventually close out if you just persist. After we had handily put away three such leads we heard the approach of cavers. John Smyre and Bill Walter had made their appointed rendezvous. John and I set off for E Passage and the upper level maze bordering Cumberland Avenue. Jeff, Jeri, and Bill remained in the network beneath Fort Sanders.

The fifth lead seemed to go nowhere. It was a 60-degree slope down 40 feet followed by a similar sand incline going up again to an apparent end. A chimney in the ceiling led on! Our upper level maze, which had been filling in so nicely, circumscribed by Cumberland Avenue, E passage, and Fort Sanders, had just broken open; we had exited the exterior wall of E Passage.

John and I ran the tape out for several 50-foot shots (we dared make them no longer for fear of missing side passages) down a flat, sandy walkway 20 feet high by 40 feet wide. Next, we heard the piercing echo of a drip that seemed to resonate from some bottomless depth. In three more shots we intersected the side of a domepit that dropped well over 50 feet. We only made a dent in this extension of the upper maze. Sixty-five stations and 1,000 feet of tedious cleanup had consumed our day of caving. Back across the sandhills to base camp we plodded for our midnight supper.

The others had no less a rewarding day. Their 1,000 feet, though not breaking into

anything large and going, included a grotto containing what they called "gypsum swords." After eating dinner and adding up surveyed footage we all bedded down for the night.

All except Bill Walter, that is. Bill's curious cuisine of cold beans and warm beer didn't sit too well with him. Nor was his sleeping arrangement quite satisfactory (an army blanket on newspapers).

"I can't sleep. I'm going off to check the breakdown at the head of the trunk passage till I get sleepy."

We arose and fired up our stoves for breakfast. Jeri asked Bill what it was he had been mumbling about when he finally bedded down at 3 a.m. Bill reconstructed his exploits of the night before.

Two hundred feet from base camp a meandering stoop passage pops out at the head of the Monster Trunk. Here, at the beginning of the large passage, breakdown is strewn about the floor and soon bars progress in one direction. Bill recounted how he started to probe this pile against the far wall, opening by opening, crack by crack. At last, a set of tight squeezes led into sinuous passage again. The passage soon came to a four-way junction, then another, and yet another. Bill had stumbled into quite a complex, little maze. In 30 minutes Bill became lost. Several hours of concerned probing led the way out, but not before he had seen one half to three-fourths of a mile of this intriguing little "city."

Since it was a Sunday and no one felt ambitious enough to cross the sandhills again, Bill's bean-inspired find proved ideal for a leisurely, second day's survey. Bill had not been exaggerating when he suggested his find was a little complicated. This wonderful little maze, Sunday City (for its convenient location to provide easy Sunday surveying), was a network of parallel and perpendicular tubes, where the passages averaged twice the width of the walls that partitioned them. Though not on the same scale as Anvil Cave, Sunday City was more complex and more complicated

9 Jeff Sims, "Xanadu", NSS News, Vol. 39, No. 8 (August, 1981), p. 172.

for the area involved. Bill excitedly took us to what he considered the main feature of the discovery, a nine-way junction! Bill was wrong, however, for less than 100 feet from this grand spectacle we found a 15-way intersection. I still don't understand how he found his way back that night…[10]

Chapter Eight: June 1978-March 1980: Deep in the Heart of Alph …The Key to the Mountain. By Jeff Sims.

Except for Randy's initial effort and the connection passage (which had yet to be tied to Randy's survey) no work had been done in Alph. Ray Lewis had explored an estimated mile of passage. Beyond our survey and Ray's brief efforts nothing was known of this section

10 Charles Clark, "Xanadu", NSS News, Vol. 39, No. 8 (August, 1981), pp172-173.

of Xanadu. Alph was indeed a mystery, and it was high time we got down to business in this section of the cave.

It wasn't until June 1978 that Randy and I returned to Alph to continue where we had left off on the connection trip. Will Chamberlin accompanied us in, while Charles, Martha, Mark, and Charlotte Stock surveyed down in Zoroaster's. Quickly, the dangling connection passage was tied to Randy's survey. From there we headed for an upper level canyon in what I term Middle Alph. A high lead from here took us to an old, dry, cobble-floored canyon. This, in turn, led to an even bigger passage. All virgin with many side leads! With the excitement of discovery as incentive we mapped late into the night …

Figure 7.19. Erica Sughrue by a wall of flowstone formations in Xanadu Cave. Photo by Bob Biddix, September 5, 2011.

Later that summer, I had to show Charles the new sections of Alph, but I insisted that we map a crawl. Little did I know that my plot would backfire. Mark and Charlotte Stock joined us, but Mark had a light failure and spent the trip in his sleeping bag at base camp. The rest of us began surveying a crawl in Middle Alph. It got tight but soon opened at a junction. I went one way, Charles went the other, to determine the best way to map. I chimneyed up 15 feet to a 30-foot-wide trunk; this was definitely the way to go! The excitement of big, virgin passage now spurred us on. The passage kept getting bigger and bigger. At one point it measured 70 feet wide and 50 feet high! We named our find the 747 Passage after a rumored trunk in the cave …only this passage was no rumor. After reaching a breakdown we started out. At Camp we found Mark snoring soundly.

March 31-April 1, 1979, Charles took Marion Smith and Gerald Moni back to the 747 Passage to make a dent in some of the numerous side passages. One hundred stations did much in extending the skeleton out from the 747 Passage. The most notable discovery was Goblin's Graveyard, a 20 by 20-foot avenue whose floor was littered with curious stone partitions and cut by a meandering, rocky trench.

After plotting up Middle Alph I discovered that most of the passages were directly under Lints Cove. So far, Lints Cove had stopped any passages running out under its southern slope. Pondering over the map with beer in hand, my search for the "Key to the Mountain" began.

An imaginary line can be drawn through points corresponding with the truncated passages at the southeastern end of Xanadu. It starts at Sunday City, runs through the Sandhill Passage's eastern breakdown and through several trunks in Middle Alph. This line runs approximately parallel to the stream and dry wash in the floor of Lints Cove on the

surface. My reasoning was that these trunk passages had to continue on the other sides of their breakdown barriers, out under Lints Cove's southern flank. Onward, perhaps, to Zarathustra's Cave.

The first attempt to find the Key to the Mountain was on January 19, 1980. It was survey trip 31, and I was accompanied by Hal Bridges, Randy Kissling, and David Bradford. After mopping up leads in the Alph Connector we found a new connection to Alph. Bradford decided all the crawling in this part of the cave wasn't quite suited to his 6-foot 4-inch, 250-pound frame. So we abandoned Dave in Bradford's Bower and headed for the southern extremities of Middle Alph.

Arriving at the point of furthest penetration we began surveying. The passage became a belly crawl that led to a 15-foot drop into a dome. By crawling to the edge, a walking passage could be seen leading off the south side of the dome. I got all excited. This was the Key to the Mountain! An easy climb down led us around the dome and into the side passage. Unfortunately, our excitement soon died in a massive breakdown. However, a drop in the floor led down 15 feet to a lower level. Maybe it was possible to get beneath the breakdown. The nature of the passage changed. We were now in an old stream passage with cobbles and debris that indicated it was subject to flooding. We ran out of time before we ran out of leads.

February 1980 Will Chamberlin and Rick Buice became victims of my sales pitch on Key to the Mountain. We began mapping at the base of the climb that Hal, Randy, and I had found in January. The crawl went the wrong direction! Instead of going south it went north. Utilizing my in-cave sketch I figured we might come out in Sunday City. Fifteen hundred feet later we popped out into the Clark Crawl just off the Sandhill Passage a half mile away from Sunday City. Rick and Will were "amazed" at my accuracy for predicting our location.

My lower level attempts at Key to the Mountain having been frustrated, Hal Bridges and I tried some upper leads in March 1980. Finding a number of interesting features including a virgin maze and the Sand Trap, we seemed at a loss for promising leads. Except for yet one more passage that ended in breakdown, most of our leads looped back into the Goblin's Graveyard.

So far, more than five miles of virgin passages have been mapped in Lower and Middle Alph. As incredible as it may seem, Alph equals the expansive Xanadu section and the complicated Zoroaster section in total surveyed footage. And in open leads it has more potential than the other sections with over 150 waiting to be mapped. Though not containing any single, outstanding feature like a Monster Trunk, Fort Sanders, or windy Zoroaster Thoroughfare (except, perhaps the 747 Passage) I have a fond attachment for this part of the cave. Because of its remoteness and lack of tourist delights, tourist have never been to Middle of Lower Alph; it remains the "private" sanctuary of the Xanadu surveyors. And the "Key" is still waiting to be turned.[11]

Chapter Nine: July 2-3, 1980 – Up and Down on the Long Cave List. By Charles Clark.
When Martha and I had moved from Tennessee Xanadu had been 11 miles long. In a little less than a year's time Jeff had inched that total forward bit by bit in the unrelenting mazes of Alph and the Evil Frog Extension until Xanadu stood at 14.5 miles. My fetish has always been to pass some other cave on the long cave list. Earlier in the year Jeff had put Anvil Cave's 12.8 miles behind him. Now, returning for a visit, Martha and I had the opportunity of helping the survey over the 15-miles mark to gun down Alabama's premier giant, Fern Cave.

Having enjoyed the luxury of four wheeling to the base of the gorge, Jeff, Laurie Adams, Martha, and I soon found ourselves at Camp II in the Zoroaster level.

"Key to the Mountain" was all I had been hearing in phone conversations and in letters. Though Jeff had coined the cute little name he never had to impress the significance of its meaning on me. Any passage that could break out under the south flank of Lints Cove had the potential of adding half again to Xanadu's already established length. A few hair-raising breakdown stacks were probed and an utterly sleezy stream crawl was mapped before we lost the urge to discover the "Key to the Mountain".

I wanted to run up the footage, so we backtracked to the series of long sewer tubes that connect Alph to the Monster Trunk of Xanadu. Though ugly and sometimes uncomfortable, these tubes never fail to provide long hours of survey and much footage (you also don't have to worry about sketching Swiss cheese). Jeff indicated an unsurveyed lead, so off we began. In several hundred feet we popped out into a small dome that also happened to be a four-way intersection. To the right was a low wide passage that ran fairly straight. A perfect lead to crank out the tape! Five hundred feet brought us to a canyon. I chimneyed up to scout an upper level.

In front of me was survey station CC-21. The place was familiar. I racked my brain and then remembered. Jeff, Martha, Jeri, and I had surveyed this down from the Monster Trunk. In fact, somewhere nearby was Assault and Battery Dome (were Martha had belted me on that same trip). After the others had tied into CC-21 they helped me try to find Assault and Battery Dome. Jeff soon found it, but I was now on the track of something else.

A few twists and turns and then I descended to a lower level, 10 feet down. Boot prints! Not virgin, I determined. Then I saw a

11 Jeff Sims, "Xanadu", NSS News, Vol. 39, No. 8, pp. 173-174.

dot smoked on the wall with JAB-12 next to it. "J Series. I'm in Zoroaster!"

Once again, I strained to remember. This was the route to the Indian footprints from the base of Connection Canyon. I called for the others to follow me. Carefully, stepping out his old survey route we soon emerged into the main throughway of Zoroaster. For the first time we had made a connection directly from Alph to Zoroaster, bypassing Xanadu and the Monster Trunk altogether.

Like any good Xanadu trip it was past midnight before we were ready to bed down. We sat up for awhile discussing our finds, planning survey strategy and boring each other with sharp wit. I totaled our footage at 1,900 feet. It would take a good 600 feet to achieve 15 miles the next day.

The next morning, walking down the main throughway of Zoroaster, I pointed to some enormous leads on the right wall.

"Did these tie into Evil Frog when you mapped them?" I asked.

"I've never been in them. I thought you mapped them" Jeff replied.

"You've never plotted them have you?"

We unpacked our survey gear and located a permanent station nearby. Each of us was silently accusing the other of total incompetency. For three years we had been walking right by this expansive gallery, down one of the most traveled passages in the cave, without ever having wondered about it (much less having entered it). It brought back nostalgic memories of the first year of the survey when the whole cave was like this. Martha ran the tape out in 100-foot shots up and down several modest sand piles. Needless to say, we made 15 miles.

Three days later Jeff, Martha, and I were laid back in our campsite at the SERA Cave Carnival, celebrating our milestone with the succulent rewards of caver's champagne (semi-cool Pabst). As usual we were patting each other on the back and marveling at our achievements. Just then Jeff noticed that

Bill Torode had pulled in. Nonchalantly, Jeff worked his way over to Bill's vehicle to "nonchalantly" inform him of Fern Cave's slight retreat on the long cave list. In a few minutes he was back.

"I thought you said Fern was 15 miles … it's 15.9 miles," Jeff informed me.

After a few shrugs and belches we all sat back down again. It was a good afternoon to sulk away our fallen pride with the stale taste of warm beer.[12]

Chapter Ten: April 15, 1981. It Ain't Over Yet…By Jeff Sims.

Putting the proverbial caving question aside (how much unexplored cave is there?), I can only guess at what lies ahead. Anyone who has surveyed a big cave with lots of virgin leads knows that anything can happen. But I can tell you this, Xanadu Cave is and will be for some time one of Tennessee's largest caves. The real goal of the survey will be to break the 20-mile mark. If we get lucky we may even connect with some of the other caves in the area.

So far, Xanadu Cave has been an unforgettable experience for the original explorers and surveyors. To map and explore virgin passage is, of course, the ultimate. Yet, after 30 trips to the cave, it is sobering to see the impact and changes made by cavers. That's right, not novices or Sunday afternoon strollers, but NSS cavers. In closing, I can only plead for visitors to Xanadu Cave to tread lightly. If the cave continues to be visited by large groups of 20 or 30 cavers the only choice is to gate the entrance to limit traffic.[13]

Interestingly, this epic narrative describes only the first 15 miles of Xanadu Cave. The map which accompanied this article shows 16.424 miles. But now, 38 years later, the surveyed length is up to slightly over 24 miles. Next, we will learn about

12 Charles Clark, "Xanadu Cave", NSS News, Vol. 39, No. 8 (August, 1981), pp174-175.

13 Jeff Sims, "Xanadu Cave", NSS News, Vol. 39, No. 8, p. 175.

the next 8 miles of discoveries made between 1981 and 1989:

1980: 11 trips, 3.8 miles surveyed. Continue finding passage in Lower and Middle Alph sections, including Key to the Mountain, Left of the Sand Trap, and additional connection to the Evil Frog Section. Cave reached over 16 miles in length.

1981: 13 trips, 3.8 miles surveyed. Discover Fifth Avenue and another connection from the lower cave to Alph, the 15 Minute Route. Continue to find more passage in the lower levels below the Wheezing Passage, between the Evil Frog and Cumberland Avenue. North Carolina cavers spend 5 days underground mapping almost a

mile. Cave reaches over 19 miles in length.

1982: 9 trips, 2.1 miles surveyed. Mapping of leads in Sunday City, Goblin's Graveyard, Kelly's Kanyon, Evil Frog--Butterfingers Route to Middle Alph, and in the Wheezing Passage.

1983: 9 trips, 1 mile surveyed. More passage surveyed in 15 Minute Route, under Cumberland Avenue, Sunday City Maze, Wheezing Passage, and Middle Alph.

1984: 6 trips; less than a mile surveyed (0.8). Mapped in Sunday City, Middle Alph, and Lower Alph.

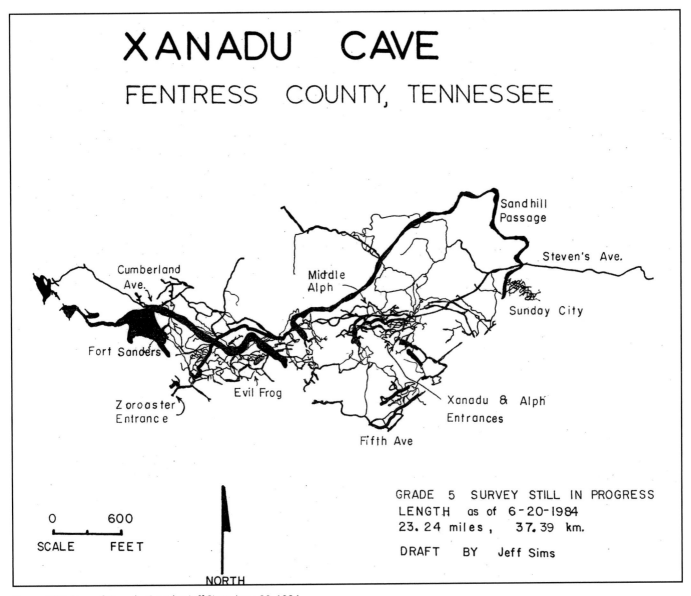

Figure 7.20. Map of Xanadu Cave by Jeff Sims, June 20, 1984.

1985: 5 trips; ½ mile surveyed. Upper levels around Marlin Pit, leads off Fifth Avenue, and Fossil Avenue.

1986-1988: No survey trips.

1989: 1 trip, last survey trip of the mapping effort.

So, mapping ended in 1989 with a grand total of 24.062 miles of surveyed cave and a vertical extent of 227 feet. This was the result of 83 survey trips spread over a 12-year period. (See Figure 7.20)

Is there more cave there to discover and survey? Probably, but this was an outstanding crew of surveyors. You will have to work hard to find anything that they missed. The surveyors give you this advice:

> The map shows several leads. Most are in maze areas and may not go far. There is probably a few more miles of cave for those willing to explore. Focusing on the edges of the map may lead to more cave. Lower wet levels may bypass collapses that stop upper passages.

Or you may be another Bill Walter and push some breakdown that no one else has been able to penetrate and break through into miles of virgin cave.

Figure 7.21. A Mastodon leg bone (Humerus) discovered in Xanadu Cave with a carbide lamp and tape measure for scale. Photo by Martha Clark, 1984.

Figure 7.22. Carol Vesely by a row of formations in Xanadu Cave. Photo by Dave Bunnell, July, 1983.

THE EVIL FROG

When you are exploring a very large cave, like Xanadu, it is very important that each passage and room have its own name. This way you can talk to your fellow explorers about where you went and how to get there. Unfortunately, with the passage of time, frequently the origin of these names is lost. With that in mind Martha Clark wrote the follow story describing the origin of the Evil Frog name:

On a survey trip in the lower levels of Xanadu in May of 1979 I was pulling tape and setting point as usual. The passage varied from 5-12 feet wide, tall and canyon like with an undulating cobble stoned floor. My carbide light was a warm yellow glow against the creamy limestone while I held it on point for Charles to take the reading. I moved ahead 40 feet or so to locate the next point while Jeff sketched. The passage narrowed. There appeared to be a side lead on the left which was upslope from where I held the tape. I shined my lamp upward into the curved ceiling alcove to see over the lip. I almost jumper back as there appeared to be large eyes staring at me. I held my lamp higher, turning if left and right trying to settle my excited imagination. But I knew almost immediately that those deep eyes set 2 feet apart in heavy brow ridges on a back-sloping head could only be those of a menacing EVIL FROG.

I shouted out what I had seen. Goosebumps rose beneath my patched denim jacket sleeves while I anxiously waited for the crew to catch up. Jeff and Charles claimed to see nothing as I cautiously started up the climb into the toad-hole of a passage, expecting a sticky tongue to wrap around my arm at any moment. I was most surprised to discover a 12-foot high alcove, 6 feet in diameter with a nearly flat sandy floor. Where had the Evil Frog gone? Two six-inch high mounds of sand covered cobble were the only hint of an overly active imagination.

I was very disappointed with the reality, but the naming of this long passage extension keeps my chill alive. It was on a later trip to the cave while driving through Cumberland County that we stopped at a roadside stand and on a whim I bought a painted concrete frog to place in the Lair of the Evil Frog. I suppose it is there to this day. Beware near the alcoves.[14]

Your mind can play funny tricks on you when you have been underground for many hours and are very tired. Here is one more story that Martha shared with us:

We were again mapping in the lower canyon levels, usually a crew of three, with the addition of Charlotte Stock. I was, as always, setting point, while Charlotte roamed around poking into side leads and returning to check in. Suddenly Charlotte said softly to me: "Did you hear that?" "What?", I whispered. "There!", exclaimed Charlotte.

I paused from reeling in the tape to listen. Nothing. "What was it like?", I asked.

"A faint moaning, kind of a hollow sound. I don't know. I don't hear it now, maybe I just imagined it."

This was repeated off and on for several more survey shots. The crew gathered together for a carbide change. Charlotte said, "I hear it again! There, can you hear it? Everybody move over here." I scooted closed to Charlotte as did Jeff and Charles.

"Yeah, I hear it now," exclaimed Charles as he reached into my bag of gorp. I held my breath to listen closer.

"Oh wow! It stopped," said Jeff.

"I didn't hear it," I sighed. Charlotte told me to take a deep breath.

"It's you, Martha! You are the cause of the wheezing in the passage! Charlotte said with delight. It was another week before I was completely over my chest cold.

14 Martha M. M. Clark, Personal communication, April 22, 2020.

Figure 7.23. Carol Vesely by beautiful formations on an upper ledge overlooking the end of the Sand Hill Passage in Xanadu Cave. Photo by Dave Bunnell, July, 1983.

Because of this, the passage was named the Wheezing Passage.[15] These place names give life and character to what are otherwise sometime just plain cave passages.

THE XANADU CAVE MASTODON BONE

While researching this book, I was fascinated to learn that the surveyors had discovered a Mastodon bone, deep inside Xanadu Cave. Martha Clark tells us the story of that find:

> In October 1984 the usual Xanadu survey team of Jeff Sims, Charles, me, plus Michele Sims were cleaning-up side leads in some far-flung section of Xanadu. We were trying to get in as many survey trips late that year as possible, as Charles and I were preparing for an impending move to Arkansas early the

next year. I was on point and went into a low, two to two and a half-foot high, but very wide crawl. The floor dipped slightly into a bowl-like depression at the end of the 40-foot shot. Near the center of the depression there was a two-foot long rock and as I crawled around it to pull the tape to the far wall, I thought it looked rather bone-like. After holding my light on point and waiting for the rest of the crew to crawl forward, I looked at it more closely.

The large end of the rock was knobby, like the joint-end of a cow's leg bone and was about 6-inches across. It looked somewhat textured while the long sides which tapered down to the smaller end were relatively smooth. The smaller end was about three and a half-inches in diameter and was open. I peered into the hollow and it had the webbed appearance like…marrow. Goose bumps swept over me as my mind spun trying to

15 Martha M. M. Clark, Personal communication, April 22, 2020.

make sense of this "rock". We were in a cave passage miles from any known entrance.

As the other team members looked at the find (we didn't move it), I scouted ahead for the next point for the survey. The passage opened up to the left and abruptly ended in a breakdown wall which had quite a bit of water dripping through it. I surmised than an entrance may have been here at one time. The low area where the bone was found had the feeling of being an animal's lair.

We returned a couple of months later to remove the bone after we decided that we could never get an archaeologist to travel that far underground to see it *in situ*. I showed the bone to a paleontologist at Georgia State in Atlanta. He identified it as the humerus bone from a Mastodon. He noted that finding mastodon bones was fairly common in quarry operations. This bone was interesting in that it was not calcified, it was just a very old bone.

Jeff and Michele took possession of the bone, with plans to have it preserved and handed over to the Gernt family, the landowners of Xanadu Cave. Michele knew someone in Indiana who could do the job. Unfortunately, with the passing of time, job changes, and moves, the bone was forgotten and its current whereabouts is unknown.[16]

Fortunately, Martha Clark did take photographs of the Mastodon bone in the cave. (Figures 7.21)

MY FIRST TRIP TO THE CAVE

Back on June 14, 1980 I made my first visit to Xanadu Cave and wrote the following Trip Report:

After reading and hearing much about Xanadu Cave, discovered a few years ago in Fentress Country I finally got around to visiting it myself. Mark Mitckes led me, Marietta Matthews, and Ken McLean to the Lower (Zoroaster) Entrance on June 14,

1980. I was very impressed at the strong wind blowing out this entrance. Shortly inside the cave I estimated the wind speed at between 10 to 15 miles per hour in a passage with a cross-section of 7 feet high and 10 feet wide. At the time, the outside temperature was in the mid 80's. This is one of the strongest, if not <u>the</u> strongest air flows I have ever encountered in a cave.

Shortly inside the Lower Entrance we were in an upper level when people appeared in the lower level. They turned out to be locals so when they asked for directions, Mark told them nothing useful. Hours later on the way back out of the cave we discovered a newly painted trail of big red arrows from this point back to the Lower Entrance. We rubbed off as many as we could with sand from the floor.

Figure 7.24. Cavers in the Sand Hills Passage in Xanadu Cave. Photo by Dave Bunnell and Philippe Crochet, July, 1981.

---

16 Martha M. M. Clark, Personal communication, April 23, 2020.

Over the Lower Entrance they had painted a large red "X" which was still wet. Fortunately they had been unable to make the climb to the upper level where we had looked down upon them and they did not find the crawlway that by-passes the climb. This gross vandalism was ironic, since we had been talking for most of the day about how clean and unvandalized the cave was. The vandals apparently rode trail bikes to the Lower Entrance.

While in the cave, we visited several formation areas, the Sand Hills, the Fort Sanders Room, and Cumberland Avenue. Xanadu is certainly a large and beautiful cave and we were all very impressed. At the Sand Hills we met a group from Atlanta which seemed to have only one person with much caving experience. They followed us to Fort Sanders and Cumberland Avenue, then out of the cave. At one point a member of their party slipped and almost fell into a 60-foot deep canyon. He just barely caught on by his hands and he lost his helmet and lamp into the canyon. In the process he hit his head on a stalagmite. Mark and I found an easy way to the bottom of the canyon and retrieved his helmet and lamp for him. It seems unlikely that this group could have found the Lower Entrance by themselves, so it is probably lucky they ran into us.

The hike back up the plateau to the cars was steep and the oppressive heat didn't help, so we concentrated on keeping a mental image of the ice-cold beers waiting for us in the cooler in the car. Mark returned to Knoxville and we cruised down the highway back to Nashville.[17]

All it takes is a few locals with spray paint to totally trash a cave.

THE XANADU CAVE CONSERVATION TASK FORCE

The following information was copied from the written introduction to the final Xanadu Cave map:

> In 1987, the Xanadu Cave Conservation Task Force (CTF) was formed in cooperation with the National Speleological Society (NSS) and the landowners, the Estate of Bruno Gernt, Inc. A lease agreement was signed with the landowner, the Estate of Bruno Gernt, Inc., and a Cave Management Plan was put in place.
>
> Part of that Management Plan is to control access to the cave's main entrances with locked gates. This is done through Access Policies in the Management Plan.
>
> The purpose of this access management is to protect and preserve the cave, rather than let it become heavily used, and vandalized, like many other caves in Tennessee have.
>
> The Xanadu Cave CTF continues to monitor the gates and controls access through keys to the gates.[18]

According to an announcement in the May, 1986 NSS News, the cave gates were built between March and April, 1986.[19]

CAVE ACCESS

Xanadu Cave is managed through a lease agreement between the Obey River Conservation Task Force and the Estate of Bruno Gernt/Allardt Land Company (EBGALC). Currently, the two managers of Xanadu Cave are Jeff Patton and Chris Kerr.[20] Anyone wishing to visit this cave must have written permission from the Obey River Conservation Task Force.

17 Larry E. Matthews, "Trip To Xanadu Cave", Speleonews, Vol. 24, No. 3 (August, 1980), pp. 62-63.

18 Jeff Sims, "Xanadu Cave, TFE94, Fentress Co., Tennessee", 2017 TCS Map Book, pp. 9-10. Copyright 2013. Used by permission.

19 Anonymous, NSS News, Vol. 44, No. 5 (May, 1986), p. 128.

20 Jeff Patton, Personal communication, January 1, 2020.

Place Names in Xanadu Cave

Alph Caverns Entrance
Assault and Battery Dome
Bradford's Bower
Butterfingers Route
Camel Raceway
Camp II
Clark Crawl
Cumberland Avenue
E Passage
Evil Frog Extension
Fifth Avenue
Fort Sanders
Fossil Avenue
Goblin's Graveyard
J Series
Jewel Box
Kelly's Kanyon

Key to the Mountain
Kublai Khan's Camel Raceway
Left of the Sand Trap
Kingston Pike
Lower Alph
Marlin Pit
Middle Alph
Monster Trunk
Sand Hills
Sand Trap
Sunday City
Wheezing Passage
Xanadu Entrance
Zoroaster Canyon
Zoroaster Entrance
15 Minute Route
747 Passage

Figure 7.25. Phreatic tubes in the Zoroaster section, are the lowest levels of the Xanadu cave system. Photo by Dave Bunnell and Philippe Crochet, July 1981.

Figure 8.1. Two cavers in the entrance to Yggdrasil Cave. Photo by Joe Douglas, June 1, 2013.

Figure 8.2. Marion O. Smith inspects thick wood boards left by the saltpeter miners in Yggdrasil Cave. Photo by Kristen Bobo, June 1, 2013.

CHAPTER 8
Yggdrasil Cave

Located relatively close to Xanadu Cave is another very significant cave: Yggdrasil Cave.[1] It has approximately one mile of explored passages, has the remains of a saltpeter mine near the entrance, and contains several large breakdown rooms and large passages. The following description was written by Ray Lewis and Alan Cressler and is in the Tennessee Cave Survey Narrative Files:

> Yggdrasil Cave is located in the middle of the gorge of the East Fork of the Obey River. The entrance is 12 feet wide by 9 feet high and opens to a tunnel looking passage that quickly lowers to a dry hands-and-knees tube for 100 feet to a large room. This room contains remains of old saltpeter workings, vats, and troughs, and stuff. A small hole at the lower, back end of the room goes down to a low passage. Follow this and take the first small hole on the left, crawl through, and then it opens up. Then there is another crawl, then a series of crawls and climbdowns. Finally, climb up to a sandy passage. We dug this open and pushed it as a belly crawl for 1,000 feet to where it suddenly pops out over a 10 to 20-foot wide by 40-foot-high trunk passage. (Bring a rope for it's 12-feet to the floor.) The lower passage is muddy and consists of several adjoining breakdown rooms.

Joe Douglas reports:

> The best feature (of this cave) is the classic saltpeter chamber. A huge pile of waste rocks, vat remnants, tally marks, and impressive water collection troughs, made of single enormous logs, the likes of which are not found in Fentress County today.[2]

---

1 Yggdrasil is the Tree of Life in Norse Mythology, an immense, eternally green ash tree.

2 Joe Douglas, Personal communication, April 4, 2020.

A 1979 TRIP REPORT

Amazingly little has been written about this cave, so the following Trip Report by Bruce Zerr provides some much-needed information about the original exploration of this cave:

> The surveying of Yggdrasil Cave in the Obey River Gorge is finally complete. The footage surveyed is a little over one-half mile.
>
> Our last trip to Yggdrasil was intended to finish mapping the cave. If nothing new was found it could be done, but time was going to be short for doing everything planned.
>
> The trip started on time and arrived at the lip of the gorge only 15 minutes late. We saw nothing unusual on the way down as we hurried.
>
> About halfway to the back of the cave I explored a side lead. In 30 feet I was in virgin cave! The crawl stayed tight for another 50 feet when it suddenly changed levels by six to seven feet. I could see around the corner and up into a four-foot-high passage. Someone smaller than I will be the explorer, namely someone that is five feet tall and weighs 90 pounds.
>
> We caught up with the group as they were entering Wiley's Slot. The next exploration spot was immediately determined to be a ceiling loop. Since we all were here, we headed to the end of the hall to check the terminal breakdown for leads. None were found, even though Robert Rainey free climbed high into the ceiling to check a couple of dark holes.
>
> Next, we headed for the Trunk Passage. The long sand crawl isn't half as bad as was expected because after 50 feet it gets progressively higher. The 12-foot drop off to the floor of the Trunk was a shock. We exited through a tight 10-inch wide slit.

This time we were to map to the end of the Trunk and then map the maze. Around the corner and about four survey shots away, we hit the big terminal breakdown pile of rock and mud. While we mapped up to the pile, the others explored for a way through. Emily Norgradi soon found a passage needing mapping on the north side. It descended for 50 feet overlooking a virgin pit. It was simple enough to get down. We found ourselves in a passage crack doubling underneath our original position. The mud became very slippery, 1 ½ - inch thick right above a 20-foot crack. Here we had a choice of leads. We took the better one through a window overlooking a room the size of a garage. We climbed down on the gooey mud which had the passage looking much like a sewer. At the base of the room, someone found a very small stream strewn with small chert nodules and bat skulls and bones. We followed the stream for about 30 more feet where the survey ended. Downstream became impassable. Upstream went another 30 feet with the same results. After checking all the leads and loops thoroughly, we headed back out and up to the Trunk Passage 50 feet above us.

Once at the top of the breakdown pile, we went back a survey station or two and tied into mapping the small maze. This maze took some time but was comparatively easy.

We were a little rushed at the end to finish a last branch that had been overlooked. With this done we headed out as fast as we could for we knew we would have only 15 minutes of twilight at best when we emerged.

EPILOG

Yggdrasil is interesting. I believe that there is further trunk passage beyond the eastern terminal breakdown that stopped us. We just can't get to it at this point. This belief is based on the size of the trunk passage. It shouldn't dead-end so quickly. Also, it is based upon the discovery of the maze. If the breakdown completely closed the trunk passage, it would have dammed the cave stream. The water level would rise behind the rock dam and eventually the water would find a series of cracks allowing it to bypass the breakdown. It would enlarge these cracks, forming a maze or until one passage pirated the water. This appears to be happening at Yggdrasil. The water dissolving the maze is coming from above; through cracks too tight to go through.

At Yggdrasil though, the water seems to be also dissolving a lower-level passage to bypass the breakdown pile. This is the muddy stream section we found, which is still tight. A sizeable lower section would not have the thick deposits of mud on everything indicating standing, quiet water. So the pool of water behind the breakdown can completely drain away using the higher maze bypass only during high flood.

At the other end of the Trunk Passage at the downstream end is a sand plug. This plug probably opens only during the time the cave floods. As the water rises, it exerts greater and greater hydraulic pressure on the plug until it goes. After the cave drains, the sand re-plugs the lower end of the syphon again until the water rises again. I bet somewhere in the gorge is a sizeable "ebb and flow" spring where this happens.[3]

It is interesting to note that although Bruce Zerr says the survey is complete "with a little over one-half mile", the Tennessee Cave Survey lists this cave as 5,000 feet long, so clearly more cave has been explored since this survey was "completed".

THE SURVEY OF YGGDRASIL CAVE

Bruce Zerr and Mike Russell were surveying Yggdrasil Cave during the 1970s. However, no final survey was ever submitted to the Tennessee Cave Survey. It is not known if a map was ever

3 Bruce Zerr, "Yggdrasil Cave Survey Complete!", Speleotype, v. 12 (1979), no. 2, pp. 2-3. Reprinted in 1979 Speleo Digest.

Figure 8.3. Marion O. Smith inspects large wooden water troughs in Yggdrasil Cave. Photo by Joe Douglas, June 1, 2013.

Figure 8.4. Kristen Bobo in a canyon passage in Yggdrasil Cave. Photo by Joe Douglas, June 1, 2013.

drafted, or not. This would be an outstanding survey project for some young cavers, as this is a large, complex, and significant cave.

SALTPETER MINING IN YGGDRASIL CAVE

Cave historian Marion O. Smith visited Yggdrasil Cave on Saturday, June 1, 2013. On this trip he was accompanied by Grace Baumann, Brian Killingbeck, Ken Pasternack, Joe C. Douglas, Kristen Bobo, and Alfred Crabtree. Here are notes from his diary for that day:

> We waded across the E. Fork of the Obey five times before going up a hollow to the 8-9-foot wide by 6-7-foot-high entrance of Yggdrasil Cave.
>
> I was the last of our group to enter the cave, at 12:57 PM CDT. After ca. 100 feet of walk/crawl there was the 30+ foot wide by 80+ foot long by 20-foot-high saltpeter room.

This room had piles representing perhaps 3 or more vats, with one being possibly a double vat within one frame. There were numerous and I mean NUMEROUS cast aside rocks in this room, including above and below a large boulder. These were out in the area with the vat dirt piles and at least 3 or more pieces of wooden troughs.

But what impressed me most was in the right alcove of the room closest to the entrance. That was the presence of a lot of wood, specifically four 10-foot-long boards 24-26 inches wide and up to 4 inches thick, the biggest (or rather the widest) I've ever seen (See Figure 8.2). Also, the end of a large trough (2-feet wide) was under a board near the cave wall (See Figure 8.3). Both Kristen and Joe did photography in this room.

At the end of the room was a 3-4-foot wide by 2-3-foot-high short passage to a 10-foot long, 20-foot high passage. This passage had a few tally marks and at least one (to me illegible) old name in script.[4]

Marion and his group continued on beyond the area of saltpeter mining. Here is his description of the rest of that trip:

Left off this passage was a crawl to another walking passage, and everyone went there. At the in-cave end of the passage the main way forward was a 25-30-foot long and very windy (coming out) crawl. The cave was cold in the front areas and everyone except Brian and me wimped out at this crawl.

Brian and I continued to traverse the cave to tour the main passage. We went down a series of slopes, climb-downs, and short crawls (and this included an 8-foot overhang climb) and one or two up climbs, the last of which led to the alleged "1000-foot belly sand crawl."

This belly crawl definitely started out as a belly crawl and Brian took the rope through. Luckily, the belly part was 100-150 feet, then it was a bit higher and lastly became actual walking size. This section, instead of being 1,000-feet long seemed only to be closer to 300-350 feet to me. It led through one more short crawl to the 10-11-foot pit into a segment of 40-foot-high passage. With Ken's 110-foot rope we used 2 semi-flaky tie-offs to rig it. Order down the drop was me, then Brian.

We toured both ways (40 feet high at first) at bottom. Left was initially big and off it was a sort of maze. We went along one narrow passage until it seemed to be ending – 200+ feet in this section. Right led up slope to 2 or 3 small rooms, a bit muddy but not too bad and seemingly the end, maybe 200 feet more.

Yggdrasil Cave is listed as 5,000 feet long, but I think the amount we saw was closer to 1,500 feet, and therefore the reported length is exaggerated. But surely the strong air exiting indicates a cave of considerable extent. Generally it is a pretty good fossil cave and

Figure 8.5. End portion of a wooden water trough left by the saltpeter miners in Yggdrasil Cave. Photo by Kristen Bobo, June 1, 2013.

if it could be moved closer to where I live I'd make a project out of it! But, since it is remote by Tennessee standards someone in the future can do that.

We headed for the entrance and Brian was the hero and took the rope out. Even so, I couldn't keep up with him (of course he is 32 and I'm 70 2/3). I was last out at 5:06 PM CDT.

Only Grace was at the entrance. It had rained and about ½ to 1 hour earlier the other 4 folks left. Grace said she hung out with Kristen and Joe in the saltpeter area a while and Kristen dug around and found more wood in the vat pile.[5]

The TCS description mentions several large breakdown rooms, but Marion's description does not. Did he miss something? How long is this

4 Marion O. Smith, Personal communication, April 5, 2020.

5 Marion O. Smith, Personal communication, April 5, 2020.

Figure 8.6. Portion of a log water pipe system left by saltpeter miners in Yggdrasil Cave. Photo by Kristen Bobo. June 1, 2013.

Figure 8.7. Remains of saltpeter vats in Yggdrasil Cave. Photo by Joe Douglas, June 1, 2013.

Figure 8.8. Pile of rocks left behind by saltpeter miners after removing the dirt for processing. Photo by Joe Douglas, June 1, 2013.

Figure 8.9. Crosshatch pattern drawn on the wall in Yggdrasil Cave. Photo by Kristen Bobo, June 1, 2013.

cave? Without an accurate survey, we just do not know at this point. But, like Marion says, the strong airflow indicates there must be a lot more cave there, somewhere. And, like Marion says, this would be a great project cave for some young, new cavers to explore and map.

CAVE ACCESS

Yggdrasil Cave is located on private property. You must have the owner's permission before you visit this cave.

Figure 9.1. Keith Filson on a ledge in a large canyon in Zarathustra's Cave. Photo by Bob Biddix, November 18, 2012.

CHAPTER 9
Zarathustra's Cave

Zarathustra's Cave is located in Fentress County, Tennessee. The Tennessee Cave Survey lists this cave as 37,118 feet (7.0 miles) long, making it one of the longer mapped caves in Tennessee.

A DESCRIPTION OF THE CAVE

Bill Deane describes the discovery and exploration of Zarathustra's Cave:

> In Fentress County, Tennessee, the East Fork of the Obey River has carved a deep gorge into the western escarpment of the Cumberland Plateau. For seven miles the river winds through a forest-cloaked limestone canyon, almost 1,000 feet deep. The rugged nature of the land and an absence of roads has created a *de facto* wilderness which is rarely visited by residents of the surrounding farms and communities. For years cavers speculated about the caving potential of the East Fork, but it was not until May, 1975 that the search began…

> **Dragon's Breath**
> When Ray Lewis and Brad Neff reconnoitered the upstream portion of the East Fork for a canoeing trip they found a dry limestone riverbed over 100 feet wide. Ray's mind began to race with thoughts of a master cave carrying the missing river. Somewhere, perhaps miles downstream, the East Fork might reappear at a giant spring. Such a spring would be well worth seeking.

> Two weeks passed and Ray returned with Jim Matthews to hike the dry riverbed. Four long miles later the two cavers approached a high limestone cliff pocked with possible cave entrances, but a large pool of water at the base prevented easy access. Ray later wrote, "One of

the holes, the only one we took a good look at, was blowing a large amount of cold air. Due to the nature of that hole, low, wet, and rough, we didn't check it but we planned to return." The cold air breathing out over the pool turned into a misty smoke called the Dragon's Breath.

> On July 4, Ray and Sid Jones explored some of the openings on the cliff face. A blowhole led to a room 50 feet in diameter and beyond to a stream passage that connected to the Dragon's Breath. They followed the stream a few hundred feet through some large breakdown rooms without reaching the end. Back on the cliff face they climbed on a narrow ledge up to a 20 by 12-foot entrance with a fine view of the river. They walked several hundred feet through passage mined for saltpeter, but time was against them. Faced with the long hike out of the gorge they reluctantly left their discoveries. The next weekend, Sid, Jay, and Ray walked into the gorge via a new dirt road cut by oil prospectors. This reduced the hike to only 1½ miles with a 900-foot drop in elevation. About 800 feet inside the Saltpeter Cave they were stopped by an unclimbable drop opening into a large lower level. A search for side leads yielded a chimney. They descended and followed a walking passage into a familiar breakdown room. The higher Saltpeter Cave entrance was now connected to the lower Dragon's Breath-Blowhole Cave. The lower cave continued up a sandy slope into a large trunk passage. They walked 2,600 feet down the trunk which averaged 50 by 30 feet in cross section, passing dozens of side leads. One of Tennessee's longest caves was revealing its secrets.

Figure 9.2. Faith Wright stands in the entrance to Zarathustra's Cave. Photo by Chuck Sutherland, May 19, 2012.

Zarathustra's Cave

Pleased with his find, Ray named it after the mythical cave described in *Also Sprach Zarathustra* by Friedrich Nietzche. "Behold, up yonder lies Zarathustra's Cave."

"My cave is big and deep and possesses many corners; where the best hidden man can find his hiding place. And close by it are a hundred secret, slippery ways for creeping, fluttering, and jumping-beast."

Yet, to Ray's disappointment, Zarathustra's Cave was not the master drainage cave he was seeking. The water flow out of the Dragon's Breath was far too small to be the resurgence of the missing river. He abandoned exploration of the cave, reported the discovery to the Tennessee Cave Survey and continued searching the gorge.

A Stroll In The Sun

The 95° heat and high humidity seemed unbearable as Jay Cox, Doug Ralston and John Smyre trudged down the East Fork towards Zarathustra's Cave. The cobblestone bed of the dry river was treacherous as the unrelenting July sun. They stumbled onto an old logging road and the walking became easier, but the heat and humidity had taken its toll. Arriving at the cave, Jay and John laid down in the cool draft of the Blowhole and did not move for a half hour. Doug finally talked them into entering the cave, but they explored for only 45 minutes.

At the next Smoky Mountain Grotto meeting, Doug described their grim march, but spoke enthusiastically of a large trunk with many side leads. I decided to visit Zarathustra's Cave. All I needed was somebody crazy enough to go hiking in the gorge.

Jay Arnold and Martha McGlasson listened as I spoke eloquently of virgin cave begging to be explored, of endless trunk passages, vast chambers, untold side leads, and, oh yes, a pleasant hike into a beautiful wilderness gorge. It was a classic suck-in.

As we drove to Fentress County, I suggested we search for an old logging road shown on the 1954 topo map that might offer a shorter route to the cave. That road was long gone, but another, recently bulldozed, served us well. We were able to drive my Bronco to the very bottom of the gorge. Fifteen minutes later, we were standing in the Saltpeter Entrance looking out over the river.

The Elephant Walk

After passing the saltpeter mining remains and looking down the unclimbable drop that had stopped previous upper level exploration, we split up to check two side leads. Martha and I explored a small passage that quickly degenerated into two very tight crawls. We returned to find Jay grinning like the Cheshire Cat. He had climbed up a chimney and had run through 700 feet of virgin cave. We followed him up into a 20 by 15-foot passage and soon reached his farthest point of exploration where two 25-foot pits dropped into a lower level. The pits were not climbable, so continuing on the same level, we walked a few more feet into virgin cave and sat down to eat lunch. As we ate, Jay named his discovery

Figure 9.3. Kristen Bobo welds the gate for Zarathustra's Cave. Photo by Chuck Sutherland, May 19, 2012.

Figure 9.4. Erica Sughrue in a large stream passage in Zarathustra's Cave. Photo by Bob Biddix, November 18, 2012.

Figure 9.5. Saltpeter vat casts inside the Saltpeter Entrance to Zarathustra's Cave. Photo by Joe Douglas, November 11, 2006.

Figure 9.6. Erica Sughrue beneath a large dome in Zarathustra's Cave. Photo by Bob Biddix, November 18, 2012.

the Elephant Walk. I remarked that a passage like this could go forever.

We fairly flew along the meandering trunk; up and down sandy slopes, over and under breakdown, with fleeting pauses to note possible side leads. Our joy and amazement increased with each step into the unknown. Perhaps this passage was endless, for after 2,000 feet it still averaged 20 feet wide and 15 feet high. We passed by displays of brownish flowstone, peered into a jagged dome-pit with a cascading waterfall and scrambled around sandy hills that reached to the ceiling. After 3,300 feet, our eager rush into darkness was momentarily halted by Martha's need to change carbide. I poked around in some holes in the ceiling for a few moments; but found nothing. Then Jay returned from a short scouting trip to gravely inform us that the pasage ended only 50 feet ahead at a flowstone choke.

Martha's Crawl

While Jay and I stared glumly at the end of the Elephant Walk, Martha found a crawlway so small we doubted that even she could fit. Blowing air spoke of more cave and after a long, tight 15 feet we stood up on the far side of the flowstone choke. No elephants would walk here. We worked our way through a series of short segments of walking passage connected by stoopways and brief crawls. Occasional patches of small gypsum flowers decorated the walls. We marveled at a narrow, well-worn trail created by cave rats that wove its way through hundreds of feet of passage. One thousand feet past the flowstone choke,

Figure 9.7. Faith Wright (left) and Lacey Crabtree (right) at the Bigalo-Jingoist Hole. Photo by Chuck Sutherland, May 19, 2012.

the cave split into three directions. "To the left," I said. After 200 miserable feet of stoopway lined with sharp breakdown, I heard mutterings of mutiny. Fortunately, our efforts were rewarded with more gypsum flowers. We followed the stoopway into a room and beyond to welcomed walking passage. Past a second room, we chimneyed along ledges which crunched like corn flakes beneath our feet. The chimney slowed Martha down and I pulled ahead without fully realizing it. Suddenly there was only blackness.

Ultima Thule

My feet sank deep into gypsum sand as I walked part way up the slope. Below me, Jay and Martha shined their lights about in silent amazement. This was beyond anything we had dared to hope for. After having explored 6,000 feet of virgin cave, we now stood in a major trunk 50 feet high and 20 feet wide. Our silence turned to gleeful laughter. We had found more elephant country. I would later name this passage Ultima Thule, the Greek phrase for an infinitely remote place.

We climbed up the steep slope past a dozen gypsum flowers 3-4 inches long. The slope leveled off and we set an exuberant pace for hundreds of feet through a 20 by 20-foot walkway. The walkway became a stoopway and then a crawlway. Beyond a second crawlway, we popped out into large passage at a Y junction. We climbed down a dirt cliff into the left branch. It was fissure-like ranging from 10 to 30 feet high and averaging 6 feet wide. We explored 500 feet before turning back at a difficult climb. The right branch started off nicely, but soon we began alternately crawling

Figure 9.8. Chuck Sutherland at the Dragon's Breath Entrance to Zarathustra's Cave. Photo by Chuck Sutherland, May 19, 2012.

over cave coral and pushing through narrow fissures. Our progress was slow. After a few hundred feet it became obvious that fatigue was setting in. We had explored 7,900 feet of virgin cave. It was time to go home.[1]

Truly, they had had a remarkable day exploring virgin cave in Tennessee.

THE SURVEY OF ZARATHUSTRA'S CAVE

Following are excerpts from Trip Reports written during the survey of Zarathustra's Cave.

1 Bill Deane, "Exploring Zarathustra's Cave", NSS News, Volume 35, No. 11 (November, 1977), pp. 223-225.

September 27-28, 1975

Our assignment was the upper level, supposed to be somewhat less large than the lower. "Don't map the right lead," said Bill Deane, "because it only goes half a mile. Map the left for a mile and a half." Barb Unger, Jim Nicholls, and I (Lou Simpson) began our part of the work, the M Survey. We tied into parties on the lower level at several places. Hours passed as we continued to map. Our short night of rest was telling on us. A party passed us, telling us to map until we found their tie-in station where they would begin mapping a side crawl. We came to a domepit at 6 p.m.

Figure 9.9. Kristen Bobo by a column in Zarathustra's Cave. Note two entrances in the far background. Photo by Chuck Sutherland, May 19, 2012.

Figure 9.10. Lacey Crabtree by rimstone dams in Zarathustra's Cave. Photo by Chuck Sutherland, May 19, 2012. (Facing page)

It was at least 50 feet deep and quite high and had a falls. Beyond this the passage got lower and I put on my kneepads, just to justify having packed them in. Finally, at station 79 I chanced to check a doubtful looking upper level lead. It opened up hugely!

Abandon the survey, it's scoop time! We charged into the upper level, where no human had ever been before. The walls were very far away! Our first lead (of three) produced breakdown and a crawl that had some nut shells and airflow. The second led to 80-foot pits, breakdown domes, and a passage with white walls and round chert nodules. This led to a dome with nut shells and leaves. Another passage in this section led to a terrifying overlook of the pits.

It was after 10 p.m. We rested for a long time, part of the way into what looked like the most promising lead yet. Jim crawled ahead, walls thirty feet away from him. Skirting a 15-foot pit, he came to what is probably the deep domepit we mapped past on the lower level. Then breakdown. Above this, it opened up! Now the walls were at least a hundred feet apart! The floor was crunchy sand. I considered this the most exciting, most pleasant virgin passage I've ever seen. We followed this magnificent place for ten minutes and stopped at some breakdown when it looked like a little effort would be needed. Happy for an excuse to return to camp, we left.

When we got back, all were asleep except Frosty Miller, who informed us that two search parties were looking for us. Unaware of our new level, they were perplexed. Eventually, they returned. We learned that 11,000 feet had been mapped that day.

On Sunday two parties returned to our new section, which I named "Heaven", to map some of it. With the Sunday mapping, the length of the cave is now 15,500 feet. I'm looking forward to many exciting trips to Zarathustra's Cave.[2]

The entire survey crew for this trip consisted of Jerry (Nugget) Black, John Bullock, Janice Cate, Bill Deane, Phil Herrell, Martha McGlasson, Frosty Miller, Gerald Moni, Jim Nicholls, Charlotte Rogers, Lou Simpson, Jeff Sims, Barb Unger, and Richard Wallace. They mapped just slightly over two (2) miles of passages.

November 27-29, 1975

Barb and I (Lou Simpson) began mapping Friday morning, bright and early, in various places in the top level, named Heaven. By noon we had mapped over 40 stations and were still going strong. We discovered some more connections between levels, pushed some virgin leads, and found walking passage to join Bob Wood and Dave Socky back at their vertical project. When we found them, Bob was getting ready to descend the second pit. We mapped to an overlook in the Rats Nest Maze and measured the total depth of the lower pit at 77 feet. Bob could have rigged the pit in one drop from this point if I had shown him the way. He moved some breakdown and found a connection to a deeper level that had been explored before.

Saturday morning the three of us mapped 1,200 feet of nice walking passage with attractive rimstone and stalactite formations near the end of it. Across from an occupied rat nest was a blowing lead that smelled like the outdoors. I followed it through a tight constriction and emerged outside! It turned out we were almost above the main entrance. This entrance is about 30 feet above the main entrance, which itself is 40 feet above the river.

Finally it was time to leave. I took a quick look at a thousand feet of the several miles of lower level passages accessible easily from the small entrances near the main entrance. I stopped when

2 Lou Simpson, "Zarathustra's Cave", C.O.G. Squeaks, Vol. 18, No. 10 (October, 1975), pp. 103-104.

Figure 9.11. Alfred Crabtree and Kristen Bobo in Zarathustra's Cave. Photo by Chuck Sutherland, May 19, 2012. (Facing page)

Figure 9.12. Erica Sughrue in a large passage in Zarathustra's Cave. Photo by Bob Biddix, November 18, 2012.

I couldn't see any walls. We had mapped 2,200 feet, which brings the total survey to about 18,000 feet.

I think the phrase "Death March" adequately describes the hike back up the valley.[3]

January 1-3, 1976

Rather than camp in the chilly entrance, we carried our gear six hundred feet inside, across a 20-foot pit, to a somewhat warmer upper level. After a brief snack and rest, we headed

for the spacious upper level half a mile into the cave, called Heaven. Zarathustra's Cave, as presently known consists of at least four main levels, interconnected at many places. The level we camped on is called the Elephant Walk. We followed this level to the climbable connections to the Heaven level at stations M-74 and M-79. A deep pit with a waterfall intersects Heaven and the Elephant Walk. A lead on the far side of this pit, between the two levels, was to be Bob Wood's main objective.

Friday, January 2, was our big day. Bob Wood, Mark Flarida, and Jim Hazlitt began rigging the

3 Lou Simpson, "Thanksgiving In Zarathustra's Cave", C.O.G. Squeaks, Vol. 18, No. 12 (December, 1975), pp. 122-123.

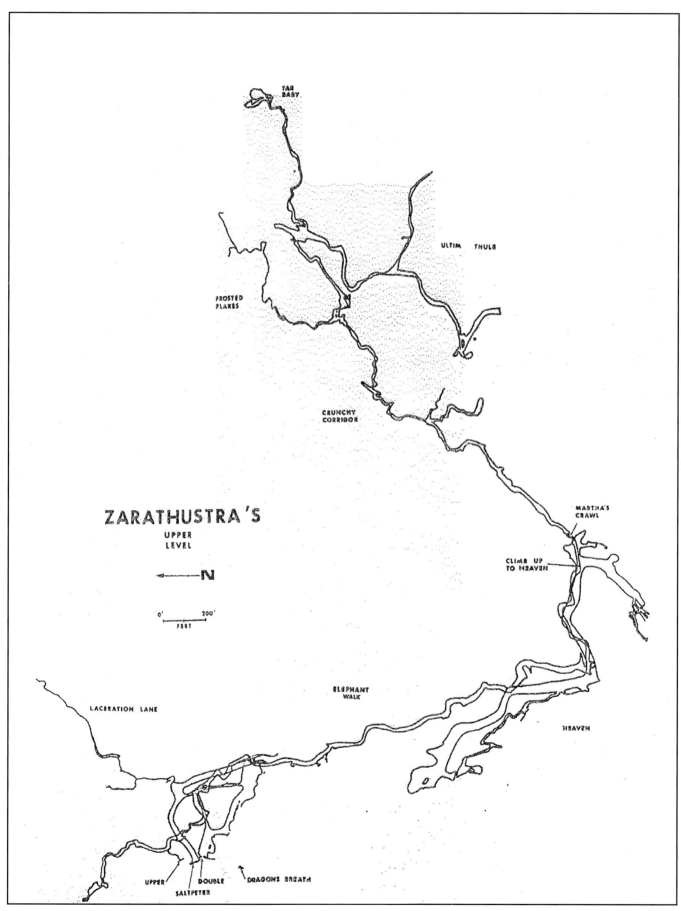

Figure 9.13. Map of Zarathustra's Cave.

waterfall pit from the Heaven level. Bob's bolt driver broke during the first bolt.

Barb and I mapped four places, including a resurvey of the northern part of Heaven, where numerous alcoves and side leads and pits needed better definition. The initial survey of Heaven had been done in a hurry and the sketch was not scaled, plotted, or oriented. In a parallel passage we explored and mapped into a breakdown room in which a waterfall was audible. I failed to get to this falls, however, since access between two horizontal breakdown blocks must await hammer and chisel next trip.

Barb and I briefly explored a virgin upper level that Bill Deane told us about. I climbed up Frosty's Falls, not named for falling water but for a falling caver, Frosty Miller. Barb found a safer route by voice connection. We only explored a few hundred feet and stopped before a perfectly decent belly-crawl because it was late. To get to this area we had to go through an extremely tight belly-crawl over rimstone.

On Saturday, January 3, Ken Smith and Joe Martin photographed the Saltpeter overlook, Bob and Mark surveyed the new connection between levels, and Barb and I mapped some of our scoop found Thursday. Jim helped either of the other two groups. Finally we were ready for the grueling climb back to civilization.[4]

May 29-31, 1976

Memorial Day 1976 saw seven cavers again in Tennessee's fabulous Zarathustra's Cave. Dave Taylor, Donna Graham, Russ Dobos, Dennis Stumpp, Dave Voelker, Barb Unger, and Lou Simpson mapped another 1,900 feet, bringing the total to around 32,000 feet mapped since the beginning of the survey in late September 1975.

Dave V., Russ, Dennis, and Lou donned respirators and made for Cleveland Canyon and the dread Black Lung Boulevard, while the other three undertook to map a gross bellycrawl near the entrance. A high lead was climbed in Black Lung Boulevard, which led to 500 feet of trunk passage. Lou nearly buried himself as he excavated the end of this trunk at "Premature Burial". He also made the unforgiveable mistake of eating a can of kippers. Not only breath, but also pig, notes, and everything else reeked of it for the remainder of the trip.

Barb, Dave T., and Donna discovered a joint-controlled maze off the lower entrance room. As might be expected, this is directly under an upper level maze and will be difficult to show on the map.

Barb and Lou pushed the long, painful bellycrawl that remained from the previous expedition. After 400 feet of additional survey, Lou encountered an unlikely chisel project and turned back. They mapped some lower level rooms and overlooks instead.

Lou suggested to the three Cleveland cavers that they dig out a lead off the Frosted Flakes Crawl. This is the passage explored by Barb Unger and Bruce Warthman in February 1976. After half an hour of digging, Russ finally got through by removing most of his clothes. There is another, even less promising dig in the small room there.

Lou and Barb explored some of the lower levels on the third day and saw the continuation of the main stream upstream—a low, hands-and-knees crawl in six inches of water. This is unexplored and might be best pushed in wetsuits.[5]

November 25, 1976

At the entrance we separated into three groups: Greg Kalmback, Mary Kalmbach, and I planned to survey near the entrance. Barb and Woody went to Cleveland Canyon to bolt a high lead. The rest went to the Elephant Walk and Heaven and eventually to Cleveland Canyon for photography and sight-seeing.

The survey party mapped a total of 511 feet in two leads, discovering about 200 feet of virgin

4 Lou Simpson, "New Year's Expedition To Zarathustra's Cave", C.O.G. Squeaks, Vol. 19, No. 1 (January, 1976), pp. 3-5.

5 Lou Simpson, "Memorial Weekend In Zarathustra's Cave", C.O.G. Squeaks, Vol. 19, No. 7 & 8 (July-August, 1976), pp. 54, 59-60.

Figure 9.14. Lacey Crabtree by rock pile left by saltpeter miners in Zarathustra's Cave, May 19, 2012. Photo by Chuck Sutherland.

canyon in the first project. One survey was through a previously flooded rimstone pool to a few rooms beyond that had been explored before by a party from Knoxville. This has to be the muddiest place in this otherwise dry cave.

Woody's bolt climb resulted in two leads, but not enough time remained in the day to even thoroughly check them out.[6]

SALTPETER MINING IN ZARATHUSTRA'S CAVE

Joe Douglas give the following information about the saltpeter mining in Zarathustra's Cave:

The upper part of Zarathustra's Cave, at least, was mined for saltpeter, which was initially processed in a series of vats located in the first

couple of hundred feet of passage inside the Saltpeter Entrance. Today, a large number of rather poorly preserved vat casts remain from the saltpeter leaching vats. The structure of the vats *may* be V-shaped. Water for the sediment processing was likely brought up from the river level. Like other substantial saltpeter operations in the East Fork of the Obey River, it is thought to date from the War of 1812 era.[7]

Marion O. Smith also provided information about the saltpeter mining operation in Zarathustra's Cave. He visited the cave on November 11, 2012 with Chuck Sutherland, Joe Douglas, Kristen Bobo, David Wascher, Emily P. Davis, Mike West, Eli Austin, and Jason Lavender. Here are his observations on the evidence of saltpeter mining:

6 Lou Simpson, "Zarathustra's Cave", C.O.G. Squeaks, Vol. 19, No. 12 (December, 1976), p. 100.

7 Joe Douglas, Personal communication, April 29, 2020.

Today, my objective was to pay more attention to the saltpeter section beyond the main 30-foot wide by 10-20-foot high entrance. There is a gate in it about 75 feet inside and Kristen opened it for me. One possible pile of dirt representing a vat was close to the entrance.

I entered at 11:06 AM CST and wandered about in the saltpeter section alone for exactly 2 hours. It was hard to say how many other leaching vats were once present, but at least 20-22 are past the gate, including 6 in the next Big Room.

In the Big Room there were at least 330 tally marks, a 3-foot section of old board, an 8-foot piece of old lumber (3+ inches thick), and a 4½-foot long, 1½-foot wide X 5-6-inch thick start of a log trough (unfinished).

The "right" passage, 25+ feet wide, which leads from the Big Room was 300+ feet long with a totally disturbed floor, very uneven, and very rocky, much man handled. This passage "ended" on that level with a 12-15-foot drop into a lower level (accessible from the two "snake eyes" entrances 75 feet south of the Saltpeter Entrance). There was a group of about 23 tally marks also.

In a smaller and more straight passage (which I seemed to have toured on 9-23-78), generally 5-6-feet wide and 3½-10-feet (but usually 7-feet) high, were three more groups of tally marks, about 30, 26, and 51, bringing the total I noticed to about 460. This passage had lots of soot marks from lamps, a good number of wooden faggots, some stacked rocks, and a 2-foot board.

There is little doubt that Zarathustra's Cave was a commercial saltpeter operation, but nothing is known about its history.[8]

---

8 Marion O. Smith, Personal communication, May 6, 2020.

Figure 9.5 Shows many saltpeter vat casts lining either side of the passage described above by Joe Douglas. Figure 9.4 Also shows piles of dirt that are remains of the saltpeter mining activity.

CAVE ACCESS

Zarathustra's Cave is managed through a lease agreement between the Obey River Conservation Task Force and the Estate of Bruno Gernt/Allardt Land Company (EBGALC). Anyone wishing to visit this cave must have written permission from the Obey River Conservation Task Force. Jeff Patton is currently the contact person for this cave.

PLACE NAMES IN ZARATHUSTRA'S CAVE

Big Room
Black Lung Boulevard
Blowhole Cave
Cough Drop
Cleveland Canyon
Dragon's Breath
Elephant Walk
Frosted Flakes Crawl
Frostys Falls
Heaven
Premature Burial
Rats Nest Maze
Saltpeter Entrance
Snake Eyes Entrance
Ultima Thule

Figure 9.15. Erica Sughrue in a large passage in Zarathustra's Cave. Photo by Bob Biddix, November 18, 2012.

Figure 10.1. Erica Sughrue prepares to rappel into Hellhole. Photo by Bob Biddix, July 26, 2020.

CHAPTER 10
Hellhole

Hellhole is located in Overton County, Tennessee. There are no horizontal passages at the bottom, but it is a very deep and picturesque pit.

A DESCRIPTION OF THE CAVE

Hellhole is described by Thomas C. Barr, Jr. in his book *Caves of Tennessee* (1961):

> Hellhole is a huge pit developed in Mississippian limestone just beneath the Cypress sandstone. The depression in which it opens is 200 feet in diameter, and its sides slope downward steeply to a vertical shaft nearly 100 feet across at the top. A wide sandstone rock shelter is at the top of the pit, and a waterfall pours into the hole.
>
> A smaller shaft parallel to the main pit extends downward for 175 feet. At -175 feet the side shaft joins the main pit. A sheer drop of 125 feet must be negotiated from this point to the bottom. Hellhole is fully 300 feet deep.
>
> From the 200 feet diameter at the top, the main shaft narrows to 60 feet in diameter, then bells out at the bottom into a chamber 80 feet across. A talus cone some 50 feet high occupies the center of this room. No passages lead off from the bottom of Hellhole.[1]

Technically, the above description by Bill C. Stewart is accurate, but by today's standards, only the bottom 180 feet qualifies as a pit. So, early explorers were extremely disappointed, to say the least, when they arrived expecting a 300-foot drop to find only a 180-foot drop. The top 120 feet is very steep, however, and a handline is recommended.

Here is the earliest reported exploration of the Hellhole:

The most famous vertical cave in Overton County, Tenn. (Livingston area) seems to be the "bottomless" pit on Hellhole Mountain. While camping in Standing Stone State Park, Tom Barr, Roy Davis, and Bert Denton were visited by a Livingston cave enthusiast, Don Dean, who has partially explored this chasm. With 11 men, a 250-foot rope, and a harness, Don was lowered into Hellhole. When he reached the end of the rope the cave was still dropping out of sight. He got out of the harness and continued downward on narrow ledges for a least 50 feet, but never reached the bottom.[2]

I have no doubt that this is an honest description of Mr. Dean's exploration. But it is not a 300-foot free-fall drop as Ed Yarbrough learned in 1961.

AN EARLY VISIT TO HELLHOLE

The following Trip Report by Edward M. Yarbrough describes one of the first visits to Hellhole after the publication of Barr's *Caves of Tennessee* (1961):

> On November 1, 1963, I hitchhiked to Nashville to join Richard Finch for a weekend of fun and frolic in the cavernous nether reaches of Overton County. Among the caves we visited was a pit called "Hellhole" which I had been to before but never descended.
>
> Hellhole has been described in an early (1955) issue of the Speleonews as well as Bulletin 64. The depth mentioned in both sources is at least 300 feet and the dimensions of the shaft are described at "100 feet in diameter at the top." I went to the pit first in 1962 and discovered that the top diameter

1 Description by Bill C. Stewart.

2 Anonymous, "300-Foot Pit Near Livingston", Speleonews, v. 2 (1954), no. 7, p. 12.

was barely 25 feet. I wrote Bill Cuddington inquiring about the possibility of two pits existing on the same mountain. He replied that the one I had seen was the only one he knew of, and even sent a picture; proof that everybody was talking about the same pit. Bill mentioned that he believed the depth to be exaggerated and suggested that I obtain an accurate measurement if I went. I did. Hellhole is 180 feet deep, quite unlike the 300 and 340-foot measurements reported by earlier explorers.

I rigged on the south (lower) end of the sinkhole; however, on this occasion it was just a matter of personal preference, since there was no water then. The descent was routine except for two minor blunders. The first mistake was unknowingly feeding the rope through a small opening adjacent to the major shaft. I couldn't see this little hole from the anchor point but when I started down I discovered that the rope was going through something I couldn't. So I sat down and dragged 430 feet of rope through the opening and tossed it over into the main pit, amid much grumbling.

After I landed on the sloping platform about 70 feet down, I took several pictures before going on. I left the camera there and negotiated the remaining 110 feet to the floor of the pit. When I had determined that there were no more drops and no passages I prussiked back up…you guessed it, forgetting all about the camera on the first ledge. Arriving at the surface like the conquering adventurer all it took to make the adventurer feel conquered was Richard's innocent comment, "Where's your camera?" I collapsed in a piteous, forgetful heap.

Since the rappelling spool was tied at the far end of the rope, I went down the second time using the carabiner and shoulder pad (a much better way to rappel, anyway). After recovering the camera I returned to the surface with my sheepish expression and began raising the rope. We then sped back to Nashville, late as usual, and the following day found me back in Memphis reminiscing about a very enjoyable weekend in the cave country of Tennessee.[3]

There is a nice profile of Hellhole that accompanied this Trip Report. It is shown as Figure 10.2. Ed Yarbrough adds the following important information:

> As far as we know the only descent (of Hellhole) had been by Cuddington in the 50's and, of course, he got the depth wrong by counting the cliff over the entrance as part of the drop. And, from his Speleonews article it appears he never got to the bottom. Tommy Hutchison and I found it in 1961 but did not go down. Then, two months after my Fern Cave trip, I hitchhiked to Nashville on a weekend and met Finch for a trip to Overton County and he accompanied me to Hellhole but did not descend it. So this was likely the second time anyone did it and the first time anyone got to the bottom. That effort revealed that there were only two legitimate drops and the total depth was about 180 feet.[4]

So, it appears that Ed Yarbrough was the first person to ever reach the bottom of Hellhole.

THE SURVEY OF HELLHOLE

Hellhole was surveyed by cavers Jeff Bowers and Frank Bogle on January 2, 1993. That plan and profile is shown as Figure 10.5. As you can see from the information on this map, the total depth of Hellhole is 243 feet, since the bottom slopes down steeply from the point where the rope reaches the bottom.

CAVE ACCESS

Hellhole is located on private property. Do not enter this pit or any other pits or caves, without the owner's permission.

3 Edward M. Yarbrough, "Vertical Views", Nashville Speleonews, v. 7, no. 4 (August, 1963), pp. 39-40.
4 Edward M. Yarbrough, Personal communication, September 21, 2020.

COPENA SKULL PIT AND SHIVER HOLE

Another interesting and significant pit complex in Overton County is Copena Skull Pit and the nearby Shiver Hole. Copena Skull Pit was first explored by David Irving, Jim Corley, and Francis McKinney on March 5, 1967. Here is David Irving's report of that trip:

On March 5, I entered what is now known as Copena Skull Pit. Jim Corley and Francis McKinney waited at the top for word from me that there was cave to explore. At the bottom, I climbed down a talus slope and stopped at a low wall separating two adjoining domes. The floor of the dome on the other side was 10 to 15 feet below me. I could see that although the climb down would be easy, getting back up might be rough. As I hesitated, uncertain about climbing down without assistance available, I glanced up at the opposite wall. There, in a niche, was a human skull. That did it! I yelled for Jim and Francis to come down. When they arrived, I climbed into the adjoining dome and retrieved the skull. The jaws were missing, but the skull was complete and in excellent condition. Our first thought was that it might be Indian, and we started looking for artifacts that would establish the skull's origin. Someone quickly noticed a "pot" half buried in the mud floor of the dome. We dug it up only to find that the "pot" was part of another skull. A few jaw pieces were found, then the jaw of a bobcat. Several limb bones were scattered about, but we couldn't tell which ones were human and which were bobcat. While Jim and I were searching this dome, Francis looked into a small side crevice off the bottom of the talus slope and found two more complete skulls. One showed pronounced flattening across the forehead and across the back, increasing our suspicion that these were Indian. This deformed skull is the one pictured on the cover. Before we left the pit, Francis discovered another human jawbone on a ledge at the other end of the

cave. We searched for artifacts, but the only man-made objects were recent.

We brought the skulls home, cleaned them, and took them to the McClung Museum at the University of Tennessee in Knoxville. There they were definitely identified as Indian probably Copena culture. This culture existed from about 500 B. C. to 500 A. D. The Copena were known to use pits as burial sites on occasion. They also practiced skull flattening. I was shown a Copena skull from a site near Nickajack; it was deformed in a

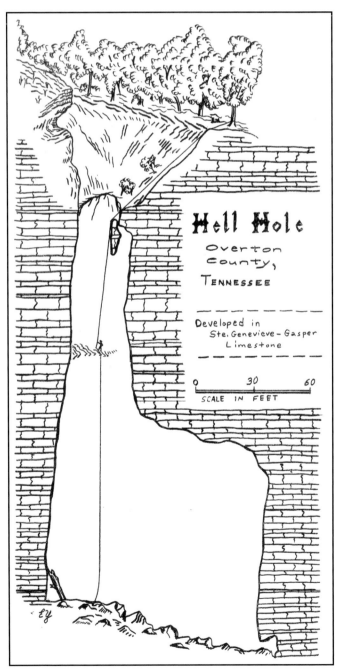

Figure 10.2. Profile of Hellhole by Edward M. Yarbrough, 1963.

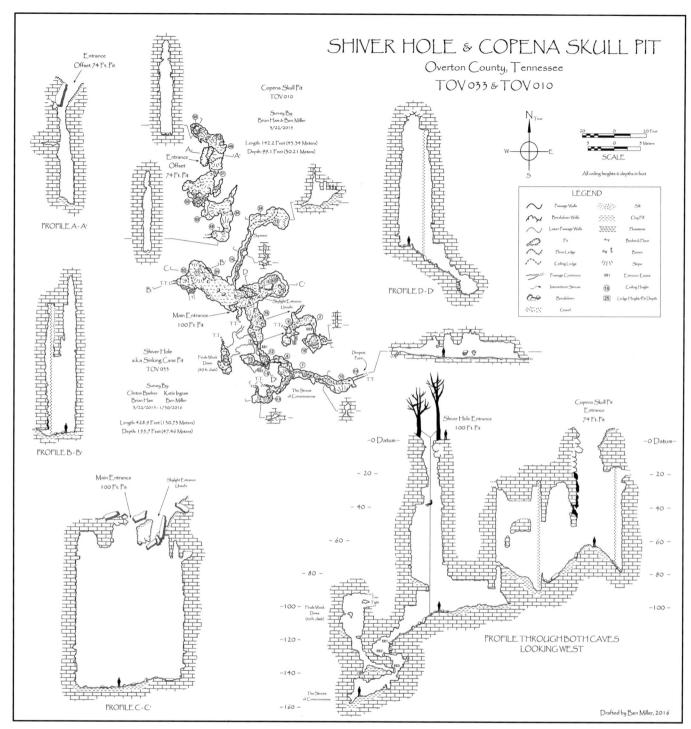

Figure 10.3. Survey of Shiver Hole and Copena Skull Pit, 2015-2016.

Figure 10.4. Ray Nelson on rope in Shiver Hole. Photo by Bob Biddix, March 1, 1998.

manner similar to the one we found. This trait is not completely distinctive, however, as skull flattening was practiced by a few other tribes and the Creeks did it infrequently as late as post-Columbian times.

The deformed skull was that of a young man about 30 years old. The two other complete skulls belonged to an old man and an old woman. The "pot" was a man about 40-50. The jawbone found at the north end of the cave did not fit any of the other skulls; thus, at least five individuals were buried in the pit. The skulls are now at the McClung Museum.

No human bones other than skull pieces had been found. The skulls might have been discarded trophies, since the Indians have been known to take trophy heads, but disposal of skulls in pits was unknown. Consequently, I headed back to the pit on October 21 with Don Mulholland to look for further human material.

After rappelling down, Don and I checked the pit at both ends of the talus pile. There was a great deal of breakdown intermingled with numerous bones of recent animals. We suspect that the talus pile is fairly modern, and any Indian material present is buried under a good deal of rock. The few pieces we found in this area were preserved when the caught in cracks or on ledges above the breakdown. Only the presence of the low wall kept the talus back from the dome in which we found most of the material and preserved its ancient mud surface. We climbed over the wall and down into the dome. I looked up to the crack where the first skull had been located and noticed a few more bones. Using sophisticated climbing techniques (I stood on Mulholland's back), I was able to reach this area and retrieve some arm bones and part of a hand which was in an articulated position. While I was digging these up, Don returned to the floor of the dome and began excavating the mud slope. He uncovered the major part of a skeleton, laying in a semi-articulated fashion beneath the crack which had held the skull. As Don

continued digging, he eventually realized that at least three individuals were involved. At this point we ceased our operations, leaving an area untouched for future excavation in a more controlled and scientific manner. The greatest disappointment was that absolutely no artifacts had been found. The artifacts would have given a better idea of the age and culture of the burials found.[5]

David Irving describes another pit, located close by:

One hundred feet south of Copena Skull Pit is a shallow depression in the hillside, floored with a jumble of sandstone blocks. Two openings in this pile of breakdown proved the entrances for Sinking Cane Pit. One entrance, a small hole, is a 102-foot drop, pleasantly close to the wall of the pit. The second entrance, east of the first, is a fissure which becomes a free-fall drop about 15 feet shorter than the first. The cave is an L-shaped well with each arm about 70 feet long. The floor is flat and free of breakdown except beneath the second entrance. The walls are vertical and smooth rising to a flat roof. In the afternoon, light pours in the first entrance and illuminates the entire west end of the pit. A narrow, winding passage leads away from the center of the "L" to a small room less than 30 feet long and 15 feet high.

Copena Skull Pit and Sinking Cane Pit come within 20 feet of each other but do not connect. The ceilings of all domes in the two pits are a roughly the same elevation. This strongly suggest that that level marks the sandstone-limestone contacts. On the hillside just above the entrances, the Hartselle Sandstone outcrops in ledges.

The two pits received a slight mention in *Caves of Tennessee* (1961) on page 344 in the description of Fancher Cave and Pit.[6]

5 Dave Irving, "Indian Burials Found", Speleotype, v. 2, no. 3 (Summer 1967), pp. 47-48.

6 David Irving, "Copena Skull Pit and Sinking Cane Pit", Speleotype, v. 2, no. 3 (Summer 1967), pp. 49-50.

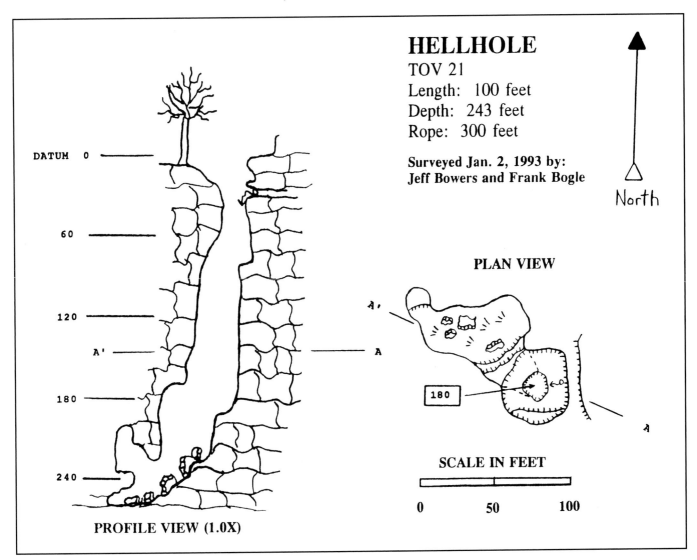

HELLHOLE

TOV 21
Length: 100 feet
Depth: 243 feet
Rope: 300 feet

Surveyed Jan. 2, 1993 by:
Jeff Bowers and Frank Bogle

North

DATUM 0

60

120

A'

180

240

PROFILE VIEW (1.0X)

PLAN VIEW

180

SCALE IN FEET

0   50   100

Figure 10.5. Survey of Hellhole by Jeff Bowers and Frank Bogle, 1993.

Figure 10.6. Photo of David Irving and the skull of a Copena Indian from the Copena Skull Pit.

Figure 10.7. Erica Sughrue on rappel in MacDonald Hole. Photo by Bob Biddix, March 19, 2017.

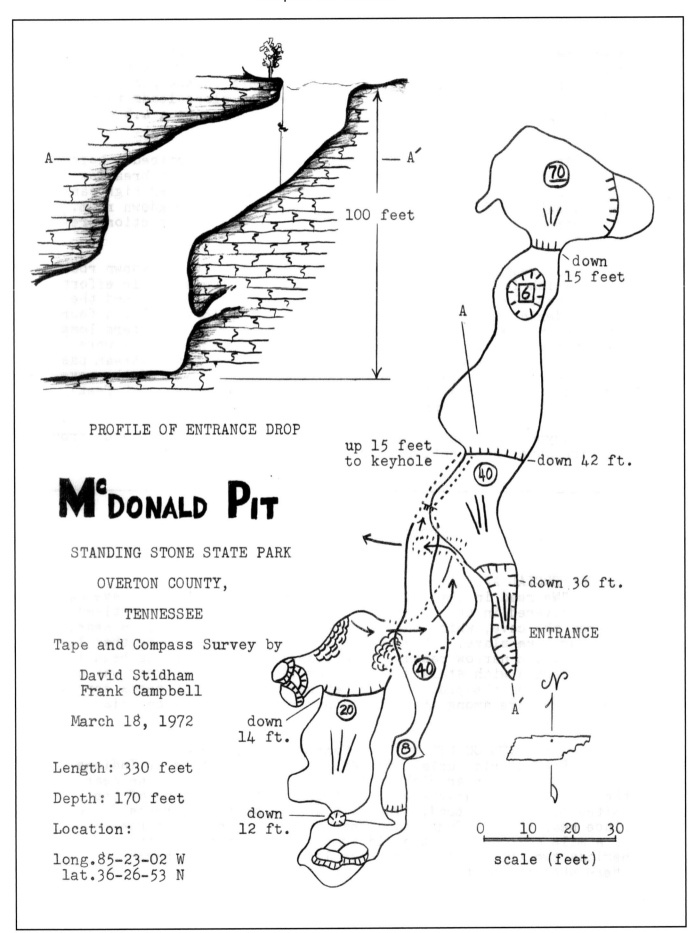

100 feet

PROFILE OF ENTRANCE DROP

McDonald Pit

STANDING STONE STATE PARK

OVERTON COUNTY,

TENNESSEE

Tape and Compass Survey by

David Stidham
Frank Campbell

March 18, 1972

Length: 330 feet

Depth: 170 feet

Location:

long.85-23-02 W
lat.36-26-53 N

down
15 feet

up 15 feet
to keyhole

down 42 ft.

down 36 ft.

ENTRANCE

down
14 ft.

down
12 ft.

0   10   20   30

scale (feet)

Figure 10.8. Survey of MacDonald Hole by David Stidham and Frank Campbell, March 18, 1972.

Sinking Cane Pit was also submitted to the Tennessee Cave Survey under the name Shiver Hole by a different explorer. That is the name currently in use for this pit.

THE SURVEY OF SHIVER HOLE AND COPENA SKULL PIT

Copena Skull Pit was surveyed by Brian Ham and Ben Miller on March 22, 2015. There is both a plan and a profile. Shiver Hole was surveyed by Clinton Barber, Brian Ham, Katie Ingram, and Ben Miller between March 22, 2015 and January 30, 2016. Again, there is both a plan and a profile. The profile through both caves looking west shows that the two caves come within approximately 20 feet of each other. This combined survey is shown as Figure 10.3.

An earlier map by D. C. Irving, J. Corley, and F. E. McKinney was prepared on March 5, 1967, but is not as detailed as the newer map. It was published in the Summer 1967 issue of the Speleotype on page 51.

CAVE ACCESS

These pits are located on private property. Do not enter these pits or any other pits or caves, without the owner's permission.

MACDONALD HOLE

MacDonald Hole (also known as McDonald Pit) is another well-known and significant pit located in Overton County. This pit was first descended by Bill Cuddington in 1954.

A DESCRIPTION OF THE CAVE

The first mention of MacDonald Hole in the caving literature was this short note in the July, 1954 Speleonews:

> Another deep pit is located in Standing Stone State Park—the MacDonald Hole. No one has ever succeeded in reaching the bottom, although several attempts have been made. Back in Civil War days, it seems that Old Man MacDonald was captured by bushwhackers

and tossed into the pit. His bones have never been recovered.[7]

Apparently Bill Cuddington visited this pit soon afterwards and did reach the bottom. Unfortunately, he did not write a Trip Report and we have no further details of his exploration. If Bill found Old Man MacDonald's remains, we will never know.

Nearly twenty years later, David Stidham wrote the following description of the cave:

> MacDonald Pit is located within the boundaries of Standing Stone State Park and Forest, in Overton County, near the Group Camp. The pit is not a new find, for it has been visited by cavers and park visitors in the past, but it did yield virgin passage on a trip in March.
>
> Frank Campbell had been to the pit before and agreed to lead a return trip. Frank drove within a couple hundred feet of the entrance in his Scout. A short walk leads to a 6-foot by 24-foot trench at the base of a bluff. The trench drops 14 feet at one end and 33 feet at the opposite end. The 33-foot drop is recommended for rigging, yet explorers in the past have climbed down the short drop on logs. A steep slope leads to a 38-foot drop. A level passage leads 42 feet to a 14-foot climb-down and a 60-foot dome.
>
> As I rappelled down the 38-foot drop, I noticed a hole 12 feet off the floor. It is possible to climb up breakdown to this keyhole. The keyhole opens into a 36-foot high canyon passage, which extends 75 feet to a small breakdown room. It appeared as if only a few people had been in this section previously.
>
> A streamlet flowed down a small hole in the breakdown room, beyond which is appeared the cave extended. With a little effort it was possible to break some popcorn encrusted rocks around the hole, widening

---

7 Anonymous, "300-Foot pit Near Livingston", Speleonews, v. 2 (1954), no. 7, p. 12.

Figure 10.9. Erica Sughrue on rope in Hellhole. Photo by Bob Biddix, July 26, 2020.

Figure 10.10. Ed Yarbrough rappels into MacDonald Hole. Photo by Harry White, 1972.

it enough to gain access to virgin passage. A 12-foot chimney entered into the upper end of a room 57 feet long and 18 feet wide. A small waterfall and flowstone mounds were developed at the lower end of the room, and a 36-foot stream passage terminated the cave at a narrow fissure. We mapped the cave, which is 330 feet long and 170 feet deep, at the stream siphon.[8]

THE SURVEY OF MACDONALD HOLE

MacDonald Hole (also known as McDonald Pit) was surveyed by David Stidham and Frank Campbell on March 18, 1972 (See Figure 10.8.)

8 David Stidham, "Old McDonald Had A Pit (Revisited)", Speleonews, v. 16 (1972), no. 3, pp. 42-44.

CAVE ACCESS

MacDonald Hole is located in Standing Stone State Park. Be sure to check with the State Park Office to determine the current access status of this pit.

WARNING:

Vertical caving is inherently dangerous. If you do not use the proper equipment and the proper techniques, in all likelihood you will die. Always seek out training from experienced vertical cavers before you ever attempt to explore pits on your own.

Figure 11.1. Erica Sughrue at the Entrance to Falling Springs Cave. Photo by Bob Biddix, October 24, 2020.

CHAPTER 11
Mill Hollow Cave

Mill Hollow Cave is located in Overton County, Tennessee. It was discovered by Lennie Fottrell and Joe Douglas on March 10 1984. With nearly five miles of explored passages, it is one of Tennessee's longest caves. Also located in Big Sunk Cane are Falling River Cave and Falling Springs Cave, which are included in this chapter.

A DESCRIPTION OF THE CAVE

The Tennessee Cave Survey lists this cave as being 25,000 feet (4.7 miles) long. Chuck Mangelsdorf wrote the following Trip Report in 1984:

> Big Sunk Cane is the local name applied to a large sinking valley situated in extreme southeastern Overton County, 6.5 miles northeast of Monterey, TN. The karst valley is developed in the Monteagle Limestone and measures 60 to 80 feet deep, a mile long, and half a mile wide, with several tributary hollows. Three separate streambeds sink at the bottom of the valley, draining an area of about four-square miles.
>
> At least a portion of this water is believed (by both cavers and local residents) to resurge in Three Forks Cave, on the West Fork of the Obey River, just over two miles north of Big Sunk Cane. Tom Barr mentioned this drainage connection in *Caves of Tennessee* (1961), and local inhabitants still relate the story of how a pig washed underground in the Cane and reappeared later in Three Forks Cave. Explorations spearheaded by Larry Johnson in 1977 and 1978 succeeded in pushing the length of Three Forks Cave to over two miles, much of which was large stream trunk passage. Before exploration of the cave was completed or a survey begun over nine-tenths of the cave was sealed off when a road construction crew blasted into the ceiling

of the entrance passage, effectively sealing off the most significant portion of the cave. The results of the damage are still visible. An artificial second entrance in the roadcut leads down over tons and tons of rock to what was formerly a deep sump, leading to the infamous "tornado alley" and the two miles long extension. Today the sump lies underneath a thick layer of rock and earth and any chance of re-entering the extension in Three Forks Cave seems remote.

Falling River Cave and Falling Springs Cave

Years passed after our explorations in Three Forks Cave, and one minor fact remained buried in my mind. Big Sunk Cane, one of Tennessee's most significant blind karst valleys, boasted only one known cave, and it was not too impressive. One day at work I called Joe Douglas and mentioned the idea of a trip to Overton County to him. He said it sounded good and the two of us set up a meeting point and agreed to try and recruit a couple other cavers to go along. On Saturday March 10, 1984 Joe and I met to go caving and a few other cavers did show up, namely: Brad Neff, Sue Neff, Lennie Fottrell, David Parr, Rodger Ling, Paula Ledbetter, Joe Webster, and Ann Wilkerson.

After we arrived at Big Sunk Cave it was decided to venture to Falling Springs Cave, which had been visited and described by both Barr and Bailey. After checking two interesting wet weather swallets our group arrived at the picturesque waterfall entrance to Falling Springs. While everyone geared up to enter the cave, I lingered back with Joe who had stumbled upon a small, deep sinkhole 250 feet away. The sinkhole looked as if it might

Figure 11.2 Erica Sughrue at the point where a wet-weather stream sinks underground in Big Sunk Cane. Photo by Bob Biddix, October 24, 2020.

contain a tiny entrance at the bottom; after Joe had moved a few loose rocks he was able to crawl into a small passage. Several minutes later he shouted to me what he had found—a good-sized waterfall dropping into what looked like walking passage. Needless to say, I quickly entered the cave.

The entrance was low and tight. The two-foot wide, one-foot high entrance passage immediately led to an awkward "S" turn, then to Joe who greeted me with a sly grin. He informed me the crawl ahead led to the 30-foot high waterfall, which I could hear roaring in the background. The drop would require ropes, he said. However, by climbing down a sheer, tight, 20-foot chimney I was able to reach the stream passage below and explore 150 feet of cave to the top of a difficult climb. Backtracking, I called up to Joe to get the others. After much shouting over the din of the rushing water he got the message.

Ten minutes later I was joined in the stream passage by Brad, David, and another caver. The four of us headed into the cave, skirted around the drop where I had stopped, and ended up in a large, blind domepit with lots of loose rocks. Returning to the ledge above the drop we noticed a small pit leading downward. Rocks tossed in fell only 20 feet, or so, but it would require vertical gear. Said gear being in the cars, we headed out of the cave.

On the surface we met the rest of the team and described the cave to them. It was decided that Brad, David, Rodger, Joe Webster, Paula, and I would return to the cave and rig the drop while the others ridge-walked in the area and searched for other entrances. Reentering the cave with several ropes we rigged the upper two-foot high ledge and fed the rope into the 20-foot pit. I descended first and did my best to clear the lip of loose rocks, which surrounded the opening. From the bottom

Figure 11.3. Erica Sughrue in the main passage of Falling Springs Cave. Photo by Bob Biddix, October 24, 2020.

of the shaft a passage led downward into a continuation of the stream passage. A couple of free climbs in the cascading water were to characterize the rest of the cave. The cave was explored to a depth of approximately 180 to 200 feet and a length of about 2,000 feet. Several sporting waterfall climbs had to be negotiated before exploration was halted at a stream siphon in breakdown. Several leads were left unchecked.

The last of the explorers exited the cave around 7 pm that evening. While waiting outside around the campfire near the sinkhole entrance we tossed around several possible names for the new cave. We finally settled on Falling River Cave because of its proximity to Falling Springs Cave and because the name so aptly described much of the cave's passage.

Lennie Fottrell and Joe Douglas had been ridge-walking while we were exploring the new cave (Falling River Cave), described their most promising find to us. They has stumbled upon a prominent entrance at the swallet in Mill Hollow. Stooping into the small entrance they'd entered a large room which immediately led to 1,500 feet or so of walking passage with many unchecked leads and a good deal of washed-in debris. This new find was dubbed Mill Hollow Cave and plans were made to return to it soon.

The next day, March 11th, Joe Douglas returned to Mill Hollow Cave with David Parr, Jim Hodson, Sue Loveless, and Joel Buckner. They explored most of the obvious passageways in the cave, extending its length to approximately 4,000 feet. The best

Figure 11.4. Erica Sughrue at the Entrance to Mill Hollow Cave. Photo by Bob Biddix, October 24, 2020.

remaining lead was a bolt climb which seemed to lead up into an upper level passage. Dates from the 1970s were seen smoked on the walls of the cave, indicating that locals had been entering the cave for the past several years. The nature of the entrance suggests that Mill Hollow Cave could have been blocked by debris sometime in the recent past. It is possible that the entrance may be covered by surface debris after any future heavy rain.

Mill Hollow Cave contained several leads in addition to the bolt climb, so a return trip was set up for July 8, 1984. Sixteen cavers arrived in Big Sunk Cane on the hot Sunday and geared up for exploring and surveying. Three survey teams entered Mill Hollow, a fourth team carried ropes, bolts, and vertical gear. The first survey team began surveying at the entrance. Joe Douglas, Larry Adams, Chuck Frase, and Paula Ledbetter were the A

team. The second group of mappers consisted of David Parr, Gerald Moni, Sue Loveless, and Buddy Shelfer. This B team went ahead to begin their survey which the A team would tie into. The third survey team, the C team, was to start knocking off side passages, gradually making its way further into the cave. Brad Neff, Sue Neff, Debbie Hannah, Sarah Johnson, and I made up the C team. The bolting team (or the Glory Boys) included Jim Hodson, Elwin Hannah, and Don Neal.

The climbers went underground first, followed closely by the B team. The A team began their survey while the C team picked blackberries near the entrance. The C team soon entered and began our survey quickly by tying into station A-5, just inside the entrance. The side passage we began to map was located on the right side of the huge entrance room. Being point man, I trudged up the breakdown

Figure 11.5. Erica Sughrue in a breakdown-floored passage in Mill Hollow Cave. Photo by Bob Biddix, October 24, 2020. (Above)

Figure 11.6. Erica Sughrue at the Entrance to Falling River Cave. Photo by Bob Biddix, October 24, 2020. (Right)

slope and off across the shelf-like edge of the room, expecting the side lead to pinch out quickly. While setting station C-2 I noticed a small hole in the floor leading down into blackness. Negotiating a steep climb the bottom was reached and passages headed in both directions, although neither seemed really promising. The C team followed, and we surveyed to the left first, down a steep breakdown slope which finally ended at a possible dig.

Meanwhile, Sue Neff had been checking out the right-hand passage. She described it as leading for 100 feet to a tight pit which might be climbable. The CB series was begun in this small passage. Reaching the small pit quickly, it was descended to the top of an even tighter drop. Both pits were eight to ten feet deep

Figure 11.7. Erica Sughrue in a large passage where flood waters have washed away all sediments and left the bare limestone floor. Photo by Bob Biddix, October 24, 2020.

and climbable. Several stations later we were surveying in virgin walking passage. The first side lead in Mill Hollow Cave had broken the cave wide open.

The passage we had entered obviously carried a stream during heavy rainfall. It was surveyed for about 500 feet, past two walking side leads, to a point where the cave opened up to 40 feet wide and 40 feet high, with a huge side passage opening on the left. Ignoring this tantalizing lead, we surveyed onward for 200 more feet to the end of the trunk at a tremendous earth fill which extended upward for 50 feet. A stream

canyon entered from the left here and crossed the borehole to the right. We decided to survey downstream, following the water. The downstream canyon averaged five feet wide and 25 feet high and was staggered with several free climbs. We surveyed on through still pools of water. Five hundred feet or so into this section of the cave we began to look for a place to terminate the survey and begin exploring. Side leads were beginning to add up and the cave was starting to get complex. Upon reaching a junction where four passages joined we set out last station of the day, CB-43. We surveyed over fifty stations, almost all of it virgin.

Figure 11.8. Erica Sughrue by flowstone formations in Mill Hollow Cave. Photo by Bob Biddix, October 24, 2020.

Figure 11.9. Erica Sughrue in a large borehole passage in Mill Hollow Cave. Photo by Bob Biddix, October 24, 2020.

As we were putting up our survey gear we heard voices coming up the passage from behind us. Brad, Sue, Debbie, Sarah, and I were joined by Elwin, David, and Buddy. They had completed a long loop through the cave which eventually led them to the large trunk passage, where they encountered our CB survey stations. They followed the route of our survey down the stream canyon and met us at CB-43. The eight of us headed on into the cave. Two thousand feet of walking passage led to a junction with a wet stream passage which took off in both directions. Elwin jumped into the deep water and swam a couple hundred feet by himself to a point where he could finally wade. Returning to us, he described the passage as being six feet high, 20 feet wide, with water and no end in sight.

A return trip with wetsuits will probably be required to explore this section of the cave.

Everyone was out of the cave around 5 pm that evening. The other two survey teams had mapped about 30 stations each, including the upper level lead which had been rigged by Elwin. The loop traversed by Elwin, David, and Buddy contained many unexplored passages, as did much of the cave. Most of the cavers present estimated the explored length of the cave to be around 8,000 feet, over one and a half miles. And this was only the third trip into the cave by Nashville Grotto explorers.

On Saturday, July 28th, David Parr, Buddy Shelfer, and I returned to Mill Hollow Cave and explored additional passages in several sections of the cave. The cave seems to be a complex drainage system for Big Sunk Cane. Throughout the entire length of the cave surface debris is seen and the cave must flood to the ceiling at times. As the survey progresses and is plotted, possible connection with Three Forks Cave and Falling River Cave are sure to be attempted. Because of the possibility of flooding, Mill Hollow Cave should be entered only during the summer and fall, or when there is no forecast for rain. Big Sunk Cane is sure to be the scene of much caving during the coming years and it is hoped that all cavers will continue to respect the property of the landowners in the area.[1]

The cavers had a very productive weekend and Mill Hollow Cave would continue to grow in length as exploration continued.

THE SURVEY OF MILL HOLLOW CAVE

This is another one of those sad stories were people spent hundreds of hours surveying a cave and no final map was ever produced. What a waste of time! At least we know how long the cave is. Gerald Moni reports that the mapping effort was led by Paul Platt and Greg Johns. Gerald says: "The cave was mapped for 5 miles but no map was produced. Everyone involved dropped out of caving years ago. I was unable to get the notes."[2]

Here is a great opportunity for a new generation of cavers to map a really long, significant cave. Who knows how much the 1984 surveyors missed? There may be miles of virgin cave just waiting to be surveyed and explored. Get out your compass and tape and go to work!

CAVE ACCESS

Current access to this cave is unknown. Please be sure you have the owner's permission before you enter this, or any other cave.

Figure 11.10. Bob Biddix in the Dismal Pursuit Entrance of Mill Hollow Cave. Photo by Erica Sughrue, October 30, 2020.

---

1 Chuck Mangelsdorf, "Big Sunk Cave - 1984", Speleonews, v. 28, no. 6 (December, 1984), pp. 109-114.

2 Gerald Moni, Personal communication, September 17, 2019.

Figure 12.1. Harold Hamilton, Ray Swallow, Roger Young, Robert Young, and Jimmy Lee Young in Robinson Cave about 1962.

Figure 12.2. Dr. McGlafin of University of Tennessee at Knoxville with Ray Swallows, Robert Young, Roger Young, and Jimmy Lee Young in Robinson Cave about 1962.

CHAPTER 12
Robinson Cave

Robinson Cave is located in Overton County, Tennessee. It is not known who first explored the cave, but clearly it was known to the local residents before it was explored by organized cavers.

A DESCRIPTION OF THE CAVE

Robinson Cave has two entrances. One is a 20-foot deep fissure which can be chimneyed, but a safety is recommended. This enters into a wide gallery 10 feet high which runs 100 feet to a large room 80 feet in diameter and 20 feet high. The second entrance is a pit 20 feet in diameter and 30 feet deep, which drops into the center of this room. A passage leads south for about 75 feet to a fissure leading down into the main passage of the cave. This drop is only 15 feet, but the rocks are quite muddy, and a rope is helpful. One is now at the beginning of the main Formation Room, which is 250 feet long, as much as 100 feet wide, and 60 feet high at the far end. Several large formations are found in this room, especially

at the far end. There are massive stalagmites which tower 20 to 30 feet high and rest on broad flowstone bases. A small waterfall issues from the ceiling and splashes onto a massive stalagmite below.

A steep climb up a breakdown slope at the far end of the Formation Room leads into a continuation of the main passage. This passage trends west for 300 feet, averaging 40 feet wide and 20 feet high, then turns southwest for 350 feet and averages 75 feet wide and 30 feet high. A small passage about 50 feet before the end of the main passage leads northwest to the top of a 90-foot pit. The rappel is free and down the very center of an impressive dome-shaped room. The entrance to the pit is clogged with breakdown and the explorer rappels through an opening only 5 feet in diameter. The pit is 20 feet wide at the top and rapidly expands to 50 feet wide at the bottom. Talus slopes down 30 more feet to a stream passage which is very small and muddy at first, but gradually opens up downstream. Several chimneys and climbs make this passage difficult to traverse. This passage has been explored for approximately 1,000 feet and may continue farther.

The most significant discovery in Robinson Cave was two skeletons of the extinct ground sloth *Megalonyx jeffersoni* found by three brothers, Jimmy, Charles, and Roger Young in December 1961. These bones were discovered in a small pit in the Formation Room and were removed by the Carnegie Museum. One specimen was taken to the Carnegie Museum, the other was given to the Tennessee State Museum, but as of 1970 this skeleton was still not on display. Skeletons of smaller animals found during the dig include pine marten, chipmunk, southern flying squirrel, red squirrel, and bobcat.

Figure 12.3. Harold Hamilton of the Carnegie Museum wraps bones in Robinson Cave, Summer of 1962.

The sloth bones were extremely fragile and had to be removed in blocks of matrix covered with burlap and plaster. If the Young brothers had not used extremely good judgment in notifying a professional paleontologist to remove the bones, they would have been destroyed. Even trying to pull one of the protruding bones out of the clay would have caused it to crumble into hundreds of useless pieces.

THE ROBINSON CAVE GROUND SLOTHS

As noted in the description of the cave, in December, 1961, three brothers (Jimmy, Charles, and Roger Young) descended a small pit inside Robinson Cave. This drop led them into a kidney-shaped chamber eight (8) feet wide and fourteen (14) feet long. They found the bones of a large and unfamiliar animal protruding from the clay mud on the floor. Rather than disturb the bones, they left and quietly informed their High School Science Teacher, Mr. Ray Swallows, of their discovery. Swallows contacted the Tennessee Division of Geology. Since there were no trained vertebrate paleontologists on their staff, Assistant State Geologist Robert Hershey contacted Dr. Craig C. Black at the Carnegie Museum of the discovery.

On May 11, 1962, Dr. Black and Vertebrate Fossil Department Associates Harold Hamilton and Allen McCrady, along with Harold Casey, also of the Museum, made a reconnaissance trip to the cave. Allen D. McCrady describes what they found:

> Two visits to the cave on this trip resulted in tentative plans for excavation and a decision as to the best technique for bringing the bones to the surface undamaged. The first trip proved quite a revelation to novice caver Black. He now knows that cable ladders will hold a man's weight and are quite safe for descents in excess of 50 feet. Upon arrival at the site within the cave, Dr. Black was immediately able to identify an almost complete skull of the *Megalonyx jeffersoni* resting on the surface of the deposit. The next day a minimum of work

disclosed the magnitude of the task. There were remains of not one, but two specimens of sloth in varying states of preservation. After determining the general limits of the area to be worked, the crew turned to the task of removing the skull. In its protective plaster jacket it was taken back to the Museum, together with the skull and one mandible of a pine marten, and fragments of jaw and skull from the second *Megalonyx* found on the surface.

On June 17, 1962, Harold Hamilton, Rita Hamilton, and Allen McCray returned to Tennessee to spend fifteen (15) more days underground in Robinson Cave.

Description of Robinson Cave and Environs

Robinson Cave, Overton County is located on the land of Walter Robinson, approximately eight miles south of Livingston, Tennessee. One climbs about half-way up a ridge, locally known as Maxwell Mountain, from Mr. Robinson's back pasture, and following a "Dry Wash", comes to the first or smaller entrance. A 20-foot fissure which can be chimneyed with a safety leads to the top of a slippery mud and rock talus at the side of a large, decorated room. Descending a three to one slope for approximately 100 feet one comes to the lowest part of the "outer" cave. From here one can see daylight from the second or larger entrance, a 50-foot pit 30 feet wide which enters the cave some 200 feet up the ridge from the first. A large talus cone occupies the bottom of this pit composed of breakdown organic matter, and soil. It supports a large colony of tree frogs and salamanders in addition to cave crickets and insects by the thousands. The whole of the "outer cave", being more or less a "Twilight Zone" is an excellent collecting area for animal forms suited to dark and damp conditions.

Proceeding from the room at the bottom of the first entrance one turns left into a chamber which narrows into a stoopway and after curving to the left approximately

Figure 12.4. Erica Sughrue by large formations in Robinson Cave. Photo by Bob Biddix, November 7, 2014.

Figure 12.5. Roy Davis exits from a pit deep in Robinson Cave. Photo by Ed Yarbrough. November, 1970.

Figure 12.6. Larry Adams by colorful stalagmites in Robinson Cave. Photo by Larry E. Matthews. February, 1978.

Figure 12.7. Erica Sughrue rappels into the entrance of Robinson Cave. Photo by Bob Biddix, November 7, 2014.

50 feet ends at a fissure leading down. This is an awkward little climb of perhaps 20 feet. Although the Young brothers have installed a log across it, it should be rigged as it cannot be chimneyed due to a coating of mud left by the passage of many feet. At the bottom of this pitch a talus leads into a huge chamber. Climbing down a "Hog Back" of talus one travels a path which must be well worn by now. It winds across the breakdown-filled room up a slope to a "notch" leading to a back potion of the room separated from the rest by high breakdown. The notch has many once-beautiful six-inch diameter stalagmites which have been thoughtlessly broken. Looking from the notch one can see what appears at first glance to be the right wall of the cave. A closer look shows it to be one side

of the smaller of two tremendous stalagmites. Down the breakdown on the other side of the notch, approximately 600 feet from the fissure entrance into the "Inner Cave", looms the base of one of the elder statesmen of all stalagmites, perhaps 40 feet in diameter. The breakdown to the left at its base conceals the 20-foot pit from which the pine marten, sloth, and bobcat remains were taken. A waterfall splashes onto the stalagmite, issuing from the ceiling 60 feet above. In a small grotto in the side of the stalagmite, the other small mammals (chipmunk, flying squirrel, red squirrel) were found.

During the many days the author and his companions spent in the cave only one short half hour could be spared for further exploration. In that time, the breakdown at the end of the room was climbed almost to the ceiling, and a passage leading off into the mountain explored for perhaps 1,500 feet. Lack of time and not the end of the cave caused us to turn back. This is not surprising, since Maxwell Mountain is composed of the same strata found in the Mammoth Cave area, with the Cypress Sandstone capping and protecting the St. Genevieve Limestone and others below. While Robinson Cave possesses the same grand scale of rooms and passages, it is vastly more decorated. Only as one progresses into the mountain does the cave take on the appearance of Mammoth—the wide, gently arched ceilings, the massive plate breakdown, the huge stream passages, now dry.

Techniques and Problems of Excavation

Although the reconnaissance trip resulted in a good plan of attack, the June party was to find the job of completing the excavation no push-over. Instead of the seven days planned, 15 working days, plus two days rest and drying out were required. Several factors contributed to the difficulty of the task.

We should have foreseen that "housekeeping" and supply problems would take considerable time. After initial supplies were exhausted their replacements had to be purchased locally and packed to stand the trip through the cave to the working site. Every caver with a modicum of experience will recognize that to carry a 100-pound sack of plaster through even an easy cave is difficult. In places Robinson Cave is not easy. Hence each item had to be reduced to manageable size and protected against moisture and mud. Five-gallon paint buckets with pressure lids served for light-weight items such as paper, burlap bags, etc. Quick-set plaster was carried and stored in one-gallon paint buckets lined with plastic bags. We were fortunate that we could use the waterfall as a source for drinking, carbide lights, and mixing plaster. We were even more fortunate in having the Young brothers and Ray Swallows to help in all major "carries", both in and out. Nevertheless, we were rarely able to travel light on our trips in and out of the cave.

It also appeared that working in 55 F. degree temperature at near 100 percent humidity was relatively more tiring then similar activity above ground. Typically, after entering the cave at 9 A.M. and working without pause except for lunch, one would begin to feel the dampness and cold around 4 P.M. We developed the habit of stopping for a cup of tea brewed on the Primus, and this kept us going until we surfaced, usually about 7:30 P.M. Perhaps the contrast between the cold dampness of the cave and the usual hot Tennessee summer outside kept our bodies from acclimating.

The major difficulty arose from the nature of the deposit itself. Upon first examination it did not appear that the bones themselves would be too fragile, or the sand and pebble matrix apparent on the surface too hard to handle. We also had hopes that both sloths would be more or less articulated—that is, the neck bone connected to the head bone, etc. On these points we were doomed to disappointment. Except for the perimeter or

Figure 12.8. Erica Sughrue at the entrance to the Sloth Pit in Robinson Cave. Photo by Bob Biddix, November 7, 2014.

the chamber where it reach four or five inches, the "sand" ended two to three inches down. Then we struck a layer of cemented pebble, sand, and clay (called Breccia by caving paleontologists) which varied from as much as one to one and a half inches in depth. Then followed nine inches of homogeneous brown clay—very wet and slippery in most places. Then in the one area where we found the larger, more incomplete sloth, this changed to a thin layer (one-half to one-eighth of an inch) of gray clay followed by a three-eighths inch layer of bright red clay followed by a brown clay interbedded with thin layers of sand. In the other sloth area the homogeneous brown clay was followed by a layer of weathered calcite and grey clay, then the red clay and brown clay again. In addition, the small sloth area had numerous active drips and splashes

falling from the ceiling and striking the bone-bearing matrix. This caused a third, or surface layer of calcite to form as an over-all crust. The small, more complete sloth remains extended down to (and into one small area) the grey clay level. Thus the second sloth was covered with four layers of material, alternating hard and soft. Bone located under the first inch or so was in a uniform condition—wet through, rotten, and fragile, much the consistency of wet chalk.

Since there was no hope of drying the bone material in place in order to impregnate it was hardeners such as shellac or Alvar, and no way of taking it out to dry without breaking it into chips and crumbs, the solution lay in using an "outside" paleontologist method. The bone, or bones to be lifted are found using a pointing trowel to chip away at the surrounding clay.

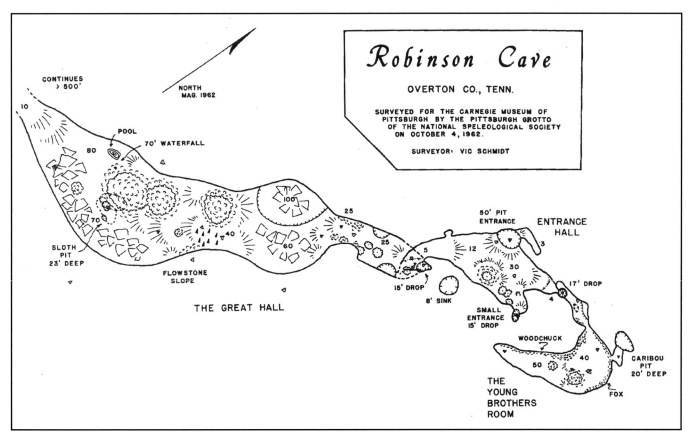

Figure 12.9. Map of the entrance area of Robinson Cave, Overton County by Vic Schmidt, October 4, 1962.

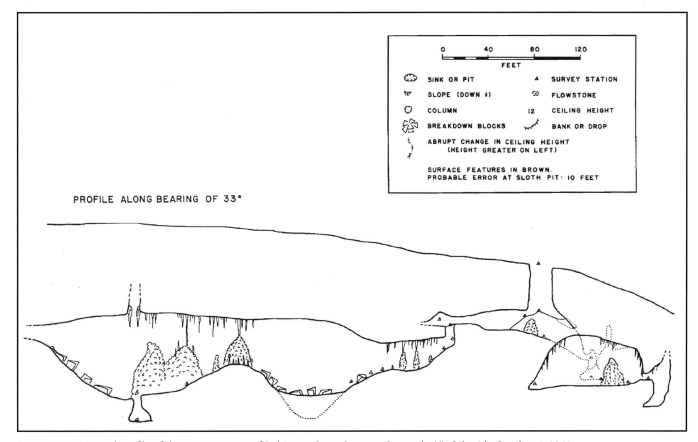

Figure 12.10. Vertical profile of the entrance area of Robinson Cave, Overton County by Vic Schmidt, October 4, 1962.

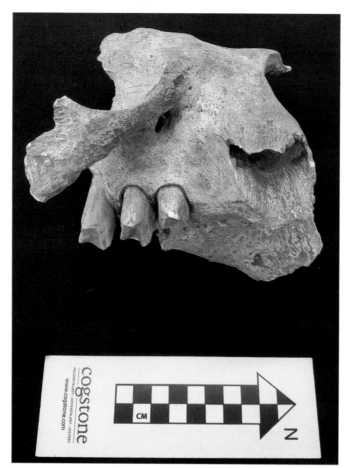

Figure 12.11. Partial skull of a *Megalonyx jeffersoni* recovered from the Sloth Pit in Robinson Cave. Photo courtesy of the Carnegie Museum.

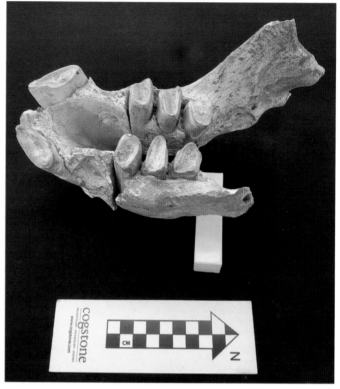

Figure 12.12. Jaws of a *Megalonyx jeffersoni* recovered from the Sloth Pit in Robinson Cave. Photo courtesy of the Carnegie Museum.

Figure 12.13. Skull of Megalonyx jeffersoni recovered from the Sloth Pit in Robinson Cave. Photo by Galen Barton.

Then smaller tools, in our case dentist's picks and probes, are used to trench around the exposed bone to find a convenient break or joint. Thus one hopes to find a manageable piece of bone or chunk of bones. The trick is now to under cut the bone(s) on three sides so that the bone is supported by a cantilever pedestal of clay. Since the next step is to enclose as much of the bone as possible by burlap soaked in liquid quick-set plaster, one tries to get as much clay out from under as possible and still leave the bone in place. In one of two cases when the support gave prematurely, the crew looked on in frozen suspense while a "block" of bones toppled with agonizing slowness into the surrounding trench. At this point, we picked up the pieces and started all over again.

In excavating the larger sloth we were hampered by the fact that the bone rested in a disorganized heap. Either the bones had been swirled about by water action or the animal had died in the breakdown above and filtered to the bottom of the pit. At any rate it was extremely difficult to isolate individual bones for removal.

Finally, the bones were quite fragile. The cancellous material which fills the center of bones is cellular in structure. It is designed to give strength with a minimum of weight. In all the sloth material the cancellous material

Figure 12.14. Erica Sughrue in the Great Hall of Robinson Cave. Photo by Bob Biddix, November 7, 2014.

Figure 12.15. Carol Lamers by a large stalagmite in Robinson Cave. Photo by Bob Biddix, November 7, 2014.

was punky and entirely lacking in strength. Evidently the bones had lain in water too long and not long enough—so long that they had been leached and not so long that they had been replaced.

Results

Over 80 plaster "bundles" of sloth were hoisted out of the cave. They averaged 15 pounds, but one or two approached 150 pounds. If it were not for the Young brothers they might have been there yet! Fragments of completely replaced bones were found under the sloth remains in the third calcite layer. These have been tentatively identified as bobcat, they are surely of the genus Lynx. Samples were taken of the various layers of matrix in the deposit. The more complete sloth skeleton is to be lodged at the State Museum at Nashville, Tennessee.

Questions Still To Be Answered

How old are the bones? How much older is the Lynx than the sloth? How did the animals get into the cave? How can we explain the various layers which composed the matrix? Where did the small sandstone pebbles found on the surface of the deposit come from? Were the red squirrel and pine marten contemporaneous with the sloth?

Acknowledgements

I should like to thank in as public a manner as possible Mr. and Mrs. Robinson for their truly Southern Hospitality. They were grand. Throughout this article Jimmy, Charles, and Roger Young were mentioned again and again. We have nothing but the highest regard for them, not only as personable friends but as co-workers of the highest caliber. Ray Swallows was the sort of teacher we wish all high

Figure 12.16. Erica Sughrue between huge formations in Robinson Cave. Photo by Bob Biddix, November 7, 2014.

schools had in abundance. Out thanks also are due to Dave Murrian and his friends from the Tennessee Fish and Game Commission who took pictures of the site and volunteered for heavy labor. Finally, we owe our thanks to Mr. Hershey and the Tennessee Geological Survey for the opportunity to vacation in underground Tennessee.[1]

THE SECOND DISCOVERY

In August 1962, the Young brothers discovered another "bone-pit" in Robinson Cave. The story of that discovery is told by Allen D. McCrady and Vic Schmidt:

After their initial discoveries in the cave and thwarted for the moment by lack of equipment

for descending the pits that terminate the high passage that Allen had looked into earlier, the Young Brothers had turned their attention to a small hole opening off one end of the Entrance Hall. Enlarging the hole somewhat they were soon able to drop down 17 feet to a lower level passage. This quickly opens into a crescent-shaped room of goodly size with ceiling heights ranging from 40 to 80 feet. The walls and ceiling are magnificently decorated, and a large column stands off to one side, nearly dividing the room into two sections. In the north wall, a small hole in the flowstone curtain leads one to the lip of a 20-foot pit. The Young Brothers had used a rope ladder here and spied, for the second time, an untouched bone deposit. Old hands at this game that they now were, they sent word to Pittsburgh about their find.

1 Allen D. McCrady, The Netherworld News, v. 10 (1962), no. 9, pp. 155-160. Reprinted in the 1962 Speleo Digest, pp 2-40 - 2-45.

Ladders were strung at the first small drop and at the new bone pit. Meanwhile, Roy Davis and a group from the Nashville Grotto arrived at the scene and accompanied Dr. Black and myself on a visit to the Sloth Pit, where Ham, Rita, and Allen had done extensive excavating on the earlier trips. A short inspection of the site assured Dr. Black that nothing of interest remained, and we headed once again for the entrance, mapping as we went. From there, Roy and I mapped our way into the new section, and I visited Allen and Ham in the new bone pit (we can now refer to this as the "Caribou Pit", as one of these critters seems to have lost a tooth here, once upon a time). I was fascinated by the careful sifting operations, and particularly by the method Al and Ham have developed for "on the spot" cleaning of some doubtful objects to determine if they are bone or stone: They simply pop them into their mouths, swish them around for a bit, and then "ptui", out comes a new specimen for little old ladies to gawk at in the museum. Al was heard to claim, "Even the guano layers aren't so bad… after all, they're 1,000 years old."

On Friday I tore myself away from watching such marvels as these and set about photographing the cave. By afternoon, both photographic and digging operations had ground to a halt, and I returned to the surface to do some hurried topographic mapping over the cave with Dr. Black, while Al, Ham, and the others probed into the high passage leading off the end of the Great Hall. The series of drops they encountered quickly exhausted available equipment and by mid-afternoon all had exited the cave.[2]

Again, the excavation was done by the Carnegie Museum of Pittsburg, Pennsylvania. The entire fauna (with one exception) of this pit was animals which live in cold climates.

They probably lived 20,000 years ago during the last great Ice Age when the weather of Tennessee was more like that of Southern Canada today. Extinct animals found in the pit were *Canis dirus*—the dire wolf, *Rangifer*—a large, extinct deer closely related to the caribou, and *Epesicus grandis*—the big brown bat. The one exception was *Dasypus bellus*—the armadillo, which only lives in climates much warmer than present-day Tennessee.[3] The armadillo may have lived in Tennessee more than 80,000 years ago, during the last interglacial period, the Sangamon Period.[4]

At the 1963 NSS Convention at Mt. Lake, Virginia, Allen D. McCrady presented a talk in the Biology Session further describing the fauna that was recovered from Robinson Cave. Here is the Abstract of that talk:

Over twenty-one working days underground in Robinson Cave, Overton County, has produced the largest and most varied fauna yet recovered from the Late Pleistocene of Tennessee. Three locations in the cave netted ten species of carnivores, 15 species of insectivores, 2 types of deer, 17 rodents, 2 species of edentates, and one proboscidean in addition to numerous birds, snakes, salamanders, lizards, turtles, millipedes, and snails. Four extinct animals, the Jefferson ground sloth, *Megalonyx jeffersoni*, the dire wolf, mastodon, and the giant *Eptesicus grandis*, indicate an age at least of late Pleistocene and one specimen *Dasypus bellus*, seems to indicate the close of the Sangamon. Three climates are inferred from the present habitats of the surviving animals. First, a climate somewhat warmer than present day Tennessee, as indicated by the armadillo; second, a climate similar to that existing now in Canada and northern United States characterized by the arctic shrew,

2 Allen D. McCrady and Vic Schmidt, "Second Interim Report: Late Pleistocene Fossils From Robinson Cave, Tennessee", Netherworld News, Vol. 11 (1963), no. 2, pp 19-27.

3 Interestingly, since this was written in 1962, the armadillo has migrated north and again lives in Tennessee.

4 Larry E. Matthews, *Descriptions of Tennessee Caves*, TN Division of Geology, Bulletin 69 (1971), pp 76-77.

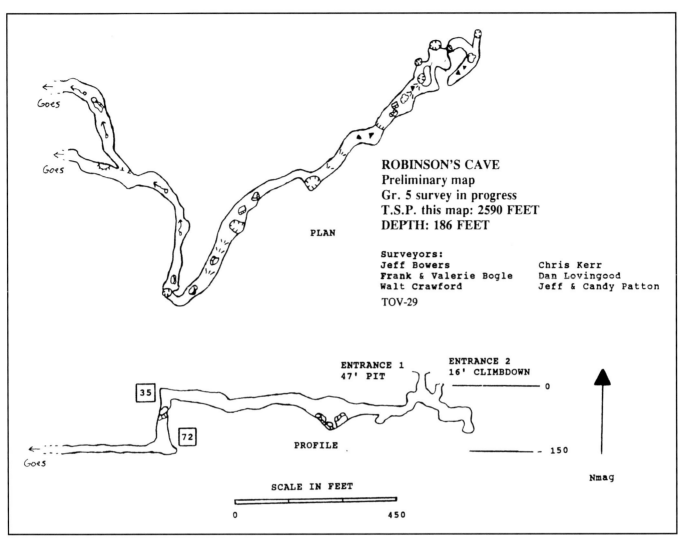

Figure 12.17. Map of Robinson Cave.

northern bog lemming, caribou, jumping mice, porcupine, pine martin, and certain other mice; and a third, dryer, northern plains climate with the thirteen-lined ground squirrel as evidence. Fluorine content studies made on representative samples of bone support the theory that the armadillo material has been in place longest and lead to the interesting speculation that deposition began at the end of the Sangamon and extended into the height of the Wisconsin. It is postulated that the material funneled into the underground cavities, where it was found by means of drains in the bottom of trap pits which once extended to the surface. Subsequent collapse, cementation and decoration by flowstone has obscured the point of entry. Several techniques novel to cave paleontology were used in excavating and recovering the material in addition to painstaking lab analysis which is continuing at the time of writing.[5]

This makes it clear that significant work had been accomplished on removing the bones from the matrix and identifying them in the year since the actual excavation. Now, the question 56 years later is whether, or not, this material is still housed in the Carnegie Museum.

WHERE IS THE SKULL?

Personnel at the Tennessee State Museum admit they had the Ground Sloth Skull at one time, perhaps in 1971, but now they do not know where it is. This is confirmed by my conversations with

5 Allen D. McCrady, NSS News, v. 21 (1963), no. 10, p. 163.

Debbie Shaw who is currently a curator at the museum. The next question is: Did they have the original skull, or did they have a well-made cast? Not everyone would be able to tell the difference.

JEFFERSON'S GROUND SLOTH

The first recorded giant ground sloth bones were discovered in 1797 in a cave in what would later become West Virginia. At the time, however, the area was still a part of the State of Virginia. These large bones were sent to Thomas Jefferson, a leading scientist of the day. Based on the huge size of the claws, and lacking a skull, Jefferson surmised that the bones belonged to some type of giant lion. Using scientific nomenclature, with *Mega* for giant and *Lonyx* for claw, the creature was named *Megalonyx*. A few years later, when more complete skeletons were found, it became clear that this was a giant form of sloth. This particular species was named *jeffersoni*, in honor of Thomas Jefferson. A very well preserved and complete skeleton of *Megalonyx jeffersoni* was discovered in Big Bone Cave, Van Buren County, Tennessee in 1810.

Giant Ground Sloths lived during the Miocene, Pliocene, and Pleistocene Epochs and ranged widely across North America. Over this vast expanse of time, there were many different genus and species. *Megalonyx jeffersoni* was the last species living before the extinction of the Megafauna. Since it's fossils are frequently found in caves, perhaps it used caves as den and hibernation sites just as bears have since the last Ice Age.

THE EXTINCTION OF THE MEGAFAUNA

North America was inhabited by a wide variety of large mammals for millions of years. These included Giant Ground Sloths, Mammoths, Mastodons, Saber-Toothed Tigers, Horses, Camels, Tapirs, Giant Armadillos, Lions, and other interesting creatures. But, for some reason, these large animals, referred to by paleontologists as the Megafauna, abruptly disappear about 12,000 years ago. Some people attributed this to the arrival of human beings at about the same time and suggested that the Indians hunted these animals into extinction. Others suggested that the Land Bridge to Asia allowed diseases to enter North America that had never been here before. None of the theories really seemed to be adequate.

The dinosaurs went extinct abruptly 65 million years ago when a large asteroid hit what is now the coast of the Yucatan in Mexico. A distinctive black layer separates the Cretaceous, dinosaur-bearing layers from the Triassic layers above where there are no dinosaurs. In this layer there is a relatively high concentration of Iridium, which is common in asteroids. Could something similar have happened to the Megafauna?

Geologists examining the strata here in North America have discovered a similar, black-mat layer that separates the older, Megafauna-bearing sediments from the more recent sediments where they are absent. This layer is relatively rich in Platinum, which is also present in comets and asteroids. There is a feature along the Atlantic Coast known as Carolina Bays. These are shallow, oval-shaped depressions, named for the vegetation growing in them. If you draw a line along the long axes of these depressions, they all converge at the current location of the Great Lakes. At that time, the Continental Ice Sheet was two miles thick at that point and the impact of a large celestial object apparently sent blocks of ice flying all over what is now the Central and Eastern United States. When these giant chunks of ice hit the ground surface, they created what we now call the Carolina Bays. Further dating in ice cores has pinpointed this impact at about 12,800 years ago. This event was not as large as the one they killed the dinosaurs, but it was large enough to impact North America and Europe.

MY FIRST TRIP TO THE CAVE

I have color slides that I took on a trip to Robinson Cave in 1978. But I am sure I went there at least ten years earlier with Kirk Holland, probably on a SERA Cave Carnival Trip. I remember that we went down the pit to the lower level of the cave and never reached the end.

THE SURVEY OF ROBINSON CAVE

The entrance area of Robinson Cave was surveyed by Vic Schmidt on October 4, 1962. This map includes a vertical profile showing the pits and the heights of the rooms. The Great Hall is located southwest from the Entrance Hall and the Young Brothers Room is located northeast of the Entrance Hall. Approximately 800 feet of passage are shown. The cave continues to the southeast, past the Great Hall, but that area was not surveyed at this time. The map states: "Surveyed for the Carnegie Museum of Pittsburgh by the Pittsburgh Grotto of the National Speleological Society on October 4, 1962." It is an excellent and well-detailed map. (See Figures 12.9 and 12.10)

There is also an undated survey of Robinson Cave by Jeff Bowers, Chris Kerr, Frank & Valerie Bogle, Dan Lovingood, Walt Crawford, and Jeff & Candy Patton. It shows 2,590 feet of cave with a total depth of 186 feet. This map shows all of the upper cave and approximately 300 feet of the lower level of the cave. This map was printed on page 32 of the 1993 SERA Cave Carnival Guidebook. (See Figure 12.17)

THE NAME OF THE CAVE

As this book goes to press I have received information from Chuck Sutherland that the landowners of the property on which this cave is located were named Roberson and not Robinson. The name Robinson Cave has been in use for over 60 years, but apparently this was due to a misunderstanding by the people from the Carnegie Museum as to the correct spelling of the owner's name. Therefore, the Tennessee Cave Survey plans to officially change the name of the cave to Roberson Cave to honor the landowners.[6]

CAVE ACCESS

Robinson Cave is located on private property. Before entering this or any other cave, be sure that you have permission from the owner.

SUGGESTED READING

John E. Guilday, H. W. Hamilton, and Allen D. McCrady published *The Pleistocene Vertebrate Fauna of Robinson Cave, Overton County, Tennessee* in the Journal *Palaeovertebrata*, Volume 2 (1969), pages 25-75. It has some great photos of the sloth skull.

---

6 Personal communication from Chuck Sutherland, October 5, 2020.

Figure 13.1. Calla Goins at the bottom of the entrance drop to the Great Saltpeter Chasm. Photo by Jim Fox, February 15, 2019.

CHAPTER 13

The Great Saltpeter Chasm

The Great Saltpeter Chasm is located in Overton County, Tennessee. This was one of the most significant new saltpeter caves located in Tennessee after the publication of *Caves of Tennessee* (1961).

A DESCRIPTION OF THE CAVE

The Great Saltpeter Chasm was first descended and explored by modern cavers on November 22, 1966 by cavers Bill Deane and John Smyre. Here is the story of how they located the pit, then returned and explored it as told by Bill Deane:

> This story begins on a very late Sunday night when three farm boys, amazed at our feats of rappelling and prusiking in a small pit, offered to lead Ron Zawislak, Jim Hodson, John Smyre, and myself to a "300-foot deep pit" which "no one has ever gone down." Following our guides along strange and devious trails, we suddenly found ourselves looking down into a fantastic pit located at the bottom of a sinkhole. It appeared in the glow of our carbide lights like the bottom had fallen out of a valley. With visions of joy dancing thru my head, I climbed down to where I could see into the pit. DOOM!!!! With my carbide lamp I could easily see the bottom which was only 60 feet down. Somehow the magic charm of the previous moments instantly disappeared and since it was quite late we trudged off without going down.
>
> Thirty-six hours later, John and I again stood at the edge of the pit. In the light of day we could easily see a major passage leading off to the north at the bottom of the pit. Rigging a 92-foot section of 7/16-inch Goldline, we rappelled into the pit. John made the drop first and disappeared down a passage heading west, which could not be seen from the top.
>
> I rappelled in and being determined to claim as much virgin cave as possible, I charged off into the north passage.
>
> Immediately the passage split at a "T" junction. The passage to the left was 50-feet wide and 15-feet high and stretched off into the darkness. I had the feeling that the passage was going to go on forever, so I went down it. My light began to act up, but even in the dim glow, it was obvious that the passage was not virgin. Thinking that the passage swung around and rejoined the passage John had gone down, I yelled out his name. There was no answer. I continued down the passage which soon became 40-feet high and 60-feet wide. Then I saw it, the most outstanding saltpeter vat that I had ever seen. It looked like a miniature log cabin and stood taller than me. We later measured it to be 7 feet high, 7 feet wide, and 11 feet long.
>
> Surrounding the vat are three water troughs. In one of these, I found a rusted, hand-made tin cup with a handle. (See Figure 13.4) I looked at it for a few minutes contemplating the fact that it had been laying there unseen and untouched since the Civil War. On the opposite side of the passage from the big vat are the remains of three small V-shaped vats. It wasn't until my third trip to the Great Saltpeter Chasm, that it was pointed out to me that a perfect handprint exists in the dried mud in the top of one of these vats. The handprint is small and is probably that of a child.
>
> I continued down the passage which was now 75-feet wide and 40-feet high. However, it soon ended at a giant breakdown. About this time, John rejoined me and once he got over the initial shock of the discovery and we had stopped jumping up and down for joy, we

Figure 13.2. Frank Campbell rappels into the entrance of the Great Saltpeter Chasm. Photo by Larry E. Matthews, July, 1976.

Figure 13.3. A caver by tally marks and torch marks on the wall of the Great Saltpeter Chasm. Photo by Ronald L. Zawislak, 1968.

started a careful search of the entire passage. Our first find was some tally marks and numbers behind the small vats. Then halfway up the breakdown in a small side dome John discovered a gigantic water trough 8 feet 2 inches long and 2 feet 8 inches wide. Richard Finch, upon seeing photographs of it, said that it was the largest water trough that he knew of in any Tennessee cave. In all there is 1,250 feet of walking passage at the bottom of the pit. The following map is a steel tape and Brunton Compass survey.[1]

There was no evidence in the cave to indicate that anyone else had entered the cave since the saltpeter mining operations had ceased. It is possible that the cave was mined during the Civil War, as Bill Deane suggests, but it is also possible

Figure 13.4. Barbara Zawislak examines a tin cup sitting in a water trough in the Great Saltpeter Chasm. Photo by Ronald L. Zawislak, 1968.

that the cave was mined even earlier, during the War of 1812.

Bill Deane returned to the Great Saltpeter Chasm in the summer of 1970 with Walt Rosenthal, Rhoda Estin, Ira Estin, and Art Gaier. Although this was planned as a photography trip,

_____

1 Bill Deane, "The Great Saltpetre Chasm", Speleonews, v. 11, no. 3 (May, 1967), pp. 53-56.

Figure 13.5. Frank Campbell stands next to the large, notched-log saltpeter vat in the Saltpeter Passage. Photo by Larry E. Matthews, July, 1976.

Figure 13.6. Harry White by wooden water troughs and the large, notched-log saltpeter vat in the Great Saltpeter Chasm. Photo by Ronald L. Zawislak, 1968.

Figure 13.7. Jim Hodson examines a small, wooden trough in the Great Saltpeter Chasm. Photo by Ronald L. Zawislak, 1968.

they did explore some leads while they were there. Bill describes the trip:

> We climbed two domes and found ourselves in cave not shown on the published map. At the end of the sandy-floored passage is a dome in which someone had placed a log. Walt and I climbed up the log and found ourselves with about 40 feet of passage and a room 12 feet high, 10 feet wide, and 18 feet long. This part was not virgin, but I climbed a 10-foot dome in the room and found about 10 feet of wet, muddy, virgin crawlway. Not much, considering the effort.
>
> We did somewhat better in John's passage, in the other end of the cave. While Art, Rhoda, and Ira were prusiking out, Walt and I pondered several high leads. We decided finally to climb to a large ledge located 50 feet down the passage just past a 10-foot dome. We first attempted to free climb the 15-foot wall with absolutely no success. I then attempted to lasso a rock projection, and after 50 attempts, or so, I finally succeeded. I climbed up hand-over-hand, and found myself even with the ledge, but 6 feet away from it. One super daddy-long-leg step and stretch put me on the ledge and I started down what I hoped would be miles of passage. Naturally my carbide light ran out of water at this moment and died. I switched to my flashlight. A quick check revealed that I was in a dome about 30 feet

long, 20 feet wide, and 40 feet high. A very careful search revealed no passage, except a lead at the top of the dome, which I could not reach. So, I climbed back down the wall and a short time later prussiked out of the pit.[2]

Bill Deane returned to the Great Saltpeter Chasm again on June 24, 1972 to check out another high lead:

> At the end of the Domes Passage in the Great Saltpeter Chasm, about 25 feet above the floor, is a major lead which has always tantalized me. On June 24, 1972, I climbed up to this passage using Jim Hodson's 30-foot climbing pole. I found about 75 feet of virgin cave, most of which was in breakdown. This was done during the Nashville Grotto's field trip for June.[3]

THE FLOOD OF 1975

Middle Tennessee had extensive rains and flooding in the Spring of 1975. I had heard rumors that this flooding had damaged the saltpeter mining artifacts in the Great Salpeter Chasm, so on June 26, 1976 Marietta Matthews, Frank Campbell, Barbara Amande, Bill Haggard, Ned McCloud, and I visited the cave to assess the damage. Here is a report of what we found:

> The three (3) V-shaped saltpeter vats have been totally collapsed by the flooding. All that remains is three irregular piles of dirt with miscellaneous posts and boards sticking out. The three water troughs which were located around the large, notched-log square vat were no longer in their original positions and had been damaged (broken) during the movement caused by the flooding. The large, notched-log square vat itself, which was the outstanding artifact in the cave, is still standing, but the notched-log frame shows considerable deterioration from the flooding and the plank

2 Bill Deane, "Sight-Seeing In The Great Saltpeter Chasm", Speleonews, v. 14, no. 5 (November, 1970), pp. 63-64.
3 Bill Deane, "The Rafters Of The Great Saltpeter Chasm", Speleonews, v. 16, no. 3, p. 43.

Figure 13.8. Ray Nelson examines a wooden water trough in the Great Saltpeter Chasm. Photo by Bob Biddix, October, 1998.

Figure 13.9. Erica Sughrue by the bottom rail of a V-shaped saltpeter vat. The groove in the left end would have emptied into a wooden collection trough. Photo by Bob Biddix, December 31, 2016.

inner-liner is now a jumbled pile of boards in the bottom of the vat where the flooding washed out all the dirt inside the vat. The "ramp" made of two poles which led up one side of the vat was washed away by the flooding.

The only significant artifact in the cave that was not damaged by the flooding was the extremely large water trough, which is in a small side passage, perhaps 20 feet higher in elevation than the saltpeter vats. The large water trough is apparently unchanged since my last visit to the cave. Obviously, the flooding did not reach this high.[4]

It was discouraging to see that these significant saltpeter mining artifacts had been damaged. Fortunately, we have good photographs of them before the flood.

4 Larry E. Matthews, "Great Saltpeter Chasm's Artifacts Damaged By Flooding", Speleonews, v. 20, no. 2 (April, 1976), pp. 17-18.

MY FIRST TRIP TO THE CAVE

I visited this cave sometime shortly after it was discovered, probably in 1967 or 1968, but I have no record of the exact date.

THE SURVEY OF THE GREAT SALTPETER CHASM

The Great Saltpeter Chasm was surveyed on November 27 & 29, 1966. A copy of that survey is shown as Figure 13.12.

ACCIDENT AT THE GREAT SALTPETER CHASM

There was a large Nashville Grotto trip to the Great Saltpeter Chasm in 1973. Due to the number of people present, it looked like it would be slow going getting in and out of the pit, so I rigged my Goldline rope. Two people went down before me, one of whom was my wife Marietta. I rigged in next with my rack and backed over the

Figure 13.10. Remains of three (3) V-Shaped saltpeter vats. These vats collapsed during the Flood of 1975. Photo by Larry E. Matthews, July, 1976.

edge. Just at I got past the lip and was hanging free, the rope broke, right in front of my face.

I remember looking back, over my shoulder to the rocks 60 feet below. "I'm dead," I thought. I remember nothing until waking up laying face down on the talus slope on the bottom.

Looking down the talus slope, I saw my wife running up the slope towards me. Meanwhile, I was laying still, amazed to be alive, but wondering what type of injuries I might have. When Marietta got to me, I asked her to check me very carefully from my feet up to my head, for any injuries, especially compound fractures. Hmmm. She didn't find anything wrong.

I very carefully rolled over onto my back and began checking the front of my body from my head down to my feet, and I couldn't find any injuries on that side of my body, either! I slowly sat up. So far, so good. Then I stood up. I still felt OK.

I later found out that the rather large group on the surface had heard me scream when the rope broke, then heard me falling and hitting the bottom. They expected the worst. They were as amazed as I was when the people on the bottom called up to them that I was still alive.

The secret to my "luck" was that I had rigged on the shallow side of the pit and that there were several ledges. As we reconstructed the accident later, it turns out that I had grabbed for the First Ledge and left deep fingerprints in the mud. That probably slowed me down just a little. I hit the Second Ledge with my face, leaving an imprint that was still there a year later. Fortunately, I hit mud. Apparently, this knocked me out. Judging from the severe bruise on one of my hips, I must have hit the Third Ledge with my hip. When I hit the bottom, I ended up face down and unconscious.

Figure 13.11. Zeke McKee, Calla Goins, and Jim Fox in the Saltpeter Passage in the Great Saltpeter Chasm. Photo by Jim Fox, February 15, 2019.

So, instead of falling 60 feet to the rocks, I fell about 14 feet…three times !!! We later measured the point from the lip where I had rigged to the bottom. I had fallen 42 feet.

Not knowing if I had any internal injuries, I decided that rather than continue on into cave, I should exit as soon as possible under my own power. I rigged into the other rope and prussiked out of the pit. Once on the surface, I did notice that I was having some trouble breathing. When I had hit the Second Ledge, mud was forced up both my nostrils! Once I pulled out the mud plugs I could breathe normally.

I did end up with an enormous bruise on my hip that took a long time to go away. That hip *might* have been cracked, but I never went to the Emergency Room to have it X-Rayed.

One effect that this accident had on me is that I went around SMILING for weeks on end, I was so happy to still be alive.

The Goldline rope that I had been using was tested by Mountain Safety Research a year later and broke under a normal load. But, at the point where it broke, it was discolored green inside, and obviously was much weaker. Whether this was a manufacturing flaw or subsequent damage to the rope, we never determined. However, several other people had accidents when Goldline rope broke during this time period and cavers no longer use this brand or type of rope.

CAVE ACCESS

This cave is located on private property. The current status is unknown. Do not enter this, or any other cave, without the owner's permission.

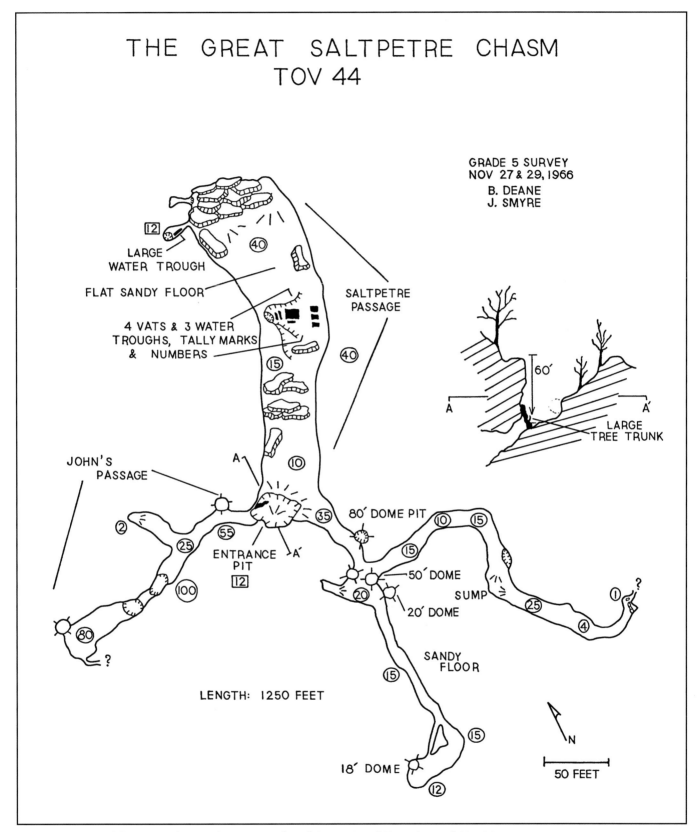

Figure 13.12. Map of the Great Saltpeter Chasm. Drawn by Bill Deane. Dated November 27 & 29, 1966.

Figure 14.1. Erica Sughrue in the main passage of Three Forks Cave. Photo by Bob Biddix, October 3, 2020.

CHAPTER 14
Three Forks Cave

Three Forks Cave is located in Overton County, Tennessee. It currently has an explored length of 7,500 feet (1.4 miles). The Tennessee Cave Survey believes that this is the same cave as the cave that Bailey (1918) described as Quarles Cave.

A 1917 VISIT TO THREE FORKS CAVE

Thomas L. Bailey's classic report, *Report on the Caves of the Eastern Highland Rim and Cumberland Mountains* (1918), gives the earliest known description of the cave:

No. 61. Quarles Cave.
Location.—On the land of Mrs. T. A. Quarles, 300 yards south of Quarles' house near the Three Forks of West Fork of the Obey River, 4 miles west of Crawford. It is in St. Louis limestone, 400 feet below the Lee sandstone.

The mouth is 60 feet wide and 15 feet high and is in open woods 50 feet west of the county road in a slight sink at the head of a small ravine. For about 65 feet from the mouth, the floor of the cave slants downward slightly but from that place back, there is a gradual upwards slope that continues through the cave with the exception of sinks at various places along the floor. At the bottom of some of these sinks a stream can be seen. There is a small spring 60 feet inside the mouth whose water sinks into the ground. The cave earth averages 6 feet, while in places there are banks of loose earth mixed with angular rock fragments 15 or 20 feet high. There is no stream on the floor of this cave, but one appears to flow underneath it. There are fragments of old shingles in one bank that may be the remains of old saltpeter hoppers and the earth seems to have been dug into in places. The cave is about 300 yards long, 35

feet wide and 20 feet high. There are a number of stalactites and some stalagmites.[1]

A DESCRIPTION OF THE CAVE

Three Forks Cave is also described by Tomas C. Barr, Jr. in his book, *Caves of Tennessee* (1961):

Three Forks Cave opens at the south side of the intersection of the Dry Hollow Road, the Sunk Cane Road, and the road north to Allred, and is readily accessible. The mouth is large and conspicuous, 25 feet wide and 10 feet high. The principal gallery of the cave averages 8 feet high and 18 feet wide; it extends S. 60° E. for 85 feet, turns N. 50° E. for 115 feet, then east for 120 feet, and ends as silt rises to the ceiling. There is a deep sump to a large stream near the end of the gallery. Local residents aver that this stream is the drainage from Big Sunk Cane. Water for drinking purposes is piped from a small side passage which was explored eastward for 100 feet.[2]

If Barr was correct and all the drainage from Big Sunk Cane drains through Three Forks Cave, then there should be miles of cave in the upstream direction. Unfortunately, it looked like the only access would be the sump, which would require cave diving. Then, in 1977, a new discovery was made by Larry Johnson and his friends. Here is Larry Johnson's story:

When I was a teenager, I use to read and re-read Barr's *Caves of Tennessee* constantly, and noticed in his description of Three Forks Cave he mentioned a hole dropping down to a

---

1 Thomas L. Bailey, *Report on the Caves of the Eastern Highland Rim and Cumberland Mountains*, TN State Geological survey, The Resources of Tennessee, Vol. 8 (1918), No. 2, pp 112-113.

2 Thomas C. Barr, Jr., *Caves of Tennessee*, TN Division of Geology, Bulletin 64 (1961), p. 351.

large, slow moving stream, and the comment that the "local residents aver that this is the water from Big Sunk Cane." So I looked at the topo and figured out Big Sunk Cane is a giant, Grassy Cove-like sinkhole located several miles away. One weekend (I think it was in 1977) me, Kevin Hancock, Frank King, and Dean Hendrix went to check it out. I think we got there late on a Friday night after school and after driving up from Nashville. Turns out the cave is virtually right on the side of the road and right in the owner's front yard. He kindly granted us permission to camp in the grassy area right in the cave's mouth. After setting up camp we went in to look at the cave and found the muddy, funnel-like hole that led down to the large stream Barr mentions. Taking a quick look, we saw that it was either going to be stoop-wading or swimming, so we came back out and got a couple of waterproof flashlights we had brought. Kevin brought

a large, red 6-volt Ever-Ready and I had a smaller 2-cell Ever-Ready Skipper. Frank only had his carbide lamp. We all changed into shorts and T-shirts because we knew we were going to get wet. Then, being "properly prepared" Kevin, Frank, and I then went back to check the stream. We found it deep but stoop-wadable, and we followed the water upstream for maybe a few hundred feet. At that point the ceiling closed down and the passage forked. To the left it sumped, but to the right the water was coming from a small, tube-shaped crawlway almost completely filled with water. As soon as we bent over to look into the crawl we were astounded to be blasted in the face by the hardest blowing wind I had ever seen in a cave; it was truly unbelievable; so hard it actually blew out Frank's carbide lamp! The wind also made a tremendous roar, but we hadn't noticed it until we stopped, due to all of the sloshing we made. (The only other

Figure 14.2. Bob Biddix at the entrance to Three Forks Cave. Photo by Erica Sughrue, October 3, 2020.

Figure 14.3. Alan Lenk stands in the entrance to Three Forks Cave. Photo by Ed Yarbrough, 1972.

caves I have ever seen with that much wind are Blowhole Cave in Cannon County, TN, Wind Cave, in South Dakota, and Lechuquilla Cave in New Mexico.)

So Kevin, who was in the front started forward. The passage was a total crawl, and the water was moving with a considerable velocity. He got to a point a few body-lengths ahead to where there was only a couple inches of airspace and backed out to let us look at it. Frank and I both got to the point of ear-dipping and also backed out. Kevin, being extremely aggressive and a good low-air-space pusher, gave it one more try. I think we held our breath with him as he pushed through the final body length and started screaming as he emerged into a giant room on the other side. Frank and I quickly followed through the low-air space, each getting the thrill and chest-heaving of total-body immersion in 53-degree water as the wind rushed past our heads. The crawl did indeed emerge into a huge, round room. We excitedly explored that, noting a couple of potential side passages, then soon

found what appeared to be the main trunk walking passage which seemed to be heading straight upstream, which we knew meant heading for Big Sunk Cane. I remember the passage as being quite large in a few places, maybe 30-feet wide by 10-feet high, but always at least walking sized. I don't remember how far we went; it was hundreds and hundreds of feet, but we were literally freezing in our wet shorts and T-Shirts, our lights were starting to get dim, and Frank was not able to get his carbide lamp re-lit after going through the wet crawl. So we turned around and headed back out. As we went through the crawl, we all agreed that a proper name for it would be "Tornado Alley". Needless to say we were all glad to get out of the cave and get warmed-up.

The next trip to Three Forks Cave was with another group including Chuck Mangelsdorf and Joel Buckner, where we used wetsuits and explored all the obvious passages to their apparent ends. I don't remember how the main passage ended, whether a sump, breakdown, or it just got low. I am also not

Figure 14.4. Erica Sughrue in the main passage of Three Forks Cave. Photo by Bob Biddix, October 3, 2020.

sure we really totally pushed everything. I remember I had cut my leg very severely on a piece of chert coming through Tornado Alley and I was in a lot of pain, so we may have left before we explored everything. After that trip, for whatever reason, we never went back to Three Forks Cave until several years later when road construction created a collapse inside the cave at the mud funnel which led to Tornado Alley and blocked future access.[3]

Joel Buckner goes on to describe the new extension:

I remember when I saw the low air space I thought they had to be kidding as it was maybe an inch or so high. The stream trunk beyond was impressively long but of modest dimensions, averaging maybe 6-8 feet high and 20-30 feet wide with only one side passage that was a short loop. But we could have missed something. I don't remember if the upstream sump looked dive-able but the passage was still a big tube, so it may be.

I did leave a going and blowing lead/dig in another part of the cave. Seems like there would be a lot of paleo upper level development considering how long Big Sunk Cane has been forming.

Some mapping was done years ago in Mill Hollow Cave (probably the main infeeder to Three Forks Cave) and I seem to recall Buddy Shelfer showing me a partial map with several miles of passage and many leads.[4]

3 Larry Johnson, Personal communication, April 18, 2020.

4 Joel Buckner, Personal communication, April 15, 2020.

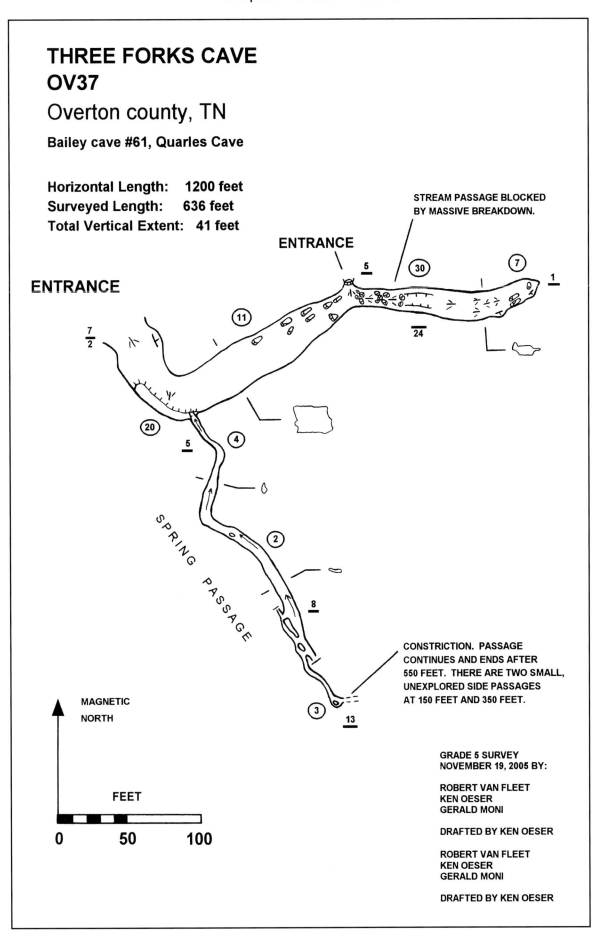

THREE FORKS CAVE
OV37
Overton county, TN

Bailey cave #61, Quarles Cave

Horizontal Length: 1200 feet
Surveyed Length: 636 feet
Total Vertical Extent: 41 feet

ENTRANCE

ENTRANCE

STREAM PASSAGE BLOCKED
BY MASSIVE BREAKDOWN.

CONSTRICTION. PASSAGE
CONTINUES AND ENDS AFTER
550 FEET. THERE ARE TWO SMALL,
UNEXPLORED SIDE PASSAGES
AT 150 FEET AND 350 FEET.

SPRING PASSAGE

MAGNETIC
NORTH

FEET

0   50   100

GRADE 5 SURVEY
NOVEMBER 19, 2005 BY:

ROBERT VAN FLEET
KEN OESER
GERALD MONI

DRAFTED BY KEN OESER

ROBERT VAN FLEET
KEN OESER
GERALD MONI

DRAFTED BY KEN OESER

Figure 14.5. Map of Three Forks Cave by Ken Oeser, November 19, 2005.

The cave had been extended in length to well over 7,000 feet. The new section was reached by crawling through the "sump" described by Barr and it consists mainly of walking stream passage which sumps far upstream. Chuck Mangelsdorf describes this large extension:

> Larry Johnson of the Nashville Grotto, and a team of neighborhood teenagers from Hermitage, spearheaded the exploration of the virgin 2-mile long extension into the "master stream trunk" of Three Forks Cave, probably in 1978.
>
> Larry was kind enough to hop in my jeep one day later in 1978 and take me to explore the caves' new borehole extension. The cave was big, long, and had a sizeable stream passage. We were wet, tired, and bloody when we emerged. The blood was mine, courtesy of a knife-sharp piece of limestone hidden in the water at shin level in the knee-deep wading. Ouch! I carried a deep scar on my right leg for many years.[5]

In 1979 Chuck Mangelsdorf learned that a second entrance to Three Forks Cave had been formed by road construction nearby. The entrance was a round hole at the base of the road cut and it was about six feet in diameter.

According to Gerald Moni, further road construction in 1979 blocked the second entrance and also the crawl from the stream to Entrance 1. The 6,000-foot stream passage is now inaccessible. The second entrance was 300 feet east of Entrance 1.[6] An interesting result of this damage to the cave is recounted by Chuck Mangelsdorf:

> When I was in college at Tennessee Tech, Ed Yarbrough and a lawyer in Cookeville represented the landowner in a civil suit for blasting damages against the roadbuilder that blasted the extension—low airspace crawl—shut by burying the connection point under tons of collapsed limestone. Cookeville

cavers Mike Sims, Elwin Hannah, and I were called to court by Ed Yarbrough in Overton County one day for trial, to testify about the magnificence of the cave that was lost due to negligent use of dynamite in widening the roadway. I believe the case was settled and no one had to testify. Which raises an interesting question—what is the legal value in damages for loss of access to a 2-mile borehole stream trunk (passage) in the northern Cumberland Plateau of Tennessee?[7]

Ed Yarbrough replied to Chuck's comment:

> I had totally forgotten about that case. I think Jerry Jared was the Cookeville lawyer. We were trying to prove the cave had commercial value but that didn't go well. The settlement was nothing to brag about.[8]

---

7 Chuck Mangelsdorf, Personal communication, April 15, 2020.

8 Ed Yarbrough, Personal communication, April 15, 2020.

Figure 14.6. Erica Sughrue at the entrance to Hilham Pit. Photo by Bob Biddix, October 3, 2020.

---

5 Chuck Mangelsdorf, Personal communication, April 15, 2020.

6 Gerald Moni, TCS Narrative File For Overton Co., TN, Edited by Andrew Gardner, November, 1993, pp 79-80.

Figure 14.7. Erica Sughure on rope in Hilham Pit. Photo by Bob Biddix, October 3, 2020.

THE SURVEY OF THREE FORKS CAVE

Three Forks Cave was surveyed on November 19, 2005 by Robert Van Fleet, Ken Oeser, and Gerald Moni. This map shows 636 feet of surveyed cave and a small, unsurveyed passage continues an additional 550 feet. (See Figure 14.5.)

The Tennessee Cave Survey lists this cave as 7,500 feet long. According to Gerald Moni, the passage that connected to most of the cave has either filled in or sumped.[9] Sounds like a great digging project for some young cavers.

Mill Hollow Cave (See Chapter 11) is located on the northwest side of Big Sunk Cave, in Mill Hollow. The sinking stream shown on the topo map flows into the entrance. It would seem likely that this is the upstream portion of the same underground stream that emerges at the rear of Three Forks Cave. If we had accurate surveys of both caves, we would know how close they come to connecting and whether it would be worthwhile to look for such a connection.

HILHAM PIT

Hilham Pit is also located in Overton County. It has a total depth of 161 feet and a large diameter room at the bottom. Some people like the fact that the entrance is only 75 feet from the road.

A DESCRIPTION OF THE PIT

The entrance to Hilham Pit is a small hole four feet in diameter. It drops 49 feet to a sloping ledge, then 24 feet more to another ledge. The last drop (86 feet) opens into a large room.[10]

ACCIDENT AT HILHAM PIT

Bob Biddix located the following notice of a fatal accident at Hilham Pit:

> While investigating a cold-case homicide near Standing Stone State Park, two sheriff's deputies and two park rangers came upon Hilham Pit. When Deputy Chad Prichard tried to get a closer look into the sinkhole with his flashlight, the ground gave way and he fell to the bottom. The pit was estimated by park rangers to be 161 feet deep. The other deputy and park rangers called to Prichard but got no response. Fire and rescue crews responded, but it became clear as they worked that Prichard had not survived the fall. It took crews several hours to recover the body.[11]

Apparently the accident occurred on April 6, 2010. As you can see from looking at Figure 14.6, it is not obvious that a deep pit is immediately inside the otherwise normal-looking cave entrance.

THE SURVEY OF HILHAM PIT

Hilham Pit was surveyed by Jeff Bowers, Joe Parrot, and Deana Daugherty on May 5, 2002. The map is included as Figure 14.8.

CAVE ACCESS

Generally accessible, but as always, be sure you have the owner's permission.

---

9 Gerald Moni, Personal communication, December 27, 2019.

10 Description by Brad Neff and David Stidham, 1973. From the TCS Narrative File For Overton Co., TN, Edited by Andrew Gardner, November 1993. Pp 36-37.

11 American Caving Accidents 2009-2010, NSS News, v. 69 (2011), no. 10, Part 2, p. 20.

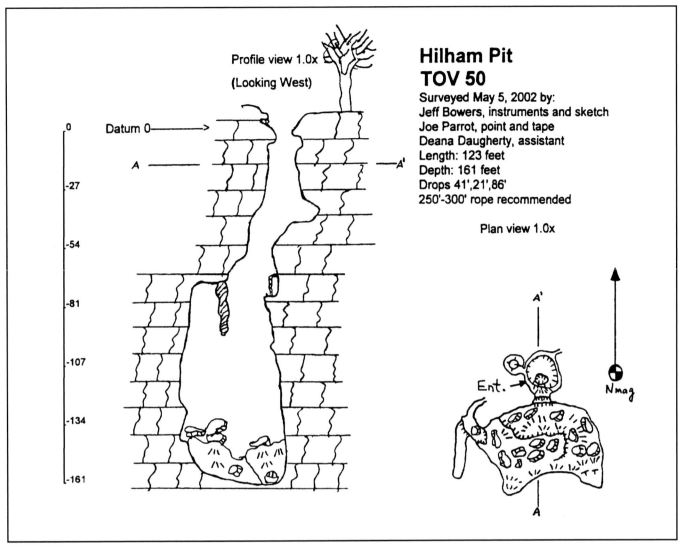

Figure 14.8. Map of Hilham Pit, Overton County by Jeff Bowers, Joe Parrot, and Deana Daugherty. May 5, 2002.

Figure 15.1. Two cavers on a ledge in Crabtree Cave. Photo by Ed Yarbrough, 1976.

CHAPTER 15
Urodela Cave

Urodela Cave is located in Overton County, Tennessee. According to the Tennessee Cave Survey, it has a mapped length of 5,847 feet, or slightly over one mile.

A DESCRIPTION OF THE CAVE

Urodela Cave has four known entrances. Caver Jerald Ledbetter provides the following description:

> The entrance is found in a small sink of the west side of the valley. The area of cave surveyed to date is made up of mostly stream passages ranging in height from one to eight feet. There would appear to be two major streams with a number of minor streams.
>
> One passage (the stream passage heading SE) would appear to exit through a collapsed spring entrance on Carr Creek. The other entrances are found in small sinks shown on the quad.
>
> A small cave named Holt Cave is found just to the north of this cave and very likely is part of this system although breakdown has stopped progress in both directions.[1]

This report was submitted to the TCS in 1974.

THE SURVEY OF URODELA CAVE

The TN Cave Survey shows this cave to have a surveyed length of 5,847 feet. The map is dated 1976. The map only shows two entrances, so clearly the cave has not been completely mapped. (See Figure 15.4)

CRABTREE CAVE

Crabtree Cave is located in Overton County, Tennessee and on the same topographic map as Urodela Cave, so for convenience, it is included in this chapter. Crabtree Cave is a multi-drop pit-cave approximately 200 feet long.

A DESCRIPTION OF THE CAVE

This cave was located and explored in 1974. Caver Ed Yarbrough tells the story:

> During the recent TCS meeting in McMinnville, Jerald Ledbetter told me about a new pit he had found near his uncle's farm in Overton County, Tennessee. He described the hole as a seventy-footer with other drops in the cave below. Apparently no one had done the other pits and only one local party had ventured in the cave at all.
>
> On October 12, I met Jerald, his brother Bill, Larry Houston of Memphis and his friend from Utah, Bill Trevithick, at the Cookeville Shoney's and we drove to Livingston for an assault on the new discovery. As we ascended the hillside in search of the cave I happened to find another pit-like opening and, thinking this to be the cave we sought, called for the others. When they arrived, however, Jerald told me I had just rigged a different pit— apparently a virgin find.
>
> We explored Mosquito Cave in less than an hour and found it to be a climbable twenty-foot pit, leading to about a hundred feet of passages and a few domes. After the little cave was explored and mapped we charged off in search of the biggie. It was not long before we were all standing at the entrance to Crabtree Cave.
>
> The first twenty feet of drop into Crabtree Cave was in a shaft measuring about five feet by seven feet, then it suddenly gave way to free fall in a spacious room. The total drop was seventy feet. The room was fifty feet wide

1 Jerald Ledbetter, TCS Narrative File For Overton Co., TN, Edited by Andrew Gardner, November, 1993, pp. 81-82.

Figure 15.2. Erica Sughrue by large flowstone formations in Crabtree Cave. Photo by Bob Biddix, December 28, 2019.

Figure 15.3. Erica Sughrue rappels into the entrance of Crabtree Cave. Photo by Bob Biddix, December 28, 2019.

and over one hundred feet long and was very well decorated with dripstone and flowstone. We soon located the deepest of the three pits that opened in the floor of the Big Room and rigged the Bluewater to a large stalagmite.

Larry and I made the rappel into the second drop and found it to be a very nice 101-foot shaft. The first portion was over flowstone and then the walls became bare limestone with some fluting. We explored several hundred feet of passages at the bottom and soon found that one climb connected with the bottom of another pit. Jerald lowered the tape from the main room, and we determined this pit to be fifty-three feet deep with a twenty-footer beyond that. Bill, Larry,

and I then climbed up the same pit we had rigged and joined the Ledbetters.

We found evidence that at least one caver had preceded us in the lower reaches— probably via the shorter drop. The earlier trip was apparently made by boys from Livingston using rope ladders.[2] The cave was unusually dry and clean throughout and no damage was detected to any formation areas.

The sketch on the following page is my own non-scientific version of the cave in cross-section. (See Figure 15.6) Jerald has promised to provide the Speleonews with a map at some later date. We finished our

2 Could this have been the Young Brothers who also explored Robinson Cave?

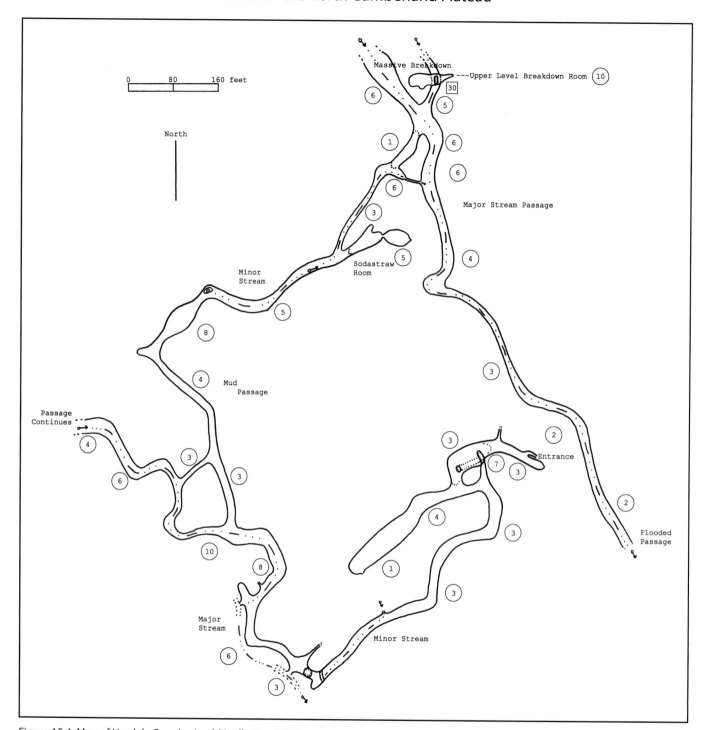

Figure 15.4. Map of Urodela Cave by Jerald Ledbetter, 1974.

Figure 15.5. Erica Sughrue by draperies in Crabtree Cave. Photo by Bob Biddix, December 28, 2019.

weekend with descents of Conley Hole and Floyd Pit on Sunday.[3]

It was another great weekend of caving in Tennessee.

THE SURVEY OF CRABTREE CAVE

Crabtree Cave was surveyed by Kristen Bobo, Sharon Jones, Marion O. Smith, and John Swartz in 2007. The map shows two plans: one for the Upper Level, which is approximately 70 below the entrance, and one for the Lower Level, which is approximately 140 feet below the entrance. There is also a Profile, which shows the vertical extent of the cave. (See Figure 15.7)

HAPPY DAY PIT

Happy Day Pit is located in Overton County in Standing Stone State Forest. John Swartz and Marion O. Smith provided the following description to the TN Cave Survey:

> The entrance is a 6-foot by 4-foot downclimb to a 120-foot pit. At the bottom a steep slope leads to a 10-foot pit. The bottom quickly ends.
> Down 25 feet from the lip of the 120-foot pit is a ledge, 20 feet wide. Traverse 70 feet (past a blind 40-foot pit) to an 8-foot pit followed by a 79-foot pit. At the bottom is a crawl to a tight (at top) 15-foot pit. Go 18 feet and up 5 feet and through a squeeze to a 10-foot pit. This leads to a room 12 feet by 8 feet. There is a too-tight crawl there with airflow.[4]

There is an excellent map and profile of this pit prepared by Smith and Swartz. (See Figure 15.14)

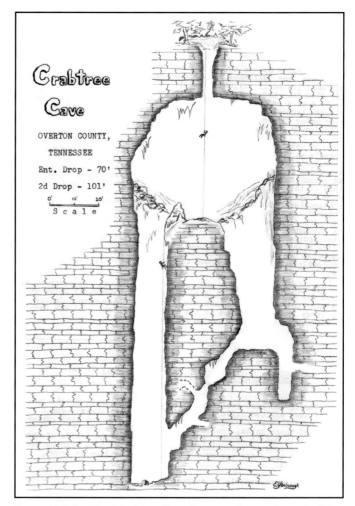

Figure 15.6. Profile of Crabtree Cave, Overton County drawn by Ed Yarbrough in 1974.

There is an enormous, scary-looking breakdown block wedged over the top of the 120-foot pit. (See Figure 15.13)

CAVE ACCESS

Current access to these caves is unknown. Please be sure that you have the owner's permission before you visit these, or any other caves.

---

3 Ed Yarbrough, "Vertical Views: Crabtree Cave", Speleonews, v. 18 (1974), no. 6, pp. 86-87.

4 Personal communication, Gerald Moni, July 31, 2020.

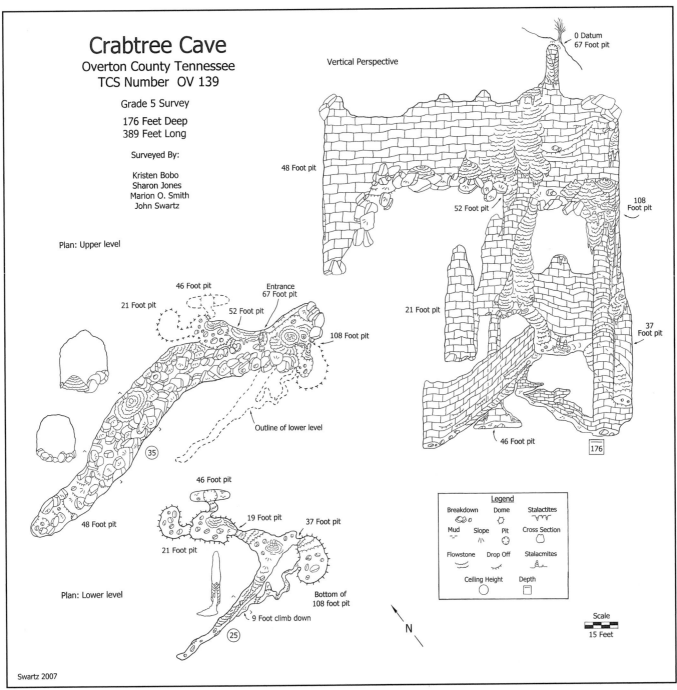

Crabtree Cave
Overton County Tennessee
TCS Number OV 139

Grade 5 Survey

176 Feet Deep
389 Feet Long

Surveyed By:

Kristen Bobo
Sharon Jones
Marion O. Smith
John Swartz

Plan: Upper level

Vertical Perspective

0 Datum
67 Foot pit

48 Foot pit

52 Foot pit

108 Foot pit

21 Foot pit

37 Foot pit

46 Foot pit

176

46 Foot pit

21 Foot pit

Entrance
67 Foot pit

52 Foot pit

108 Foot pit

Outline of lower level

35

48 Foot pit

46 Foot pit

21 Foot pit

19 Foot pit

37 Foot pit

Bottom of
108 foot pit

9 Foot climb down

25

Plan: Lower level

Legend

Breakdown	Dome	Stalactites
Mud	Slope	Cross Section
	Pit	
Flowstone	Drop Off	Stalacmites
Ceiling Height	Depth	

N

Scale

15 Feet

Swartz 2007

Figure 15.7. Map of Crabtree Cave, Overton County by John Swartz, 2007. (Above)

Figure 15.8. Erica Sughrue at the entrance to Happy Day Pit. Photo by Bob Biddix, July 18, 2020. (Bottom right)

Figure 15.9. Erica Sughrue (Left) and Bob Biddix (Right) in a large, breakdown-floored room in Crabtree Cave. Photo by Bob Biddix, December 28, 2019. (Above)

Figure 15.10. Erica Sughrue on rope in Crabtree Cave. Photo by Bob Biddix, December 28, 2019. (Facing page)

Figure 15.11. Human bones in Crabtree Cave. Photo by Bob Biddix, December 28, 2019.

Figure 15.12. Erica Sughrue rappels in the main room of Crabtree Cave. Photo by Bob Biddix, December 28, 2019. (Above)

Figure 15.13. Erica Sughrue at the top of the 120-foot pit in Happy Day Pit. Note the huge breakdown block wedged over the top of the pit. Photo by Bob Biddix, July 18, 2020. (Facing page)

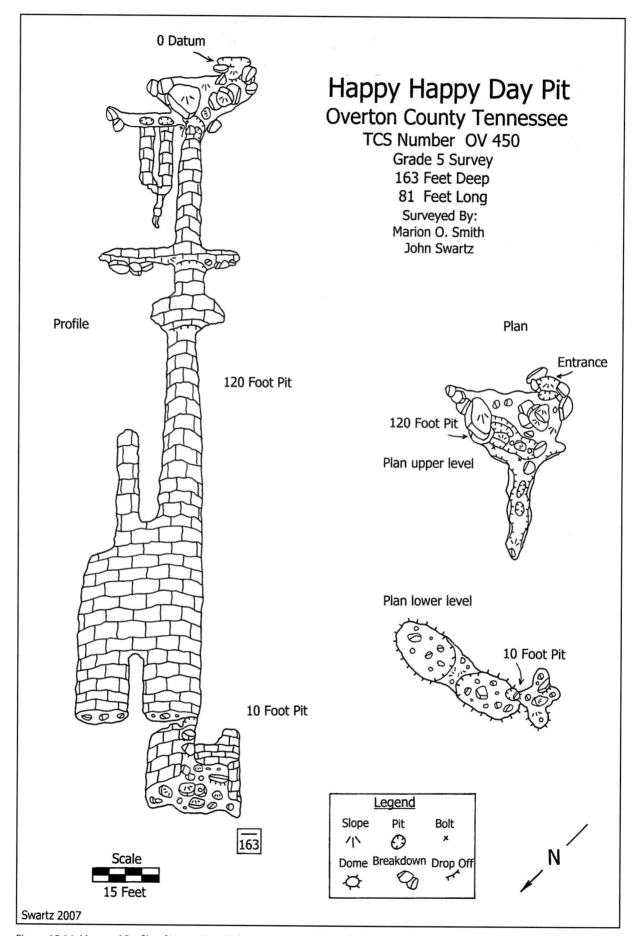

0 Datum

Happy Happy Day Pit
Overton County Tennessee
TCS Number OV 450
Grade 5 Survey
163 Feet Deep
81 Feet Long
Surveyed By:
Marion O. Smith
John Swartz

Profile

Plan

Entrance

120 Foot Pit

120 Foot Pit

Plan upper level

Plan lower level

10 Foot Pit

10 Foot Pit

163

Scale

15 Feet

Legend

Slope	Pit	Bolt
/|\	⊕	x
Dome	Breakdown	Drop Off

N

Swartz 2007

Figure 15.14. Map and Profile of Happy Day Pit by Marion O. Smith and John Swartz, 2007.

Figure 15.15. Erica Sughrue on rope in the 120-foot pit in Happy Day Pit. Photo by Bob Biddix, July 18, 2020.

Figure 16.1. Ken Pasternack in a passage in Abbott Saltpeter Cave. Note rocks stacked on ledges by saltpeter miners. Photo by Bob Biddix, February 22, 2020.

CHAPTER 16
Abbott Saltpeter Cave

Abbott Saltpeter Cave is located in Pickett County, Tennessee. It has a surveyed length of 1.8 miles. This cave was mined extensively for saltpeter. Its exploration was well documented by expert cavers John Barnes and Lou Simpson.

THE EXPLORATION AND SURVEY OF ABBOTT SALTPETER CAVE

Lou Simpson and John Barnes wrote the following Trip Reports in 1977. They give an exciting account of the exploration and survey of this interesting cave.

May 8, 1977 (by Lou Simpson)
On Sunday, some of us explored Abbott Cave, in nearby Pickett Co., TN. Several dates on the walls were from the 19th century, and there was ample evidence that the cave had been mined for saltpeter. A long crawl went beyond an old excavation (all covered with fine dust and looking virgin) to an extension that ended in a small room with a strongly blowing hole. There is about half a mile of dry cave.[1]

May 29, 1977 (by Lou Simpson)
On May 29, a group of eight, including Lou Simpson, Don Pollock, Peter Kupferman (Los Angeles, CA), Tom Patterson (N. Carolina), and Bill Thoman (Lexington), mapped half a mile in Abbott Cave. Bill and Lou began digging out the blowing crawl at the end of the 1,000-foot crawl.[2]

June 25, 1977 (by John Barnes)
Beth Albright, John Barnes, Barb and Lou Simpson, Paul Soliday, Scott Spinner, and Dave Taylor. We left the Sloan's Valley fieldhouse for Abbott Cave in Tennessee. We talked with a Mr. Pyle, whose house is the closest to the cave, and learned of a large sinkhole 1,000 feet behind his house, of which Lou had been previously unaware. We hiked to the cave and entered the second entrance, which is a 4-foot wide by 1-foot tall hole in the bluff. Scott, Paul, and I were going to survey a 200-foot long canyon, then photograph some graffiti in the cave (some items dated back to the 1830s, when Abbott was mined for saltpeter). Beth and Barb were going to survey another section of cave, after which they would join Lou and Dave at the dig site 1,000 feet deeper into the cave.

We surveyed our canyon, tying into the main passage survey, then started exploring and looking for graffiti. We were specifically looking for a drawing of a man wearing a top hat.

We decided to take a quick look at the dig and started heading down the stoopwalk passage. After crawling another 900 feet, one-third of it on our stomachs, we finally heard Lou and Dave. Another 100 feet of crawling led us to the dig site. The dig had begun at a 6-inch by 2-inch hole that blew a lot and emitted an occasional bat. The previous trip had yielded a 2-foot long tunnel. Lou, Dave, Paul, and Scott had dug about 3.5 hours all told and lengthened the tunnel to 10 feet when they finally gave me a chance. Lou dragged me out of the tunnel an hour later, with the tunnel 19-feet long, the hole blowing like mad, and only 3-feet to go before the ceiling looked high enough to bellycrawl. Lou claimed that the idea was to leave the dig in a very promising state, so we would be sure to return and continue it.[3]

July 1, 1977 (by John Barnes)
Lou and Barb Simpson and I (John Barnes) drove down to the Sloan's Valley fieldhouse Friday, July 1, having a four-day weekend to spend caving. We

---

1 Lou Simpson, "May 7-8, Triple-S, Table, and Abbott", Cave Cricket Gazette, v. 2 (1977), no. 3, p. 8.

2 Lou Simpson, "May 29-30, Wolf River, Abbott, and Hail", Cave Cricket Gazette, v. 2 (1977), no. 3, p. 8.

3 John Barnes, "Abbott Cave Trip Reports", Cave Cricket Gazette, v. 2 (1977), no. 4, p. 10.

Figure 16.2. Ken Pasternack in the entrance to Abbott Saltpeter Cave. Photo by Bob Biddix, February 22, 2020.

left Barb at the fieldhouse, then Lou and I headed down to Pickett Co., Tenn. En route to Abbott Cave we stopped at Allen Pile's house and asked him to show us the sinkhole about 1,000 feet west of his house.

At 7:00 p.m. we finally entered the cave and headed down the 1,000-foot crawlway. It took just ½ hour to reach the dig site at the end of the crawl, as we were very hopeful of breaking into virgin cave. I dug about 3 feet of tunnel, finally passing the hoped-for end of the tunnel. Meanwhile Lou was having difficultly moving the fill down the tunnel and several times I was blocked in. Alas, when I could at last peer over the edge of the fill, the ceiling to the left and in front sloped down to the level of the fill within seven feet. However, ten feet to the right appeared to be a slight dip. We now started tunneling to

the right, and at this point the ceiling was about 4 inches above the fill, so I could stuff the dug-up fill alongside the tunnel, instead of forcing Lou to haul out all the pieces. After nearly 3 hours of digging, having advanced ten feet, I asked Lou to take a look and see what he thought. He dug about a yard through the top 4 inches of fill, which was very friable, and said that he had entered a bellycrawl. However, he kept his promise (the previous weekend he promised to let me precede him if the tunnel did open into more cave, because of the amount that I had dug), and came back out after turning around in the new cave.

We assembled our packs and headed back into the tunnel. A short squeeze from the end of the tunnel to the bellycrawl, which changed to a low hands-and-knees crawl. This terminated, but a

Figure 16.3. Erica Sughrue in a joint-controlled passage in Abbott Saltpeter Cave. Photo by Bob Biddix, February 22, 2020.

low (9-inch high) room at the left connected to a stoopwalk passage. I ran along the passage until I reached another room about 24 inches high and about 30 feet across. A few breakdown blocks at the right obscured what appeared to be another stoopwalk. I crawled over the blocks, while Lou was still trying to catch up, and headed down the passage, having to slow down when I reached formations and when the ceiling began to drop. Halfway along the passage I climbed over a half-cone formed by rimstone dams. The passage was down to 18 inches high by 3 feet wide when I saw an orange salamander with black spots and eyes. A couple of feet farther I suddenly stepped into a 6-inch deep pool of water behind a rimstone dam. I traversed about another 8 feet and saw a dense group of formations ahead. I decided to go back and get Lou, and about 100 feet from the beginning of the passage heard him yell that he had found walking passage. After a little confusion on my part as to where we had entered the room, we started along the left side of the room.

Back at the room we noticed a ledge at the entrance of the walking passage. We squeezed under it and climbed down into a small room that had blowing air. We finally decided that the air was coming under a ledge with 4 inches between the ledge and the fill. This will require another dig. After an hour and a half of scooping, we decided to head out without doing any mapping, as we would be an hour overdue as it was. The crawlway was much harder to get through on the way out, as we were bushed. At 1:15 a.m. we exited the cave and headed back to the fieldhouse. We arrived at the fieldhouse at 3:15 a.m. and found Barb very worried about what had happened to us.[4]

July 2, 1977 (by John Barnes)

About 9:30 a.m. Dave Taylor came down from the barn, bringing John "Rocky" Rockwood, Gary Carpenter, and Terry Bliss with him. They had planned to go to Sawdust Pit, but when we told them of the 1,000 to 2,000 feet of virgin cave we had found, they talked Barb into going with them to start mapping the new section. Lou and I were too tired to go back down the crawl again so soon, so we planned to make a ground survey to Abbott Cave and to some of the other entrances we had found in the immediate area.

We returned to Abbott Cave and headed in to look for graffiti and photograph important items. Several names and dates indicate that the cave was known as early as 1835, and many dug pits, wood pieces, tally marks, etc., indicate that the cave was once mined for saltpeter. After an hour of this the surveying party reached us, having surveyed about 300 feet in the tunnel, the passage to the Starfish Room, and part of the righthand passage.

We will resume mapping in the new section of Abbott in a couple of weeks and have hopes of doubling the cave's size.[5]

July 16, 1977 (by Lou Simpson)

Personnel: Barb and Lou Simpson, Beth Albright, Mary and Greg Kalmbach.

Barb, Mary, and Beth went directly to the Star Room in Abbott Saltpeter Cave and began surveying into the lead past the tight spot at some flowstone. John Barnes had stopped pushing this crawlway because it lacked airflow.

Greg and I finally entered Abbott, soaking wet from sweat in the 95-degree heat. We quickly negotiated the long crawl (1,000 feet) and Greg was very impressed with the Bicentennial Dig, the thirty-foot tunnel. We had brought along a 16 mm wrench for use as a digging tool since I had left my field shovel in my trunk and we came in Kalmbach's van. We used this effectively to dig out two short leads. One had an exciting small hole through which another room could be seen, but it looked hopeless even with hammer and chisel. We then proceeded to the Star Room, left notes for the survey party, and tried the other promising lead in the new section: the low crawl that John thought might be diggable. This had good airflow.

Digging briefly to ease access (with the wrench)

---

4 John Barnes, "Abbott Cave Dig Halted", C. O. G. Squeaks, v. 20 (1977), no. 9, pp 69-71.

5 Ibid.

Figure 16.4. Erica Sughrue in a large passage in Abbott Saltpeter Cave. Photo by Bob Biddix, February 22, 2020.

Figure 16.5. An old name, James K. Rielman, scratched on the wall in Abbott Saltpeter Cave. Photo by Bob Biddix, February 22, 2020.

Figure 16.6. Pick marks left in the dirt by saltpeter miners. Photo by Bob Biddix, February 22, 2020.

Figure 16.7. Erica Sughrue examines wood pieces left from saltpeter vats in Abbott Saltpeter Cave. Photo by Bob Biddix, February 22, 2020.

Figure 16.8. Tally marks scratched on the wall in Abbott Saltpeter Cave by saltpeter miners. Photo by Bob Biddix, February 22, 2020.

Figure 16.9. Erica Sughrue by pick marks left in the dirt by saltpeter miners in Abbott Saltpeter Cave. Photo by Bob Biddix, February 22, 2020.

Figure 16.10. Erica Sughrue and Ken Pasternack in a cobble-floored passage in Abbott Saltpeter Cave. Photo by Bob Biddix, February 22, 2020.

Figure 16.11. An old name, Abbott, and the date 1894 scratched on the wall in Abbott Saltpeter Cave. Photo by Bob Biddix, February 22, 2020.

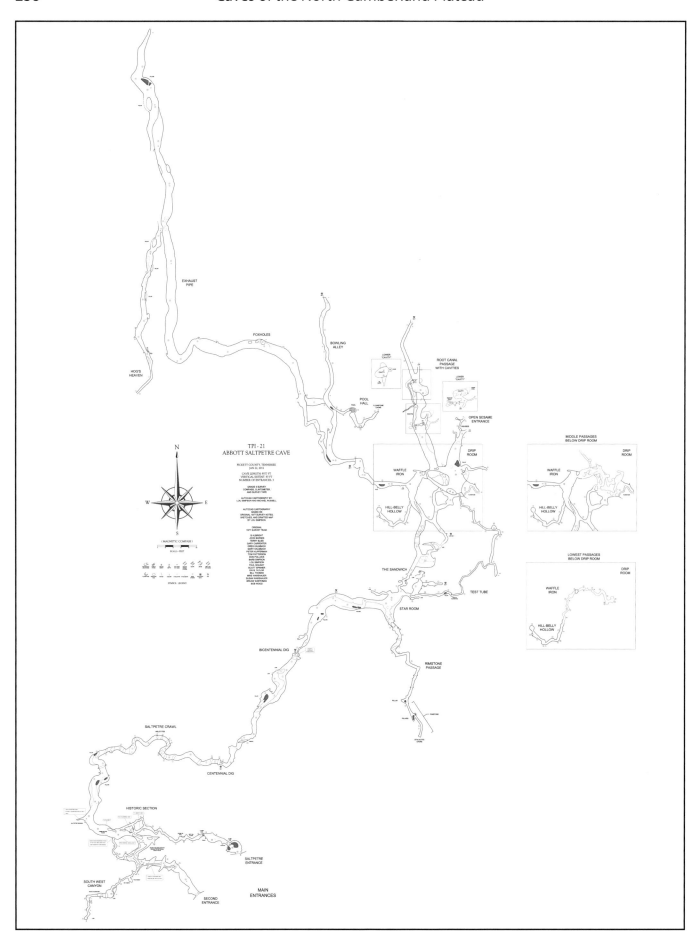

Figure 16.12. Map of Abbott Saltpeter Cave,

I found that the low crawl, while tight, was passable (barely). Pushing my helmet, I headed for the black space ahead. It opened up enough to stand. Greg struggled through with our packs. We bounded over the breakdown into a small room having several leads. We chose one that seemed to have airflow and spent the next hour trying to get through the tight leads it went to.

Finally we began mapping out. After four stations we came back to the small room and I suggested that Greg push a lead that looked like just a come around. Amazingly, it wasn't just a come around, but had a big crawlway branch that continued. We sped through several hundred feet of crawlway and emerged in an eight-foot high room with a couple of leads to the sides. These we ignored and continued on ahead. Soon we were in a much larger room, with several leads and a deep sloping hole on the right. We crossed this hole, noting that it had leads in it and continued, climbing up breakdown. Eventually we reached a room fifty feet high and heard someone shout! We looked up and saw three lights, WAY UP THERE! Barb, Mary, and Beth had also discovered this new part of the cave!

They thought we had gotten in by our pit entrance. They shouted that they had explored a large upper level and had also found an entrance from the inside. They tried for over an hour to dig their way out but were stopped by a large rock. They got their heads out this entrance and Mary left her bandana there as a marker. After a few vain attempts to find a climbable route between the levels it was decided that we didn't have any more time (we had left word at the fieldhouse that we'd be back by 12 and it was already 10) so we headed back toward the Star Room and the Abbott Entrance, so far away. Greg and I numbed by the huge rooms, the gigantic forty by forty feet flowstone wall, and the maze of passages, took a few turns and were soon lost. How can you get lost in virgin cave? When you have made loops and don't realize it. After a calming rest, we looked again and figured it out. Before leaving, we checked one more walking lead. It went. We turned around, finally, when it became necessary to stoop-walk and choose which way to go. You'll hear more![6]

July 29, 1977 (by Lou Simpson)

A new entrance had been discovered from the inside on July 16 by Barb Simpson, Beth Albright, and Mary Kalmbach. They were unable to get through, however, so Mary left her bandana just outside he small opening as a marker. The proto entrance was blocked by a large slab standing on end.

Barb convinced me that it would be worthwhile to try to find this entrance by dumb luck outside instead of laboriously mapping the rest of the way to it inside and then mapping to it on the surface. "It looked fairly level around the entrance," she said. So we looked for two hours in the hot, sticky afternoon of July 29 before entering the Saltpetre Entrance to get out of the rain. We crawled once more through the long Saltpetre Crawl, the Bicentennial Dig that resulted in the discovery of all this new passage, the Star Room, and finally the tight Test Tube, where we continued the survey through the Drip Room and to the area of the new proto-entrance, where the air was very hot and steamy. There we found Mary's bandana—in the cave! A rat must have brought it inside. I got out my hammer and chisel and, after about an hour of digging and hacking, including sawing through several inch-thick roots, Barb managed to squeeze past the edge of the obstructing slab and out of the cave! Now everything depended on Barb's effective use of the hammer. Fortunately, she was able to enlarge the opening enough for me. We then looked up and down the steep hill ("fairly level"?) and realized that we hadn't looked for the entrance here at all during our abortive ridgewalk. After another hour, we managed to move the massive breakdown slab. The Open Sesame Entrance was now open.[7]

---

6 Lou Simpson, "Breakthrough!", Cave Cricket Gazette, v. 2 (1977), no. 4, pp 11-12.

7 Lou Simpson, "Abbott Saltpetre Cave", Cave Cricket Gazette, v. 2 (1977), no. 5, pp 14-16.

July 30, 1977 (by Lou Simpson)

The next day was very productive as three survey teams entered the new entrance. Bob Wood installed a bolt so we could rig my cable ladder for easy access to the lower levels. It was necessary to chimney down part of the narrow crack before getting on the ladder. The narrowness made using the ladder difficult. John Barnes and Bruce Warthman had entered the Open Sesame Entrance earlier that day, intending to map the Sandwich Route to the new lower levels. So they went in by way of the Test Tube. Bob Wood, Mary Kalmbach, and Greg Kalmbach began mapping the seemingly endless Exhaust Pipe. Barb and I started mapping at the ladder and tied in with John and Bruce's survey. We discovered an easily climbable route back to the entrance level by a route near the Flowstone Overlook. John was nearly at the top of the ladder when I informed him of the new route. He preferred to climb back down the ladder and use the new route.

When the Exhaust Pipe mapping crew finally came out of the cave at 11 PM, they had mapped 26 stations and turned back at a low, wet crawl. Barb, Bruce, and I took our sleeping bags into the Historical Section and slept soundly there for the next nine hours. John left for the NSS Convention. The Kalmbachs and Bob spent the night in their vehicles. We were able to camp in the field near the barn and even obtained a key to the gate on the road from the owner, Otto Pile.[8]

July 31, 1977 (by Lou Simpson)

Bruce, Bob, Barb, and I mapped the Bowling Alley and Pool Hall, side leads of the Exhaust Pipe. Bob crossed a chest-deep pool of water and called back data to Bruce, who didn't have to cross the water. The total survey for the three-day weekend was 0.77 mile and the length of the cave was now 1.31 miles.[9]

August 6, 1977 (by Lou Simpson)

Our next trip to Abbott was August 6. While George Kingston and Jean Delaney toured the Historic Section, Bob Wood, Barb, and I mapped and explored pits in the Root Canal, the high level near the new entrance. We connected two pits and explored a third. The third was 45 feet deep and had a three-foot pool. Bob pendulumed to a ledge near the bottom and explored the area. When he attempted to loop the free end of the rope around a breakdown block to avoid a rapid pendulum swing, the rock was pulled into the water. Above, we heard a big splash and didn't see Bob's light for a while, as he pendulumed even more wildly than he'd anticipated, striking the far wall of the pit. His ascent of the rope was remarkably fast. We began digging at the north end of the Root Canal (passage noted for its tree roots) as it seemed to continue.[10]

August 19, 1977 (by Lou Simpson)

At last the week-long expedition we had planned all summer began. On Friday, August 19, we entered the Open Sesame Entrance with Beth Albright and proceeded to the 26th station at the remote virgin north end of the Exhaust Pipe. Two stations later it got too low to continue! We returned to station #1020 and mapped the going lead to the south. This finally got very gross and low, appropriately named Hog's Heaven. The small stream flowed under the wall five stations before the south end of the passage.[11]

August 22 & 27, 1977 (by Lou Simpson)

On August 22, after digging open a blowing hole a quarter mile west of Abbott, Mike and Susie Warshauer, Tom Patterson, Barb, and I mapped some loops and minor side leads near the new entrance. Barb, Susie and I returned to the cave August 24 to push leads in the Root Canal, including the dig, which ended, and a narrow lead near the entrance, which did also. Tom Patterson and John Barnes mapped the Rimstone Passage south out of the Star Room on August 27. The total Survey is now 1.68 miles (8,864.3 feet). Another trip should be made to push a few remaining possibilities. Remember that at one point, before the Bicentennial Dig, we were down to one lead—the strongly blowing one that we dug out.[12]

December 28, 1977 (by Lou Simpson)

Tom, Barbie, and I drove to Fentress County, Tennessee, where we dropped off the making of two pizzas at the Copleys' and headed for Abbott Saltpeter Cave in Pickett County. We pushed six leads in the Exhaust Pipe, but all ended or were come arounds. We dug for over an hour in soft sand and gravel at station #1005, but at that point it didn't look like it went, so we quit digging. The rat was present at its nest near the open Sesame Entrance. Some air was blowing out, but not a lot.[13]

April 22, 1988 (by Lou Simpson)

We drove to Wolf River Cave for a glance at the entrance. Then we drove north from there, back into Pickett County to go to Abbott Saltpeter Cave. We asked permission at the Gary Williams home. We were able to drive as far as the gate to Otto Pile's property. We parked there and walked about a mile to the first two entrances, which are across from a large boulder in the streambed and about fifty feet up the hill. The weather was very good, and the spring colors made our hike very pleasant. We went into the middle entrance, climbing down a log. The area around these entrances was mined for saltpeter in the mid-nineteenth century. We found three signatures in one place with the year 1853. My map shows that there is a date of 1838 in the cave. We visited the other of the two nearby entrances, noting two long, red spotted salamanders on the wall, then began the Saltpeter Crawl.

The cave is 1.68 miles long and has three entrances. The third entrance was our goal for the day. This entrance, along with a mile of the cave, was discovered following a 1976 dig through almost complete fill in the Saltpeter Crawl. An older, shorter dig, the Centennial Dig, already existed part of the way to the new dig, the

Bicentennial Dig. The Bicentennial Dig is about 30 feet long. It begins just beyond the massive pile of "dirts" (cubes of clay we dug out of the crawlway) that was removed from the dig. Harry said the dig wasn't tight compared to the section beyond, where it "opens up to a belly crawl" and the digging stopped. I told Harry Goepel that John Barnes deserves credit for most of the digging since he was able to work much harder than everybody else because he had very strong arms from swimming.

I hadn't looked at the map for a while, which made finding the way to the third entrance interesting. We explored several of the passages leading out of the Star Room before we finally found the Pancake, which I later realized was named the Sandwich on the map. There appeared to be some possible digs to do, which rekindled my interest in trying to connect Abbott to Rotten Fork. Of course, I was no longer familiar with Abbott, so might have just been lost. Each time we thought we were in some new crawlway; we discovered a survey station. After about an hour of disorientation, we emerged into the Waffle Iron, named for the anastomosis ceiling in the Junction Room where the Exhaust Pipe leads off to the northwest.

Now we searched again for the route over and through breakdown. We arrived at last at the base of a fifty-foot high flowstone cascade. We climbed and chimneyed to the upper level and squirmed out of the third entrance. We emerged from the low shelf onto the steep hillside and enjoyed the view of the massive sandstone bluffs across the canyon. We had been in the cave for three and a half hours. The red tape we had used to mark the entrance is still on the trees.[14]

SALTPETER MINING IN ABBOTT SALTPETER CAVE

The following information concerning the evidence of saltpeter mining in Abbott Saltpeter Cave appeared in the December, 1977 Cave Cricket Gazette.

12 Ibid.

13 Lou Simpson, "Hard-Core Holiday", Cave Cricket Gazette, v. 3 (1978), no. 1, p. 4.

14 Lou Simpson, "22 April 88, Pickett State Park, Pickett Co., TN", Cave Cricket Gazette, v. 13 (1988), no. 6, p. 67.

There are some sets of tally marks. Mining evidence includes shallow depressions, wood, and a partially buried vat. Much gravel has been placed on ledges.[15]

Cave historian Marion O. Smith visited Abbott Saltpeter Cave on April 19, 1980 with Gerald Moni. Here are Marion's observations from that trip:

> We fumbled into the cove and still had trouble finding Abbott Saltpeter but finally Gerald found the 2nd Entrance and I found the 1st Entrance (both about 40 feet above the streambed) and at 4:55 we entered the cave. I wandered around in the first 1,200 feet of sort of maze-like saltpeter passage. A steep incline near the 1st Entrance led to an old still site. Some metal scraps were there. A drip of water was nearby. If there had been a saltpeter vat there before the moonshiner, he removed all discernable traces. A little farther along the passage was dry and somewhat narrow, though high. The miners piled a lot of rocks on the sides. We wandered around the larger passages and then some crawls. We apparently were headed for the dig that Lou Simpson & Co. (c. 1976) found about 7,000 feet of new cave, but soon quit. Old names were scattered along the walls. One date appeared to be 1838 but I didn't notice any name with it. In the larger passages we found old cut wood, lots of board fragments, a couple of poles with an augured hole (one of which had a wooden peg in it), plus some pick marks. I could not actually find a spot where I could conclusively say that was where a vat was. Some of the wooden boards, small logs were mostly covered by cobbles. So, the cave was definitely mined for saltpeter, but I can't say how large the operation was, but possibly it was for local consumption by one or two families over a long period.[16]

Marion returned on October 2, 1999 with Gerald Moni, Alan Cressler, Paul Aughey, Debby Johnson, and Andy Zellner. Here are his comments from this trip:

> Moni and I entered the western most crawl entrance and the other four entered the main saltpeter entrance and inside we met. There was no Civil War graffiti and the main saltpeter area had had a lot of work done. Lots of rock placed on ledges, soot, a few tally marks, rock steps near the Saltpeter Entrance, and two or three possible vat piles of dirt, some wood fragments plus a still site.
>
> Alan and Paul found some crude Indian points just inside the entrance and far inside, in "rooms" between crawls, a few probable Indian torch stoke marks were located. A lot of mining had been done here, including dig marks.[17]

Like so much of the saltpeter mining that took place in this region, we do not have historical records to tell us the dates of the mining operation or who operated it. It could have occurred during the War of 1812, the Civil War, or both.

HISTORICAL NAMES AND DATES IN ABBOTT SALTPETER CAVE

The following information concerning old names and dates in Abbott Saltpeter Cave appeared in the December, 1977 Cave Cricket Gazette:

> Charles Gibbs talked with Luther York, who I believe is the son of Sgt. Alvin C. York, concerning the historical authenticity of the graffiti in the saltpeter mine section of Abbott Cave, Fentress Co., TN. Mr. York wrote:
> "The names found in the cave you refer to are all familiar to me except that of S. P. Flowers. I knew Sam William very well. He was killed in a tractor accident in 1924. Yes, I would say the names on the walls of the cave are authentic."

---

15 Anonymous, "Abbott Graffiti Confirmed", Cave Cricket Gazette, v. 2 (1977), no. 7, p. 24.

16 Marion O. Smith, Personal communication, May 11, 2020.

17 Ibid.

The following graffiti are scratched on the walls in Abbott Cave:

John Crabtree, 1838
T. F. S., 1857
S. T. Flowers, 1858
H. T. F. 1858
Stokely Crabtree, Feb. 25, 1870
F. Abbott, 1894
M. E. Hughes, Jan. 25, 1915

Smoked graffiti include:

James K. Rielman, 1853
Sam William, Oct. 28, 1918
A.D. Crabtree, Oct. 1945
Frank Pile, Jan. 14, 1947

There are numerous other illegible or semi-legible graffiti.

The present owner of the property is Otto Pile. The former owner was Abbott, who was preceded by Sam Williams.[18]

Marion O. Smith also looked for old names during his visit on October 2, 1999. He copied the following inscriptions:

S. Johnson 1813
J. _____ 1838
W. D. C. O. 1853
James K. Ridmorr 1853
Shadrad _____ 1853
J. T. Abbott 1894
G. G. Williams 1899
E. N. Pile 1899
Luke Williams Oct. 28, 1918

He also found the date 1809 with no name or initials. The 1809 and 1813 dates are especially interesting, since they could indicate mining during the War of 1812.[19]

CAVE ACCESS

Current access to this cave is unknown. Please be sure you have the owner's permission before you enter this or any other cave.

PLACE NAMES IN ABBOTT SALTPETER CAVE

Bicentennial Dig
Bowling Alley
Canyon
Cavities
Centennial Dig
Drip Room
Exhaust Pipe
Flowstone Overlook
Foxholes
Hill-Belly Hollow
Historic Section
Hog's Heaven
Junction Room
Open Sesame Entrance
Pool Hall
Rimstone Passage
Root Canal Passage With Cavities
Saltpeter Crawl
Saltpeter Entrance
Sandwich Route
Second Entrance
South West Canyon
Star Room
Test Tube
The Pancake
The Pits
The Sandwich
Waffle Iron

---

18 Anonymous, "Abbott Graffiti Confirmed", Cave Cricket Gazette, v. 2 (1977), no. 7, p. 24.

19 Marion O. Smith, Personal communication, May 11, 2020.

Figure 17.1. Erica Sughrue by amazingly carved limestone in Big Jordan Cave. Photo by Bob Biddix.

CHAPTER 17
Big Jordan Cave

Big Jordan Cave is located in Pickett County, Tennessee. It currently has a surveyed length of 5,392 feet. Although there is little information about this cave, it is included in this book since it is over one mile long.

A DESCRIPTION OF THE CAVE

Big Jordan Cave is described by Thomas C. Barr, Jr. in his book, *Caves of Tennessee* (1961).

> Big Jordan Cave has two mouths 35 feet apart. The upper is 30 feet wide and 10 feet high, and the lower is 10 feet by 10 feet. The cave consists of a room which trends north for 150 feet from the upper mouth to an impenetrable breakdown. A lower level stream passage is developed, but the stream apparently flows only in wet weather.[1]

Since the current surveyed length of this cave is slightly over a mile long, it is apparent that Tom Barr did not enter the stream passage, which is a crawlway. Jeff Sims, who was one of the surveyors, reports that the crawl at the entrance is very tight, but once you make it through the crawlway you come out into an 80-100 foot wide stream trunk passage that is up to 40 feet high, in places![2] That was a very exciting discovery.

When you look at the map of the cave, it is apparent that the "impenetrable breakdown" that stopped Barr separates a small section of this trunk passage, the Entrance Room, from the rest of the trunk passage. It is fortunate that a crawl bypasses this breakdown and allows access to the rest of the cave.

Jeff Sims reports that between the tight crawl near the entrance and the wet nature of the cave, very few people visit this cave.[3]

THE SURVEY OF BIG JORDAN CAVE

The surveyed length of Big Jordan Cave is 5,392 feet. This is the length given on the December 18, 1976 map. The map is labeled "In Progress", but no subsequent map has been submitted to the Tennessee Cave Survey. The cave continues as wet, low crawlways. Perhaps if someone pushed this cave they would break out into more trunk passage.

CAVE ACCESS

Current access to this cave is unknown. Please be sure you have the owner's permission before you enter this, or any other cave.

---

1 Thomas C. Barr, Jr., *Caves of Tennessee*, TN Division of Geology, Bulletin 64 (1961), p. 362.

2 Jeff Sims, Personal communication, May 13, 2020.

3 Ibid.

Figure 17.2. Erica Sughrue by a remarkably scalloped floor in Big Jordan Cave. Photo by Bob Biddix.

Figure 17.3. Erica Sughrue in a large passage in Big Jordan Cave. Photo by Bob Biddix.

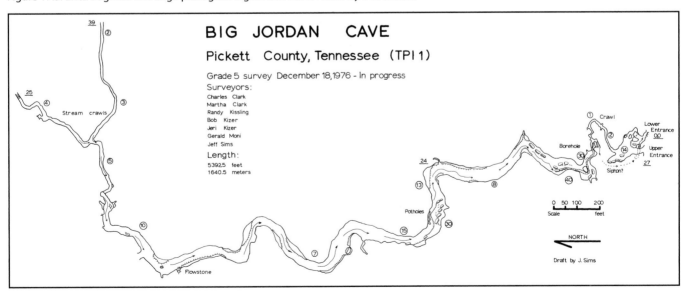

Figure 17.4. Map of Big Jordan Cave, December 18 , 1976.

Figure 17.5. Erica Sughrue on rappel on one of the massive sandstone cliffs that line the top of the Cumberland Plateau in the Big South Fork National River and Recreation Area. Photo by Bob Biddix, May 9, 2015.

Figure 17.6. Ken Pasternack at the entrance to Big Jordan Cave. Photo by Bob Biddix.

Figure 17.7. Erica Sughrue in Big Jordan Cave. Photo by Bob Biddix. (Left, same page)

Figure 17.8. Erica Sughrue by a pool in Big Jordan Cave. Photo by Bob Biddix. (Facing page)

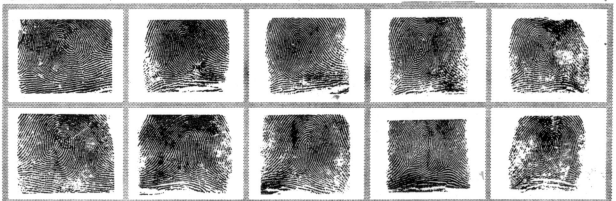

INTERSTATE FLIGHT - ASSAULT TO MURDER,
ATTEMPTED BURGLARY; BANK ROBBERY

Entered
NCIC

WANTED BY FBI

I.O. 4649
(Rev. 11-12-76)

BILLY DEAN ANDERSON

FBI No. 650,125 C

NCIC: PO1414PIPIPITTTTCICI

| 14 O 14 U | Ref: 14 |
| I 22 Tt | 24 |

ALIASES: Bill Dean Anderson, Billie Dean Anderson, James Forster, William David Upchurch

Date photographs taken unknown

Photograph taken 1973

DESCRIPTION
AGE: 42, born July 12, 1934, Fentress County, Tennessee (not supported by birth records)
HEIGHT: 5'8"   EYES: blue or green
WEIGHT: 160 to 170 pounds   COMPLEXION: fair
BUILD: stocky   RACE: white
HAIR: brown   NATIONALITY: American
OCCUPATIONS: artist, mechanic, laborer, tree surgeon, farmer
SCARS AND MARKS: scar across nose, scar left side of forehead, surgical scar right side of stomach, surgical scar lower spine
REMARKS: reportedly wears braces on both legs, suffers from atrophy of legs, and may be wearing long hair and beard.
SOCIAL SECURITY NUMBER USED: 314-36-7484

CRIMINAL RECORD
Anderson has been convicted of robbery, carrying a concealed weapon and assault with intent to commit murder.

CAUTION
ANDERSON, WHO IS BEING SOUGHT IN CONNECTION WITH AN ARMED BANK ROBBERY AND AS AN ESCAPEE FROM A TENNESSEE JAIL, HAS BEEN CONVICTED OF ASSAULT TO MURDER LAW ENFORCEMENT OFFICERS. ON AT LEAST THREE OCCASIONS HIS SHOOTING AT INVESTIGATING LAW ENFORCEMENT PERSONNEL INCLUDED FIRING AT POINT-BLANK RANGE WHILE EXITING STOPPED VEHICLE AND WITH RIFLE FROM AMBUSH. CONSIDER ARMED, EXTREMELY DANGEROUS AND AN ESCAPE RISK.

Federal warrants were issued on August 8, 1974, at Knoxville, Tennessee, and on September 28, 1976, at Indianapolis, Indiana, charging Anderson with unlawful interstate flight to avoid prosecution for the crimes of assault to murder, attempted burglary, use of a deadly weapon in commission of a felony, and habitual criminal statute (Title 18, U. S. Code, Section 1073), and bank robbery (Title 18, U. S. Code, Section 2113(d), respectively.

IF YOU HAVE INFORMATION CONCERNING THIS PERSON, PLEASE CONTACT YOUR LOCAL FBI OFFICE.
TELEPHONE NUMBERS AND ADDRESSES OF ALL FBI OFFICES LISTED ON BACK.

Identification Order 4649

Director
Federal Bureau of Investigation
Washington, D. C. 20535

Figure 18.1. FBI Wanted Poster for Billy Dean Anderson, November 12, 1976. Provided by Kay Wood Conatser.

CHAPTER 18
Billy Dean Anderson's Hideout Cave

Billy Dean Anderson's Hideout Cave is located in Pickett County, Tennessee. The surveyed length is only 1,060 feet, but it has such an interesting and unusual history it was chosen for inclusion in this book.

A DESCRIPTION OF THE CAVE

Caver Darlene Anthony wrote the following fascinating history of Billy Dean Anderson's Hideout Cave:

> We first heard about Bill Dean Anderson in the obituaries of the **Knoxville News-Sentinel**. Sometime in mid-July, the FBI had surrounded his mother's home in rural Fentress County and had there "blown him away, Bonnie-and-Clyde style," for resisting arrest. A fugitive from justice for nearly five years, local rumor reported that he had hid in a cave in the area all of that time. There are around 200 caves on report in Fentress County alone, and many in neighboring Pickett County as well. We had no idea where his cave could be located, except for these few clues: Billy Dean was a near-cripple (from a 1962 shoot-out), and therefore couldn't get around as far or as quickly; and his mother's house was located in Pall Mall, Tenn. The story slept in the back of our heads for nearly six weeks.
>
> Then a friend of ours from nearby Grimsly, Tenn., told us that the local authorities had located the cave and had relieved it of an arsenal of weapons, some personal belongings, etc. The news media published many photographs of various sheriffs and sheriff's aides posing in Billy Dean's cave. Our friend suggested that we get in touch with the sheriff's office in Jamestown, Tenn., and see if we could further explore the cave. (The authorities weren't quite sure at that point whether there was more than one entrance to the cave. The entrance they had used was a 12-foot deep hole leading down to the walking-room cave. Could Billy Dean have been stout enough to chimney up and down this hole?)
>
> This sounded quite adventuresome to us, especially after a summer of mapping Fentress County borehole. The sheriff put us in touch with the landowner, who readily volunteered to drive us to the area in his truck. As we walked up the logging road in the hills, we soon realized that we weren't the only curious ones. Every man, woman, child, grandfather, etc., was beating a path a blind man could follow up to the cave. They had even built a wooden ladder for easier access! Our carbide lamps and other cave gear were a real oddity in a world of flashlights and flashbulbs. We spent about an hour exploring the known cave passage and digging into virgin leads. We decided to put off mapping the 800-foot estimated cave until a later date.
>
> So it was that on a Sunday afternoon in late September, thwarted from big stuff in the Gorge due to high water in the Obey (River), we agreed to map what we had named Billy Dean Anderson's Hideout Cave. Aided by several Nashville Grotto members, we spent four and a half hours mapping a total of 1,060 feet of cave. Fully one-third of the cave was virgin unexplored territory, opened up by digging. The rest of the cave was either heavily

Figure 18.2. Ken Pasternack in the entrance to Billy Dean Anderson's Hideout Cave. Photo by Bob Biddix, January 19, 2020.

trafficked by local booty-seekers or had at least been scooped by one person.

Billy Dean evidently saw most of his cave at least once and made good use of his living space. In the entrance area, out of planks and rocks, he built a sleeping platform. A sleeping bag made of army-type blankets was found there. In the passage directly behind his bed, he built wooden shelves out of crates for a pantry. We found jars of peanut butter, cooking oil, home-canned jellies, etc., still on the shelves. Beyond his pantry area was an incredible collection of crushed tin cans. We later found two more areas of tin can accumulation.

In the back of the main room there is a small domepit, where water trickles down the wall constantly. Billy Dean pressed a sheet of metal against the rockface and was able to funnel water down into a waiting plastic

Figure 18.3. Kay Wood Conatser in the Entrance to Rile Pile Cave. January 20, 2015.

Figure 18.4. Ken Pasternack by Billy Dean Anderson's bed. Photo by Bob Biddix, January 19, 2020.

Figure 18.5. Ken Pasternack by sheet metal and plastic jugs used to collect drinking water. Photo by Bob Biddix, January 19, 2020.

milk jug. We counted no less than 36 of these gallon jugs, most of which were filled with water and capped, ready for use.

He also used a small foyer off of the main room as a storage area for potatoes, onions, and other produce. Locals tell us he had a small truck garden in the valley below his cave. Evidence found in the cave seems to agree with this.

Having mapped all the passage we could push into; we left the cave. Passing through the pantry and sleeping area, the wreckage and debris reminded us sharply of the human story associated with the cave. The foods are rotting and fouling the clean cave air. Locals who visit the cave plunder and vandalize, looking for souvenirs. They come to see Billy Dean's Hideout, not the cave.

Emerging from the odors below into the fresher evening air, we saw the tree where Billy Dean notched the passing years, standing silent as a sentinel above the cave entrance. We noticed it bears the silver spray-painted letters: Crabtree Was Here.[1]

A BRIEF HISTORY OF BILLY DEAN ANDERSON

Billy Dean Anderson was born on July 12, 1934 and died on July 7, 1979. At some point, he joined the Army, but received a psychiatric discharge.

Billy spent considerable time in prison and in 1962 he was shot and crippled by a TN State Trooper. Due to this injury, he drew a disability check.

---

1   Darlene Anthony, NSS News, November, 1979 (Volume 37, No. 11), pp 262, 271.

Figure 18.6. Erica Sughrue by empty containers in Billy Dean Anderson's Hideout Cave. Photo by Bob Biddix, January 19, 2020.

On December 30, 1973, Billy and his wife Betty were attempting to break in and rob the Candlelight Club near Jamestown, TN. They were caught in the act by Deputy Web Hatfield, Jr., who they shot and seriously injured. Billy and his wife were soon arrested, but his wife got off by offering to testify against him.

Later, while Billy was in prison, Betty hid a small saw blade in a box of cigars and was able to give to box to him. He and his cellmate used this saw to cut a hole in the wall of their cell in Wartburg, TN. On the morning on August 5, 1974, a jailer discovered that both men had escaped.

Wartburg was in Morgan County, just southeast of Fentress County. Billy was able to live off the land and work his way northwest to the bridge that crosses Clear Fork and leads into Fentress County. He was able to mail a letter to Glen (Squirrel) Evans at Pall Mall, telling him where he was hiding and asking him to come pick him up. On August 15, 1974, Squirrel picked up Billy at the bridge and hid him in a hunting dog box in the back of his pickup truck. That same day, Billy robbed the Marrowbone Bank of $13,418. He and Squirrel headed north to Muncie, Indiana where he had friends and relatives. After a few days there, he moved south to Bald Rock, Kentucky where he had more friends. Here, he took up residence in a cave to hide from the FBI. When the weather got cold, he moved into an old log barn at the old homestead where he was born. He was soon visited by his stepfather Omer Hughes and his mother Ina in a tobacco patch on a nearby farm. Shortly after this, Hag Wood showed him

Figure 18.7. Erica Sughrue by a beautiful parachute formation in Billy Dean Anderson's Hideout Cave. Photo by Bob Biddix, January 19, 2020.

Figure 18.8. Erica Sughrue by water storage jugs in Billy Dean Anderson's Hideout Cave. Photo by Bob Biddix, January 19, 2020.

Figure 18.9. Erica Sughrue in a large passage in Billy Dean Anderson's Hideout Cave. Photo by Bob Biddix, January 19, 2020.

the entrance to the cave where Billy would live for the next four and one-half years.

The cave that Billy Dean Anderson chose to live in was not well known. On July 6, 1979, as he walked from his Hideout Cave, around the slope of Lynch Pinnacle Mountain, he passed another cave known as Rile Pile Cave. His friend Hag Wood had tried to get Billy to use this cave for his hideout, but Billy had decided that it was too well known. Up the mountain from Rile Pile Cave was another cave that he was familiar with, Russell Caverns. Russell Caverns was a saltpeter cave that his grandfather had taken him to when he was twelve years old. Also on the slope of this mountain was the famous Bugger Hole. Billy stopped by the Bugger Hole on that fateful last day of his life, while walking to his parents' home in Pall Mall. He slipped in their back door about 8:50. After visiting his parents and some other friends, Billy left at five minutes past midnight.

As he was crossing a field behind his parents' house on his way back to his Hideout Cave he encountered two FBI agents who shot him for resisting arrest. He died there in the field.[2]

THE SURVEY OF BILLY DEAN ANDERSON'S HIDEOUT CAVE

Billy Dean Anderson's Hideout Cave was surveyed by Darlene Anthony, John Hoffelt, Chris Kerr, David Parr, and John Yust on September 30, 1979. The map is shown as Figure 18.10. The cave has a length of 1,060 feet and a depth of 46 feet

RILE PILE CAVE

The entrance to Rile Pile Cave is on a southwest-facing hillside. It is a 6-foot long, 3-foot wide, and 10-foot deep chimney that continues as a walking phreatic passage for 108 feet. The cave continues another 30 feet as a dirt-floored crawl with blowing air before becoming too tight to continue. A three-foot long wooden handle and a chisel were found in this branch and it looks like the dirt floor may have been mined. On exiting,

just to the right of the entrance climbdown, a slot continues as a walking passage for 102 feet from the junction, then ends.[3]

Kay Wood Conatser reports that this cave has been well-known locally since the mid-1880s. She recalls that she played in the cave when she was a child.[4]

Rile Pile, for whom the cave is named, was a moonshiner who hid in the cave in late 1884 and early 1885, after he shot and killed a revenuer and the man who turned him in. He was born in 1855 and died in 1938.[5]

RUSSELL CAVERNS

The entrance to Russell Caverns is located in a sink. Inside the entrance is a large tunnel 7-8 feet high and 50 feet wide. Bruce Zerr reports the remains of 6-8 saltpeter vats. All the wood has rotted away and only mounds of dirt are left. It is reported to be a complex cave with 3,300 feet of explored passages.[6]

This cave is notable in that Billy Dean Anderson's grandfather had taken him to it when he was twelve years old. Anderson stopped here to rest on his way home on the last day of his life.[7]

Marion O. Smith visited this cave on August 16, 1987 with Patricia Anthony, Gerald Moni, Ray Gregory, Chip Cahill and Mike Russell. He noted:

> From Bugger Hole we walked to Russell Caverns, which was once owned by Mike's kinfolks. The entrance is in a ravine and is a ledge dropping into an entrance in a sink underneath and almost next to the same road which is below Bugger Hole. A stoop climb leads to a 40-foot wide entrance room with major passages leading left and right. Mike

---

2 Kay Wood Conatser, "Billy Dean Anderson: A Criminal Life", 2013, 252 pages.

3 Justin Huffman, Report filed with the Tennessee Cave Survey, 2020.

4 Kay Wood Conatser, Personal communication, June 23, 2020.

5 Kay Wood Conatser, Personal communications, June 21 and 23, 2020.

6 Bruce Zerr, "TCS Narrative File For Fentress Co., TN", September, 1995, pp 78-79.

7 Kay Wood Conatser, "Billy Dean Anderson: A Criminal Life", 2013, p. 220.

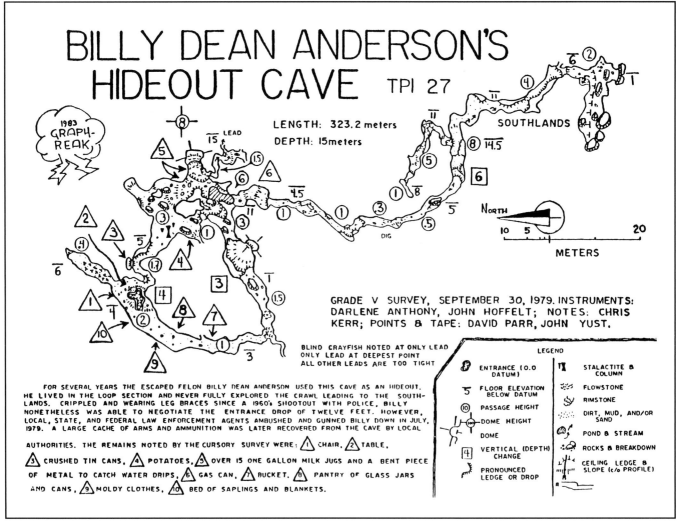

BILLY DEAN ANDERSON'S HIDEOUT CAVE TPI 27

1983 GRAPH-REAK

LENGTH: 323.2 meters
DEPTH: 15meters

SOUTHLANDS

LEAD

North

10 5 20
METERS

GRADE V SURVEY, SEPTEMBER 30, 1979. INSTRUMENTS: DARLENE ANTHONY, JOHN HOFFELT; NOTES: CHRIS KERR; POINTS & TAPE: DAVID PARR, JOHN YUST.

BLIND CRAYFISH NOTED AT ONLY LEAD
ONLY LEAD AT DEEPEST POINT
ALL OTHER LEADS ARE TOO TIGHT

FOR SEVERAL YEARS THE ESCAPED FELON BILLY DEAN ANDERSON USED THIS CAVE AS AN HIDEOUT. HE LIVED IN THE LOOP SECTION AND NEVER FULLY EXPLORED THE CRAWL LEADING TO THE SOUTHLANDS. CRIPPLED AND WEARING LEG BRACES SINCE A 1960's SHOOTOUT WITH POLICE, BILLY NONETHELESS WAS ABLE TO NEGOTIATE THE ENTRANCE DROP OF TWELVE FEET. HOWEVER, LOCAL, STATE, AND FEDERAL LAW ENFORCEMENT AGENTS AMBUSHED AND GUNNED BILLY DOWN IN JULY, 1979. A LARGE CACHE OF ARMS AND AMMUNITION WAS LATER RECOVERED FROM THE CAVE BY LOCAL AUTHORITIES. THE REMAINS NOTED BY THE CURSORY SURVEY WERE: △1 CHAIR, △2 TABLE, △3 CRUSHED TIN CANS, △4 POTATOES, △5 OVER 15 ONE GALLON MILK JUGS AND A BENT PIECE OF METAL TO CATCH WATER DRIPS, △6 GAS CAN, △7 BUCKET, △8 PANTRY OF GLASS JARS AND CANS, △9 MOLDY CLOTHES, △10 BED OF SAPLINGS AND BLANKETS.

LEGEND

ENTRANCE (0.0 DATUM)

5̄ FLOOR ELEVATION BELOW DATUM

⑩ PASSAGE HEIGHT

DOME HEIGHT

DOME

4 VERTICAL (DEPTH) CHANGE

PRONOUNCED LEDGE OR DROP

STALACTITE & COLUMN

FLOWSTONE

RIMSTONE

DIRT, MUD, AND/OR SAND

POND & STREAM

ROCKS & BREAKDOWN

CEILING LEDGE & SLOPE (c/o PROFILE)

Figure 18.10. Map of Billy Dean Anderson's Hideout Cave, 1979.

Figure 18.11. Erica Sughrue at the entrance to Russell Caverns. Photo by Bob Biddix, September 2, 2018.

Figure 18.12. Mark Hobbs rappels into the Bugger Hole. Photo by Bob Biddix, September 2, 2018.

Figure 18.13. Erica Sughrue by large mud cracks in a passage in Russell Caverns. Photo by Bob Biddix, September 2, 2018.

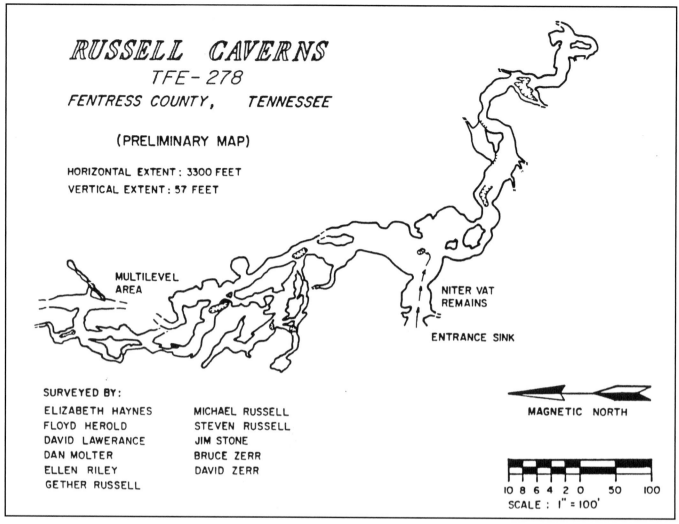

Figure 18.14. Map of Russell Caverns, Undated.

said the cave was 3,000+ feet long. I explored perhaps 30 feet of virgin cave. Russell Caverns is also a saltpeter cave. At least 2 and probably 3 vats are in the entrance room and at least one was a square vat. One of the left passages had a good bit of stacked rocks.[8]

There is a map in the TN Cave Survey Files that is labeled "Preliminary Map". It is undated and does not show ceiling heights, but it does give a horizontal extent of 3,300 feet and a vertical extent of 57 feet. (See Figure 18.14)

8 Marion O. Smith, Personal communication, June 16, 2020.

CAVE ACCESS

Unknown at the present time. Always be sure you have the owner's permission before going into these or any other caves.

SUGGESTED READING

Kay Wood Conatser published the book *Billy Dean Anderson: A Criminal Life* in 2013. It is a thorough history of Billy Dean Anderson's life.

Figure 18.15. Erica Sughrue at the bottom of the entrance drop to Billy Dean Anderson's Hideout Cave. Photo by Bob Biddix, January 19, 2020.

Figure 19.1. Erica Sughrue by rimstone dams in Bunkum Cave. Photo by Bob Biddix.

CHAPTER 19
Bunkum Cave

Bunkum Cave is located in Pickett County, Tennessee. It has a surveyed length of 6,216 feet and a vertical extent of 41 feet.

A 1917 VISIT TO BUNKUM CAVE

Thomas L. Bailey's classic report, *Report on the Caves of the Eastern Highland Rim and Cumberland Mountains* (1918), give the earliest known description of the cave:

Nos. 36 and 37. Bunkum Cave.

Sample No. 36 was taken just inside the mouth while No. 37 was taken farther back.

Location.—At the head of a hollow 1 1/2 miles east of Obey River, on the land of Irving Amlett, a half mile southeast of Bloomington, and less than half a mile from the Byrdstown road. It is in Mississippian limestone about 100 feet above the Chattanooga black shale.

The mouth of this cave is probably larger than that of any other cave in the State and of course is correspondingly imposing. It is 150 feet wide and 65 feet high. A creek flows out of the cave and a small stream falls in a cascade from the thin ledge of limestone over the cave's mouth. The large stream flows through the entire length of the cave and forks several times. As many as 75 Indian skeletons and many relics have been dug up from the mouth of Bunkum Cave. The earth in the mouth is 10 or 15 feet deep and is mixed with large boulders. This earth is quite dry and seems to contain much niter. There is also niter on the ledges projecting from the walls. There is a much larger quantity of earth in the mouth than there is farther back. The mouth is located in woods and the scenery surrounding it is quite wild. The main passage of this cave is 35 feet wide, 25 feet high and fully a mile long, and has a fork probably as long.

Most of the earth in the back of the cave has been worked over by the stream, and probably contains little niter. In many places there are wide ledges on which are beds of earth 2 or 3 feet thick which contain gypsum crystals, and in places a thin coat of white gypsum is found on the rocks. Toward the upper end of the cave there are many large, beautiful, and bizarre stalagmites, stalactites, and columns, some of which are pure white. The east fork of this cave contains a remarkable series of water-formed calcite terraces that extend for over a hundred yards in length while the vertical distance from the top to the bottom of the series is about 40 feet. Each terrace averages about 8 inches in height and forms a series of arcs or semi-circles that are themselves indented into smaller arcs in a peculiar manner. The top of each stop or terrace is a shallow basin filled with the clearest and stillest water imaginable. The rims of these pools vary from an eighth of an inch to a foot in thickness and have been built up by the water which trickles over them in a thin sheet. Some of the pools in the basin-like depressions on the top of the terrace are 4 feet deep and the water is so clear that they seem empty. An old still was once located in the mouth of this cave and the name Bunkum originated from applying this term to the still.[1]

1 Thomas L. Bailey, *Report on the Caves of the Eastern Highland Rim and Cumberland Mountains*, TN Sate Geological Survey, The Resources of Tennessee, Vol. 8 (1918), No. 2, pp 117-118.

Figure 19.2. Looking out the entrance of Bunkum Cave. Photo by Chuck Sutherland, August 5, 2017.

A DESCRIPTION OF THE CAVE

Bunkum Cave is described by Thomas C. Barr, Jr. in his book, *Caves of Tennessee* (1961):

> The entrance to Bunkum Cave is one of the most impressive cave mouths in Tennessee. It is located in a steep-walled ravine and is continuous with a large, semicircular rock shelter which marks a prominent drop of the little stream that traverses the ravine. The path to the cave circles over the top of the mouth, and one may clamber down on ledges at the far side of the gully in which the cave opens. The mouth itself is fully 100 feet wide and 50 feet high, and the cave stream flows from it to join the surface stream of the ravine.
>
> The main avenue of the cave is 750 feet long. Near the mouth it is wide and spacious, averaging 20 to 30 feet wide and 15 feet high, but toward the back of the cave it becomes smaller. The cave trends east for the first 150 feet, then east-southeast.
>
> Two lateral passages are developed. At 380 feet the first side passage opens to the left and extends northeast for 220 feet to a low bedding-plane crawl over rough gravel. This crawlway, which was explored for 325 feet, contains fragments of leaves and sticks and is probably sinkhole fed. Near the junction with the main passage is a pronounced saw-cut trench in the middle of the lateral passage, with shelves on either side representing an earlier level of the floor now abruptly truncated in hanging junction fashion by the main passage.

Figure 19.3. Donna Capps in the entrance passage to Bunkum Cave. Photo by Steve Capps, August 2, 2019.

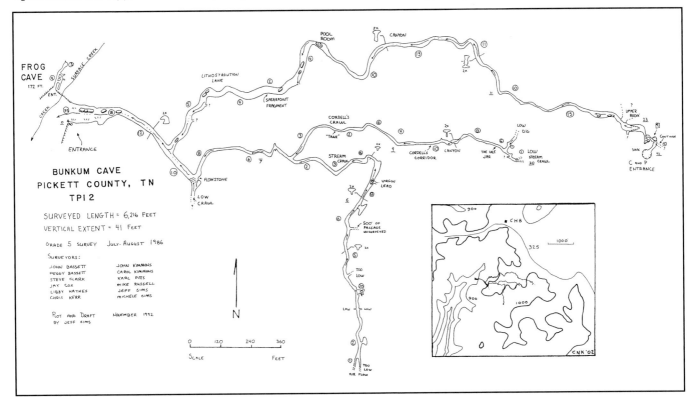

Figure 19.4. Map of Bunkum Cave by Jeff Sims.

Figure 19.5. Steve Capps and Donna Capps in a stream passage in Bunkum Cave. Photo by Steve Capps, August 2, 2019.

At 525 feet a short passage extends to the right, penetrable for only 75 feet. It runs southeast and contains many rimstone pools. There are few other dripstone formations in the cave.[2]

From the above description, it is clear that Barr only saw about 1,370 feet of cave. Since the current surveyed length is 6,216 feet, he clearly did not push the low, wet passages.

William Hull, Cordell Hull's father, used the cave entrance to house a moonshine still.

2 Thomas C. Barr, Jr., *Caves of Tennessee*, TN Division of Geology, Bulletin 64 (1961), pp 363, 364.

The Survey of Bunkum Cave

Bunkum Cave was surveyed during July and August of 1986. The final map was drafted by Jeff Sims in November, 1992. One side passage entrance on the map is labeled: "500' of passage unsurveyed". Several other leads are labeled "low" and one is labeled "low dig".

This map shows a second entrance to the cave, called the C and P Entrance. The name "Tank" is written on the wall in the Cordell's Crawl Passage. "Tank" was Standiford R. Gorin, NSS #478.

Figure 19.6. Erica Sughrue in the stream passage of Bunkum Cave. Photo by Bob Biddix.

Prehistoric Visitors To Bunkum Cave

The huge mouth of Bunkum Cave, along with the water supply flowing out of the cave, naturally lends itself as a natural shelter. A 1992 survey of the cave by the Tennessee Division of Archaeology found evidence that the cave had been occupied during the Middle Woodland Period (1,000 BC to 1,000 AD).

Place Names In Bunkum Cave

C and P Entrance
Cordell's Corridor
Cordell's Crawl
Lithostrotian Lane
Pool Room
The Uile Jar

Figure 19.7. Zachary Cunningham in a stream passage in Bunkum Cave. Photo by Chuck Sutherland, August 5, 2017.

Figure 19.8. Erica Sughrue in a stream passage in Bunkum Cave. Photo by Bob Biddix. (Facing page)

Cordell Hull Birthplace State Park

Bunkum Cave is located in Cordell Hull Birthplace State Park, which is approximately 5 miles west of Byrdstown, TN. This is a small park, consisting of 58 acres. The park was created in 1997, but the portion containing Bunkum Cave was not purchased until 2002.

Cordell Hull (1871-1955) served as a Representative in Congress from 1907 to 1931. He then served as a Senator in Congress from 1931-37, until he was appointed Secretary of State by President Franklin D. Roosevelt on March 4, 1933. Hull played a pivotal role in the creation of the United Nations in the mid-1940s. He had to resign as Secretary of State on November 27, 1944 due to ill health, shortly before the final ratification of the United Nations Charter in San Francisco. He was awarded the Nobel Peace Prize for his efforts in establishing the United Nations.

The Park has a refurbished representation of the log cabin where Hull was born in 1871 and a museum housing a number of Hull's personal items, including a replica of his 1945 Nobel Peace Prize. The cabin is on the National Register of Historic Places (1972).

Cave Access

Bunkum Cave is located in Cordell Hull State Park. There is a 2.5-mile loop trail leading to the entrance of the cave. A permit is required to explore the cave beyond its lighted area.

Figure 20.1. Erica Sughrue on rope in Devils Descent. Photo by Bob Biddix, February 6, 2021.

CHAPTER 20
Devil's Dungeon Cave

Devil's Dungeon Cave is located in Pickett County, Tennessee. The Tennessee Cave Survey lists this cave at 11,000 feet long. This sounds like an estimated length. According to the TCS Files, Devils Dungeon Cave is located across from Big Jordan Cave in an outcrop and a stream flows from the cave in wet weather. The cave drains Rocky Creek Hollow.

THE EXPLORATION AND SURVEY OF DEVIL'S DUNGEON CAVE

Joe Morgan, Barb Simpson, and Fred Anderson wrote the following Trip Reports in 1981. They give an exciting account of the exploration and survey of this interesting cave.

May 9, 1981 (by Joe Morgan)

Devil's Dungeon is a cave located in the Miami Valley Grotto's caving area in Tennessee. On Saturday May 9, I succeeded in sucking in Lou Simpson, Bruce Warthman, and John Barnes to look at and explore a cave that I had found on a previous trip several weeks earlier. Upon arriving at the cave entrance I found that the air flow was much stronger than I had remembered. We geared up and entered the cave and I found that I had forgotten my kneepads, a bad mistake in this cave. After going through short, low, muddy crawl it soon opened up into a fair-sized room about 20 feet high with two going leads. We pushed the one which had air flow, a hands and knees crawl, which after a short distance opened into another room about five feet high with a hands and knees crawl leading out of it. This, after a short distance, opened into another room about 10 feet high with another crawl leading out of it. I could no longer take the crawling without knee pads, so I waited in this room while the others pushed ahead.

According to Louis, the crawl continues until it comes to a belly crawl in water, which, after a short distance, opened up into a large room 50 feet high and 70 feet long with a dirt slope up one side. This was the extent of the push. There are four going leads out of this room: an upstream passage, a downstream passage, and two dry tubes located 10 feet straight up the wall at the top of the dirt slope. Due to the large amount of air flow, this cave has a very good chance of being large. No mapping was done because it was supposed to rain, and it was after other caving activities. All of the cave we saw was virgin. A return mapping and push trip is being planned.[1]

May 23, 1981 (by Barb Simpson)

Joe Morgan failed to show up from Speleofest Saturday morning, so Lou, Tom Patterson, and I drove down to Tennessee without him to begin the mapping of Devil's Dungeon. Joe's scoop was protected, however. Tom, Lou, and I put in about ten shots but were unable to get into the main part of the cave since it was sumped shut.[2]

August 15, 1981 (by Fred Anderson)

It was 2:00 in the morning, Saturday, August 15. Joe Morgan and I had just arrived at the Fieldhouse, expecting to find the usual hoard of people littering the bed floor, porch, and barn. Instead, we found only Doug Stecko.

The three of us had planned to start mapping and exploring Devil's Dungeon in Pickett County, Tennessee. There appeared to be only one problem—a problem that seems to ruin about half of all cave trips. It looked like rain, and Devil's Dungeon was no place to be in the rain. John Barnes had seen water gushing out of the entrance on at least two occasions. Others had

---

1 Joe Morgan, "Big Scoop In Devil's Dungeon", Cave Cricket Gazette, v. 6 (1981), no. 4, pp 41-42.

2 Barb Simpson, "Devil's Dungeon: Pickett Co., TN", Cave Cricket Gazette, v. 6 (1981), no. 5, p. 53.

Figure 20.2. The entrance to Devils Dungeon Cave. Photo by Bob Biddix.

been able to penetrate the cave for only a short distance before coming to a sump.

We awoke to a cloudy, though not dangerous looking sky, and so decided to go to Devil's Dungeon. We headed south into Tennessee.

The mile hike from the car to the cave was a hot one. Crossing over a creek bed, Joe noted the low water level. That was a good sign. Arriving at the small, unimpressive entrance to Devil's Dungeon, the three of us sat on rocks and dried off in the cool wind blowing from the cave.

Our first attempt at surveying the cave proved to be worthless. Joe was determined to do this survey in metric "for greater accuracy." However, after putting in six survey stations, our ignorance of the metric system got the best of us as we found it difficult to estimate passage dimensions that way. Instead of continuing an inaccurate survey,

we decided to come back the following week and start over, using the English system. For now, we would explore.

After crawling for a good 20 minutes, we came to the one section of the cave that we were afraid might be sumped shut. It wasn't. In fact, the water was so low that we were almost able to stay out of it by keeping our bodies wedged between the mud and the ceiling and wall to the right.

Emerging from the crawl, we found ourselves in the big room with the high leads. We could see that most of them would have to be bolt-climbed. There was one lead, though at the top of a steep, 30-foot mud slope, that beckoned us onward. Joe led the way, kicking steps into the mud as he climbed.

Once at the top of the mud slope, we followed a canyon back to an intersection with a dry

Figure 20.3. Erica Sughrue rappels into the entrance of Devils Descent. Photo by Bob Biddix, February 6, 2021.

streambed. Downstream, the passage was interrupted by a 15-foot pit, at the bottom of which was another stream passage, this one with water flowing in it. Beyond the pit, the upper stream level intersected another canyon and then continued on the other side. It was here that we turned back to explore upstream.

Upstream of where we had entered this dry stream level, we found a formation area. The formations, mainly stalactites, stalagmites, and soda straws, were few and far between, but quite beautiful. There was one truly spectacular piece of white bacon, two feet wide and four feet high, hanging from the wall and dripping water onto a two-foot high stalagmite surrounded by cobbles. This was, without a doubt, one of the prettiest formations I have ever seen in any cave. The passage continued as a low crawl.

Heading back downstream, we found a high dry crawl going off to the left. We named it the Dead Bat Passage because of the numerous bat skeletons we found in the undisturbed sand. After crawling about 100 feet, we came to what every caver dreams about—VIRGIN TRUNK.

The trunk was about 30 feet high and 50 feet wide and was interspersed with piles of breakdown. A small stream was flowing through it. Joe, Doug, and I explored downstream and found that the trunk soon became low and wet. Exploring upstream, though, the trunk continued large and dry. Climbing to the top of a breakdown pile about 300 feet from where we had entered the trunk, Joe suggested that we leave the cave.

Joe reasoned, "If we push it, we might find that it ends just around the bend. Then we'll be disappointed But if we leave now, we'll be psyched to come back next weekend and explore some more. Let's quit while we're ahead." We exited the cave, planning our return trip the following Saturday.[3]

August 22, 1981 (by Fred Anderson)

A telephone description of Devil's Dungeon to Bruce Warthman earlier in the week was all it took to convince him to come along for our second attempt at mapping the entrance crawl. Joe had decided that the crawl would have to be mapped before anymore exploring could take place. Joe, Bruce and I were accompanied by Steve Bucher and two of his friends from Richmond who just happened to be at the Fieldhouse that weekend.

Using the six original survey stations which we had put in on the previous Saturday, and then adding more as we went along, we spent about three hours mapping the entrance crawl. Its total length was just over 700 feet, the last 100 feet of which was in water. Once in the Big Room, we surveyed to the top of the 30-foot mud slope so that we would have a permanent station that would not wash away in flood waters. This done,

3 Fred Anderson, "Descent Into Devil's Dungeon", Cave Cricket Gazette, v. 6 (1981), no. 7, pp 75-77.

we left our survey equipment behind to push ahead into virgin cave.

When we reached the intersection of the Dead Bat Passage and the trunk, Bruce, Steve Bucher, and Steve's two friends went wild. Steve and his friends were impressed with the size of the trunk. Bruce was impressed with its virginity.

The six of us entered the trunk and headed upstream to the point were Joe, Doug Stecko, and I had quite one week before. At this point Bruce was permitted to lead the way so that he could experience the thrill of being "the first".

A short distance beyond the point where Bruce began leading the way, the trunk did a hairpin turn, almost doubling back in the opposite direction. It then curved to the left and continued.

At one point along the trunk there were two large domes, each 50-60 feet high. There were small bones at the bottom of one. These could indicate another entrance or at least a sinkhole in the area of the domes.

About 200 feet beyond the domes, the trunk became choked by breakdown. While everyone was either resting or checking for side leads, I entered the breakdown and began crawling up and down within it.

The breakdown was discouraging, but everywhere I turned within it, I found a way to go. Realizing that there might be a way to get through to the other side where the trunk would surely continue, I called out to the others.

"Hey !!! This breakdown goes. Are we gonna push it or are we gonna leave?"

I should have known. Just like the week before, Joe wanted to quit while we were ahead. I emerged from the breakdown, secretly glad that I had been talked out of continuing, for I was tired.

The worst is over in Devil's Dungeon as far as mapping is concerned, until someone finds another 700-foot crawl. Now remains the good part of the cave, including all the side leads that have not yet been checked. Joe Morgan estimates that we've seen about two miles in Devil's Dungeon so far, but there are four miles of ridge, and that could mean a lot of cave.[4]

4 Ibid.

September 5, 1981 (by Fred Anderson)

The anticipation was great as we drove south toward Tennessee. In my car were Tony Hughes, Bruce Warthman, and Jerry Barnes. In Barb Simpson's were Joe Morgan and Robert Phelps. Exploration of the cave had only begun three weeks before with numerous leads yet to be pushed.

In the cave, we split into two parties. Joe, Tony, and Jerry would start mapping at the top of the 30-foot mud slope in the large room at the end of the entrance crawl. From there, they would map to the first "T" junction and then go right and survey into virgin cave. Barb, Bruce, Robert, and I would start by putting in a station at the "T" junction and mapping to the left, into the formation area and beyond—also virgin.

In the formation area, Robert checked a side lead to the left and reported crawling to a crack through which he could see what appeared to be a room. He said he might have been able to squeeze through it, but we encouraged him not to do it right then because the rest of us were eager to continue mapping the passage we were in.

Beyond the formations, our passage became low and fairly wet, although it was possible to stay pretty much out of the water by sitting on rocks. Eventually, we arrived at an intersection with a taller and somewhat drier side lead to the right. We opted to map the side lead, forsaking the wet crawl for another trip.

The side lead was about ten feet high and three to five feet wide. We name it the Chocolate Cake Passage because the mud in one area resembled chocolate cake that had been sliced with a knife.

At the end of the Chocolate Cake Passage, Robert discovered a small hole about four feet up in the right wall. The hole could not have been more than a foot and a half in diameter and appeared to be too small for anyone larger than a Munchkin to fit through. Naturally, I tried.

I exhaled. I tried going through with my arms extended, then with my arms at my side. I tried squeezing through on my side, and then my back. I huffed, I puffed, I moaned, and I groaned. I could not fit. Then, Robert tried. It was not easy, but he made it with a combination of twisting, grunting, and pushing against my upheld hands with his feet. When he finally popped through on the other side, we heard an echo.

Robert began exploring, describing the passage as he went. He told how it got bigger and bigger, and how he had to stop when he reached what he estimated to be a ten-foot drop into an even larger passage. When Robert returned to the hole, I tossed our survey tape to him and we surveyed to his side of the hole. He then squeezed back through the hole with the aid of my wrists which he used as handholds. Because of the tightness of the hole and the fact that my pulling Robert through it resembled an obstetrician delivering a baby, Barb suggested calling the lead Bob's Birth Canal. Everyone agreed and then headed out of the cave, cold and tired.

We hiked back to our cars in the dark and were joined moments later by Joe and his team. They described how they had surveyed the downstream portion of the "T" junction and had continued across a pit, to the other side of a canyon, and beyond, into virgin cave. The passage in which they spent most of their time, they found, intersected with the trunk. The canyon which they had crossed over earlier turned out to be the far downstream portion of the trunk. The total length of both surveys was about 2,500 feet. Not bad for a day's work.[5]

September 6, 1981 (by Fred Anderson)

Barb Simpson, Bruce Warthman, and I returned to Devil's Dungeon, bringing an eager Tom Patterson with us.

Our assignment from Joe (Morgan) was to begin mapping the trunk, starting downstream. The reason Tom had come on this trip was because I had promised him we would begin mapping the trunk. What I didn't tell him—because I did not realize it—was that the far downstream part of the trunk was low and nasty. It was the kind of passage that has so much wet mud of the walls and ceiling that setting a legible survey station is impossible.

The four of us eventually worked out way into the nice big part of the trunk which averaged 45 feet high and 30 feet wide. Barb complained that she didn't like to map such large passages because they're hard to sketch, but you'd never know it from seeing her meticulous work. That day, we surveyed close to 1,000 feet.

September 19, 1981 (by Fred Anderson)

Joe Morgan, Bruce Warthman, and Barb Simpson returned to Devil's Dungeon, bringing Lou Simpson, John Barnes, and Carolyn Herel. I was not along, but Lou reported finding a few sinkholes in the surface above the cave. Meanwhile, Barb, Bruce, and Joe were inside, mapping the Dead Bat Passage and then several hundred feet in the Trunk for a total survey of about 1,600 feet.

After ridgewalking, Lou, John, and Carolyn entered the cave and made their way to the breakdown at the end of the trunk, where Lou put his hammer to work on a possible lead in the breakdown. Lou was not able to break through the lead but noted some surface debris in the breakdown which could indicate an entrance or at least a sinkhole somewhere above.[6]

September 26 (?), 1981 (by Bill Allendorf)

After the 700-foot crawl into the Dungeon, we rested. Fred Anderson and Barb asked me if I was too exhausted to continue. "No, I think I can go on." I said coolly, wiping the mud from my glasses. "That's good," replied Fred, "because you're in now." "What's next?' I asked.

Barb looked around the junction and answered, "Fred and I are going to start mapping down this way (pointing towards the lead to the main passage). Bruce can show you down to Bob's Birth Canal where you and Doug are going to be digging."

After a short rest Bruce Warthman escorted me down a passage past a large drapery formation to

---

5 Fred Anderson, "Return To Devil's Dungeon", Cave Cricket Gazette, v. 6 (1981), no. 6, pp 87-88

6 Fred Anderson, "Return to Devil's Dungeon", Cave Cricket Gazette, v. 6 (1981), no. 7, pp 88-89.

Figure 20.4. Bear bones at the bottom of Devils Descent. Note carabiner for scale. Photo by Bob Biddix, February 6, 2021.

a non-descript room. He pointed to a small hole in the upper half of the wall.

"That's' the Birth Canal???" I said, as I took quick mental measurement of the crack and compared them with my own torso. Presently Bruce returned to Barb and Fred for the mapping while Doug Stecko and I got to work on the Canal. After a couple cubic feet of clay, I noticed that my trencher was scraping rock. Dejectedly, I announced to Doug that we had been stopped dead.

Doug begged me aside and crawled up for a look. With a garden trowel, he attacked the floor of the Canal and soon found that the rock was only a thin veneer of flowstone. Within an hour we had broken up all but the last foot of the floor and scooped out several inches of the underlying clay. We broke for lunch with the crawl still

too small for the likes of Joe Morgan, but wide enough that I had a good chance to get through.

"Well, here I go, " I said, as I reached the end. I'm through and it's a beautiful world over here."

Beyond this, I found a ledge overlooking a bend in a canyon, disappearing into darkness at both ends. A marker at this ledge marked Robert Phelp's furthest exploration. I was standing at the brink of virgin cave.

In one direction, the canyon was wide. To the right, the canyon became narrow and twisty with a precarious ledge extending above. It was then that I heard Fred's voice coming from down the larger of the canyon passages. I called and blew my whistle. Fred acknowledged me, but due to muffling of the rocks we could not communicate further. After reporting this to Doug I returned to the Birth Canal to help him through.

Figure 20.5. Raccoon skull at the bottom of Devils Descent. Photo by Bob Biddix, February 6, 2021.

Due to his smaller size Doug did not have the same trouble coming through the Canal that I had encountered. He slithered through in a few seconds and stood with me at the sheet of flowstone on the other side.

Doug followed my lead to the formations. We sat on the ledge overlooking the canyon and shouted to Fred for a while. It was decided that Doug would sit on the ledge and wait for the mapping party to come up through the canyon while I crawled down from the ledge and navigated the narrower section of canyon to the right.

What I found at the end of the passage was another room with some large boulders, a low watery lead that may go somewhere, but the most promising of all: a tall wall of glistening flowstone with a trickle of water coming from above and a high, boulder-strewn lead with a pronounced airflow. After seeing all this, it was time to head back to Doug.

We returned finally to Bob's Birth Canal and Doug scampered through with sickening ease. After fifteen minutes, I was through. Doug had performed his first Caesarean Section on a 6' 3" nerd. Bob's Birth Canal had been robbed of its first potential victim.

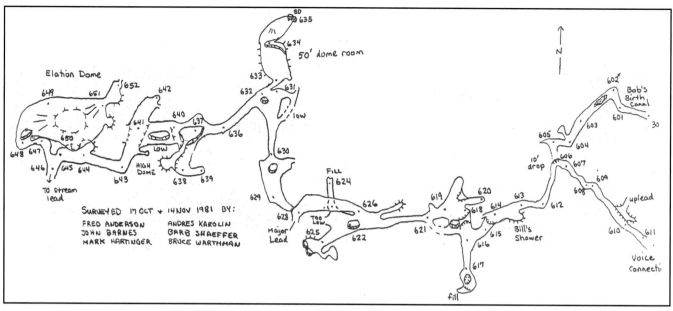

Figure 20.6. Map of the "Beyond The Birth Canal" portion of Devil's Dungeon Cave by Barb Shaeffer, 1981.

Back at the junction where we had left the others, we sat and waited for the mapping party to return. Gradually noises became audible to us: splashes and groans and grunts that meant the mappers were coming through a low, wet belly crawl. After five minutes of these sounds, Barb, Fred, and Bruce emerged from the darkness. They had barely mapped 16 stations in five hours. Fred claimed it was the worst trip he had ever been on. When they heard of my big scoop, their muddy faces brightened somewhat. Barb complained of getting cold, and we decided that we should get out as quickly as possible.[7]

October 17, 1981 (by Barb Shaeffer)

Mark, Bruce, and I surveyed beyond Bob's Birth Canal while Doug dug, and Fred explored. The passage, a twisty canyon, finally "T'd" into a taller canyon about eight feet above the floor. Fred returned after having been lost a while in the right lead and recommended we survey the left lead first. It quickly reached a dome room with only a low bellycrawl dig continuing on. It undoubtedly connects to that low, wet lead Fred, Bruce, and I had surveyed two weeks earlier since Doug and Bill heard our voices through it then.

Mark, Fred and I mapped the right lead while the others explored. We quit in the area Bill had described as a shower stall. I guess Bill's imagination is better than mine. Or maybe most domes look like shower stalls. We had surveyed just a little over 200 feet that day.[8]

November 14, 1981 (by Barb Shaeffer)

Bruce Warthman, Andy Karolin, John Barnes, and I reached the entrance to Devil's Dungeon at 1:30 PM. The 700-foot crawl seemed longer than usual. We made our way through the Birth Canal and followed the canyon to the right to Bill's Shower. The area had lots of domes and was very complex. We tried to map all the short side leads as we went but had to leave one major one for the next time. In one room there were many possibilities, so we all checked to see which way to go. Through a little canyon, I peered up a hole into blackness. It turned out to be a huge dome room fifty to seventy-five feet high and sixty feet across. I followed it up and up expecting to find an entrance any time. I was finally stopped by a tricky climb up to a tight window. For a moment I understood clearly why I go caving and decided the room should be named Elation Dome to match the excitement I felt in finding it. Back at the junction, I checked another hole that went down to a rather low stream passage. I followed it

7 Bill Allendorf, "Beyond The Birth Canal - OR - Stecko's Caesarean Section", Cave Cricket Gazette, v. 6 (1981), no. 7, pp 89-92.

8 Barb Shaeffer, "Devil's Dungeon Update", Cave Cricket Gazette, v. 7 (1982), no. 1, p. 3.

Figure 20.7. Bob Biddix on rope high above the Big South Fork River. Photo by Bob Biddix, May 9, 2015.

in both directions far enough to determine that it went and returned.

We left the stream passage for a later date and mapped Elation Dome. John climbed up high enough to peer through the window at the end. Sure enough, it went on. But that also will have to wait for the next trip. This time the survey for the day totaled over 700 feet and we still made it out of the cave and back to Monticello in time to eat at Pizza Hut.

In summary, there are four leads remaining in Bob's Birth Canal alone: The major side lead at 628, the window in Elation Dome (652), and the two directions of the low stream crawl (646).[9]

It sounds like there are going leads here for some modern cave explorer to follow up on. Go for it!!!

___

9 Barb Shaeffer, "Devil's Dungeon Update", Cave Cricket Gazette, v. 7 (1981) no. 1, p. 4.

THE SURVEY OF DEVIL'S DUNGEON CAVE

Caver Lou Simpson reports that he has seen a map of this cave, but there is no copy in the TCS Files.[10] It is always sad when people spend hundreds of hours surveying, yet no finished map is produced. Barb Shaeffer did publish a map of the "Beyond The Birth Canal" portion of the survey in the January 1982 Cave Cricket Gazette. (See Figure 20.6)

PLACE NAMES IN DEVIL'S DUNGEON CAVE

> Big Room
> Bill's Shower
> Bob's Birth Canal
> Chocolate Cake Passage
> Dead Bat Passage
> Elation Dome

DEVILS DESCENT CAVE

Located close to Devils Dungeon Cave, but 200 feet higher in elevation, is Devils Descent. Gerald Moni and Kristen Bobo give the following description:

> The pit entrance is 12 feet wide by 18 feet long. The pit depth is 118 feet. The bottom is 50 feet across. Two short climb ups end quickly. A bear skeleton is found at the top of a 6-foot climb up.[11]

The pit is located on the west slope of Rotten Fork Valley.

CAVE ACCESS

Current access to these caves is unknown. Please be sure you have the owner's permission before you enter these, or any other caves.

___

10 Lou Simpson, Personal communication, December 27, 2019.

11 Gerald Moni, 2002 and Kristen Bobo, 2014, TCS Narrative File For Pickett County, Tennessee, p. PI-13 - PI-14.

Figure 21.1. Calla Goins by a saltpeter vat and water troughs in the Great Saltpeter Chasm. Photo by Jim Fox, February 15, 2019.

CHAPTER 21

Saltpeter Mining in the Caves of the North Cumberland Plateau

A number of caves in the Upper Cumberland Plateau area covered in this book were mined for saltpeter. Saltpeter mining was an important industry in Tennessee during both the War of 1812 and the Civil War. Saltpeter is the main ingredient of gunpowder and during both of those time periods there was an extremely high demand for gunpowder. Even in times of peace, gunpowder was needed for self-defense and hunting.

The mining of caves for saltpeter dates back to at least the American Revolutionary War. Mining first began in the east in the caves of Virginia and what is now West Virginia, then spread westward. By 1810 caves in Kentucky and Tennessee were perhaps the most important saltpeter mines in the country. Mammoth Cave and Great Saltpeter Cave in Kentucky and Big Bone Cave in Tennessee are the biggest and best-known saltpeter caves. Big Bone Cave in Van Buren County, Tennessee is reported to have produced 2,000,000 pounds of saltpeter between 1811 and 1815.

MANUFACTURE OF GUNPOWDER

Gunpowder is made by grinding together specific amounts of charcoal, sulfur, and saltpeter. Saltpeter is the name given to a family of nitrogen-containing compounds (nitrates) that are normally found in the soil. On the surface of the Earth, plants constantly remove these nitrates from the soil and rainwater dissolves these highly soluble compounds, washing them into the streams and rivers, which eventually flush them into the oceans.

Due to these conditions. Surface soils are unable to accumulate significant amounts of nitrates except in a few rare desert localities. Cave, on the other hands, sometimes provide an environment in which nitrates have a chance to accumulate over long periods of time. There are no plants to use the nitrates in the cave dirt and in some caves there are no dripping waters, running streams, or annual floods to remove these chemicals as fast as they accumulate. The very best saltpeter caves were dry and dusty.

The Earth's atmosphere is rich in nitrogen, 78%. Naturally occurring bacteria in the soil have the ability to remove nitrogen from the air and convert it into nitrogen compounds (nitrates). This process is accelerated by the presence of organic matter. In caves, the frequent accumulations of bat guano, cave rat guano, cave cricket guano, and other organic debris significantly contribute to the production of saltpeter in the cave dirt.

Recent studies also indicate that the oak-hickory forest in the southeastern United States has relatively high levels of nitrates in the soils which tend to migrate though the limestone into the dirt of dry caves.[1]

The mining of saltpeter required the construction of leaching vats near or in the

---

1 Carol A. Hill and Paolo Forti, *Cave Minerals of the World*, 1986, Adobe Press, Albuquerque, New Mexico, 238 pp.

cave. These leaching vats were built from local materials using simple hand tools. For this reason, the details of craftsmanship and construction vary from cave to cave.

Next the miners excavated the saltpeter-bearing dirt and filled the saltpeter vats with it. Normally, the vat was lined with straw to help prevent dirt and water from leaking through the cracks between the planks. Water was poured into the vats until the dirt was saturated.

The water dissolved the highly soluble saltpeter and then slowly drained out of the bottom of the saltpeter vats into wooden collecting troughs. The saltpeter bearing solution (called "liquor") was then taken outside the cave for processing. A lye solution was prepared by leaching water through oak and hickory ashes. Interestingly the leaching vats used to produce lye were almost identical in construction to the saltpeter leaching vats, although usually smaller in size.

Concentrated potash lye liquor was then added to the saltpeter liquor until no further turbidity was produced. This not only converted the dissolved calcium nitrate ($CaNO_3$) into potassium nitrate (K_2NO_3), which is the type of saltpeter necessary to manufacture gunpowder, but it caused some other unwanted minerals in solution to precipitate out so that they could be easily removed by straining.

The resulting liquid was then strained, and the remaining liquid was poured into a large iron kettle where it was boiled until much of the water evaporated leaving behind crystals of saltpeter. These crystals were then removed, dried, packed in bags, and shipped to a powder mill where they would be ground with charcoal and sulfur to make gunpowder.

Listed below are some of the more significant saltpeter caves located in the North Cumberland Plateau area:

BUFFALO CAVE

Buffalo Cave is described in great detail in this book in Chapter 1. Tom Barr (1961) describes

12 saltpeter vats and 2 wooden water troughs. Clearly, this was a major mining operation.

CAMPBELL SALTPETER CAVE

Campbell Saltpeter Cave is described in detail in this book in Chapter 3. Although this is a 3-mile long cave, only the very front section of the cave was mined for saltpeter.

YGGDRASIL CAVE

This cave, located in the middle of the gorge of the East Fork of the Obey River, was a major saltpeter mining site. The cave contains leaching vats, water troughs, and evidence of dirt removal. Yggdrasil Cave is described in great detail in this book in Chapter 8.

YORK CAVE

York Cave is described in great detail in this book in Chapter 3. According to Barr (1961), York Cave was mined extensively for saltpeter during the Civil War, but Marion O. Smith disagrees and thinks the mining occurred during the War of 1812. Evidence of dirt removal and saltpeter vats are located throughout the cave. This was another major mining operation. (See Figure 21.4, 21.5, and 21.6)

SALTPETER CAVES BY COUNTY

Below is a list of all the known caves that were mined for saltpeter in the area covered by this book.

Fentress County

Blue Ridge Saltpeter Cave
Buffalo Cave
Campbell Saltpeter Cave
Cat Pen Saltpeter Cave
Copley Saltpeter Cave
East Fork Saltpeter Cave
Hideout Saltpeter Cave
Manson Saltpeter Cave
Mountain Eye Cave System
Russell Caverns

Yggdrasil Cave
York Cave

Overton County
Allred Saltpeter Cave
Cooper Saltpeter Cave
Copeland Saltpeter Cave
The Great Saltpeter Chasm

Pickett County
Abbott Saltpeter Cave
Eastport Saltpeter Cave
Holt Saltpeter Cave

SUGGESTED READING

The book *Big Bone Cave* by Larry E. Matthews (May, 2006) goes into great detail about the history and techniques of saltpeter mining in Tennessee caves. It includes numerous photographs of saltpeter mining artifacts in both Big Bone Cave and other Tennessee caves. This book was published by the National Speleological Society and was still in print at the time this book went to press. ISBN 978-1-879961-24-1.

Figure 21.2. Large wooden water trough in the Great Saltpeter Chasm. Note carbide lamp for scale. Photo by Larry E. Matthews, July, 1976.

Figure 21.3. Ken McLean stands behind a saltpeter vat in Cobb Creek Saltpeter Cave. Photo by Larry E. Matthews, 1979.

Figure 21.4. Erica Sughrue stands next to two huge saltpeter vat casts in York Cave. Photo by Bob Biddix, February 25, 2017.

Figure 21.5. Pick mark left in dirt by saltpeter miners in York Cave. Photo by Bob Biddix, February 25, 2017.

Figure 21.6. Erica Sughrue by large casts of saltpeter vats in York Cave. Photo by Bob Biddix, February 25, 2017.

Figure 21.7. Rock wall in Campbell Saltpeter Cave showing where dirt was removed and pick marks. Photo by Bob Biddix, December 15, 2019.

Figure 22.1. The cave cricket, *Hadenoecus opilionoides*, in the Mountain Eye Cave system. Photo by Bob Biddix, October 17, 2020.

CHAPTER 22
The Biology of the Caves of the North Cumberland Plateau

The caves that are located in the area of the North Cumberland Plateau, as defined by this book, are biologically rich and diverse. Some of these caves carry large amounts of surface water that drains into them. This surface water carries in organic materials that provide food for the animals inside the cave. Other caves contain bats and the excrement (guano) from these bats is another important food source in some of these caves. Cave cricket guano is also an important food source in other caves.

The animals that live in caves are generally divided into three groups depending upon their degree of specialization to subterranean life. Animals that are so specialized that they can live only in caves are referred to as *troglobites*. Animals that spend part of their lives underground and part on the surface are referred to as *trogloxenes*. Animals that can live in caves, but also live in cool, moist habitats on the Earth's surface are referred to as *troglophiles*. Animals from all three of these categories live in the North Cumberland Plateau area and are discussed below. Other animals occur in caves either by accident, or do not fall into one of the above categories.

Listed below are the various animals that have been reported, so far, from the North Cumberland Plateau area. This list is rather short since no comprehensive biological inventory has been conducted for these caves.

Bats

White Nose Syndrome (WNS) is a disease that was first identified in Howe Caverns in New York state in February, 2006. Since that time it has spread across most of the eastern United States and Canada. White Nose Syndrome is caused by a fungus, *Pseudogymnoascus destructans*, which was apparently introduced from Europe, most likely by European bats hitch-hiking in containers on ships. European bats have natural resistance to the fungus, but American bats do not and it has been deadly to most species of bats in North America.

White Nose Syndrome is spread from bat to bat and human beings apparently play no significant part in its spread. However, the State of Tennessee has used the epidemic as an excuse to close access to almost all caves on state owned property.

Gray Bats are present in Mountain Eye Cave System and Wolf River Cave in the summer.

Indiana Bats, *Myotis sodalis*, use Cornstarch Cave in Fentress County as a winter hibernation site. Please do not enter this cave from September 1 through May 15. Wolf River Cave contains the second-largest hibernation colony of Indiana bats in the Southeast. In 2002 the winter colony numbers between 2,400 and 2,500 bats. Indiana Bats are also present in the Mountain Eye Cave System.

Rafinesque's Big-Eared Bats are present in the Mountain Eye Cave System and Wolf River Cave in the summer.

Figure 22.2. A cluster of bats in Wolf River Cave. Photo by Erin McKee, May 3, 2020.

Bears

At one time, Black Bears (*Ursus americanus*) were quite common in this area. However, hunters exterminated them from most of Tennessee by the early 1900s. They were reintroduced to the nearby Big South Fork National Recreation Area and are well established there. As they expand outward from there, in all likelihood they will again use caves as dens and hibernation sites.

Blind Cave Fish

The southern blind cave fish, *Typhlichthys subterraneus*, is likely present in this area, but is not mentioned in the Trip Reports for the caves listed in this book.

Cave Beetles

Tennessee caves contain a wide variety of cave beetles. In all likelihood, the caves in this study area contain cave beetles, no inventory has been

Figure 22.3. Two bats in Abbott Saltpeter Cave. Photo by Bob Biddix.

conducted, to my knowledge. Cave beetles are reported from Wolf River Cave.

Cave Crayfish

The stygobitic blind crayfish *Cambarus barri* is reported from Cornstarch Cave, Fentress County and Redbud Cave, Fentress County. Blind cave crayfish are also reported from Wolf River Cave.

Cave Crickets

There are six (6) distinct species of cave crickets in Tennessee. None of them have overlapping ranges.

The cave cricket *Hadenoecus opilionoides* is found in caves in Fentress, Overton and Pickett Counties. This is the only cave cricket known to occur in these counties.[1] This species also occurs in Clay, Putnam, Van Buren, and White Counties. (See Figure 22.1)

Cave Millipedes

Cave millipedes are common in Tennessee. In all likelihood, the caves in this study area contain cave millipedes, but there is no inventory of them in the caves in the area covered by this book.

Garland Cave Millipede (*Pseudotremia garlandae)* is reported from Redbud Cave, Fentress County.

Cave Rats

The cave rat is also known as the Allegheny Wood Rat, *Neotoma magister*. It is a cute little animal that looks (to me) a lot more like a hamster than a rat. Out West, this same animal is referred to as the Pack Rat, due to its habit of carrying various objects back to its nest. Cave rat nests are occasionally encountered in caves of this area and the nests tend to be close to an entrance where the animal can go outside to forage for food. Such an entrance may be Cave Rat sized, and not human sized.

---

1 Theodore H. Hubbell and Russell M. Norton, "The Systematics and Biology of the Cave-Crickets of the North American Tribe Hadenoecini (Orthoptera Saltaloria Ensifera: Rhaphidophoridae: Dolichopodinae)", Museum of Zoology, University of Michigan, 1978, 124 p.

Frogs

There are no true troglobitic frogs, but they can frequently be found in the entrances of moist caves. Sometimes they are washed deeper into caves by floodwaters.

Isopods

Isopods are frequently found in Tennessee caves. In all likelihood, they occurs in the caves in this study area, but there is no inventory of them in the caves in the area covered by this book.

Pseudoscorpions

Pseudoscorpions are arachnids. They have two pinchers in the front, like true scorpions, but they do not have a stinger and tail. They are very small and are rarely noticed by the average caver. A new species of pseudoscorpion was discovered by Kristen Bobo in Wolf River Cave in August 2013. (See Figure 22.4)

Wolf River Cave Pseudoscorpion (*Kleptochthonius bobo*) is reported from Wolf River Cave, Fentress County. (See Figure 22.4)

Raccoons

The raccoon (*Procyon lotor*) frequently ventures into caves and its footprints can be seen in the mud along cave streams. Somehow, they are able to navigate in total darkness and seem to have no trouble finding their way in and out of caves.

Figure 22.4. The Wolf River Cave Pseudoscorpion (Kleptochthonius bobo). Photo by Kristen Bobo, August, 2013.

Figure 22.5. A Cave Salamander in Briar Cave. Photo by Bob Biddix, May 23, 2020.

Figure 22.6. Spider with egg case in Russell Caverns. Photo by Bob Biddix, September 2, 2018.

Salamanders

The Cave Salamander (*Eurycea lucifuga*) is reported from Redbud Cave, Fentress County. (See Figure 22.5)

Spiders

Spiders are frequently encountered in caves. Some are true troglobites. (See Figure 22.6)

SUGGESTED READING

Charles E. Mohr and Thomas L. Poulson produced a wonderful book on these animals, titled *The Life of the Cave*. Mc-Graw-Hill Book Company published this book in cooperation with *The World Book Encyclopedia* in 1966. The book is part of a series of books, called "Our Living World of Nature." This book contains exquisite color photographs of cave life accompanied by a text that is easily read by the non-scientist. Although this book is out of print, you may be able to find it in your local library. If not copies are generally available at on-line book and auction sites.

Thomas C. Barr Jr.'s *Caves of Tennessee* (1961) contains a chapter titled "Animal Life In Tennessee Caves" on pages 28-54. It is an extremely helpful guide to the variety of cave life found in Tennessee caves.

Figure 22.7 . A cluster of bats in a Fentress County cave. Photo by Bob Biddix.

CHAPTER 23
The Geology of the Caves of the North Cumberland Plateau

THE BASICS OF CAVE FORMATION

The caves of the North Cumberland Plateau (and all major caves in Tennessee for that matter) are formed in limestone. Limestone in Tennessee tends to be a hard, grayish rock that occurs in layers, called "beds." Many of the road cuts in Fentress, Overton, and Pickett counties will show you a cross section of these limestone beds. Limestone is the rock that is quarried locally in these counties to make gravel, so if you live in this area, you see limestone rock outcrops and limestone gravel almost everywhere you go.

Limestone is a sedimentary rock. The term sedimentary rock simply means that these rocks form from material deposited by wind or water. For example, another sedimentary rock known as sandstone forms when wind or water has accumulated beds of sand grains that become buried and cemented together to form a hard rock. When deposits of clay particles become buried and cemented together to form a hard rock these sedimentary rocks are called shale. Limestone, however, forms in clear, warm tropical seas, such as occur in the Caribbean. It you were to travel to the Bahaman islands today, for example, you could observe limestone forming on the floor of the ocean. The source material for the limestone is the slow accumulation of corals and seashells. Occasionally, the mineral calcite precipitates directly from ocean water and accumulates on the ocean floor. These round pellets are called oolites. If you look carefully at the limestone rocks in this area, you will frequently see fossil shells, corals, and other traces of animals that lived in those prehistoric, tropical seas.

Now, you are probably asking yourself, "How could there have been a *tropical* sea over this portion of Tennessee? Tennessee is in the temperate zone, not the tropical zone." The answer to that question is what geologists refer to as "continental drift." The continents are not fixed in place. They "float" on the lower layers of the Earth and can actually move as much as a couple of inches each year. So over hundreds of millions of years they have moved thousands of miles. When the limestone deposits of this area formed during the time period known as the Mississippian Period, approximately 320 to 360 million years ago, what is now Tennessee was located close to the equator. The major beds of limestone on the escarpment of the Cumberland Plateau in which caves are formed are known as the Warsaw Limestone, St. Louis Limestone, Monteagle Limestone and the Bangor Limestone.

What makes limestone so uniquely suitable for the formation of caves is that it is slightly soluble in water. We are all familiar with items that are highly soluble: sugar and salt, for example. If you place a teaspoon of salt in a glass of water and stir for 30 seconds, it disappears. A chemist would say, "The salt went into solution." If you put that same glass of water in a pan on the stove and boiled it until the water all evaporated, the salt would stay behind as a deposit on the bottom of

Figure 23.1. Erica Sughrue stands beneath unusual lines on the ceiling of York Cave. Photo by Bob Biddix. (Facing page)

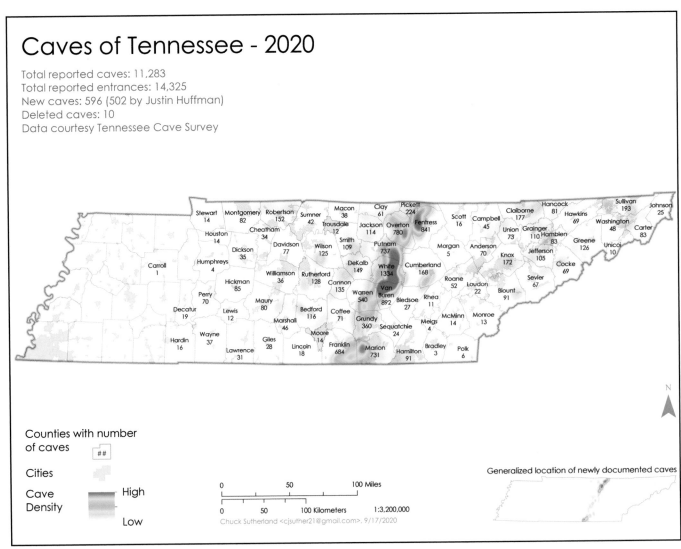

Caves of Tennessee - 2020

Total reported caves: 11,283
Total reported entrances: 14,325
New caves: 596 (502 by Justin Huffman)
Deleted caves: 10
Data courtesy Tennessee Cave Survey

Counties with number
of caves   ##

Cities

Cave
Density   High

Low

0   50   100 Miles

0   50   100 Kilometers   1:3,200,000

Chuck Sutherland <cjsuther21@gmail.com>, 9/17/2020

Generalized location of newly documented caves

N

Figure 23.2. Cave Density Map of Tennessee by Chuck Sutherland, 2020.

the pan. So the salt does not "go away", it just goes from a solid form to a dissolved form and back to a solid form. If you took a drink of water from the glass you would know instantly that the salt was in the water.

If you tried the same experiment with small pieces of limestone rock, you could stir the glass all day and you would not see any change. It would take months or even years for the same amount of limestone to dissolve, and you would have to use much more water. That is why we say limestone is only *slightly* soluble. However, when you have thousands and thousands of years available, the water naturally moving through the Earth's crust can dissolve and carry off the millions of tons of limestone necessary to create the large caves like those described in this book.

Limestone is barely soluble in pure water, but *pure* water is not present in nature. Rainwater dissolves carbon dioxide from the air, which makes a mild solution of carbonic acid. As the rainwater filters through the soil, the water becomes more acidic by picking up organic acids and more carbon dioxide. Therefore by the time the rainwater becomes groundwater, it is mildly acidic and can more easily dissolve limestone and form caves.

Although the area that is now Tennessee was underwater for at least 400 million years, it rose above sea level approximately 65 million years ago and has been above sea level ever since. During this time, erosion has worn down the surface to its present shape. But also, slightly acidic water has been dissolving away the limestone to form the many caves that we have now. In middle Tennessee, this water initially moves down the cracks in the limestone (geologists refer to these as "joints"), then move out horizontally along the spaces between the beds of limestone (geologists refer to these as "bedding planes"). Naturally, the water follows the easiest path and with time the water slowly dissolves the limestone and forms cave passages. Much of this solution to form large caves goes on beneath or close to the water table.

Once cave passages develop to the point that there is significant stream flow underground, physical erosion can also occur and speed the growth of the cave passages. As the surface stream cuts downward, the cave passages eventually become higher than the surface stream level. Then the water drains out of the cave passages leaving behind an air-filled cavity that we call a cave.

THE GEOLOGY OF THE NORTH CUMBERLAND PLATEAU

The Cumberland Plateau is a large, inland plateau that extends northward from Alabama and Georgia, through Tennessee, and into Kentucky. On its western edge in Tennessee, it is approximately 1,000 feet high and the bottom half of this escarpment exposes thick beds of limestone. In the North Cumberland Plateau area, both the Bangor limestone and the Monteagle Limestone are thick and for millions of years they have been subjected to erosion. This erosion has resulted in one of the more cave-rich areas in Tennessee. Not only are caves very numerous in this area but they can be exceptionally large.

In North America, the Carboniferous Period is conveniently subdivided into the Mississippian Sub-Period, which is dominated by marine sedimentary rocks and the Pennsylvanian Sub Period, which is dominated by terrestrial sedimentary rocks that are especially rich in beds of coal. The Pennsylvanian Sub Period occurred from approximately 325 million years ago to 286 million years ago, a time period of 39 million years.

The top of the Cumberland Plateau is relatively flat and consists of Pennsylvanian conglomerates, sandstones, and shales, with an occasional bed of coal. These rocks are not cave forming rocks and the top of the plateau is cave free, except for an occasional rock shelter. These Pennsylvanian formations form what geologists refer to as a caprock. These rocks are resistant to erosion and form a hard surface for the Cumberland Plateau. These Pennsylvanian formations formed at the mouths of ancient rivers, where rivers carrying their sediment loads from further inland built up thick delta deposits where the rivers emptied into the sea. These areas would have looked much like southern Louisiana today, where the Mississippi River deposits thick beds of sand and gravel, silt, and clay and where vast swamps accumulate organic matter, which will form future beds of coal.

The rain that falls on top of the Cumberland Plateau does not move downward into the ground

Figure 23.3. Erica Sughrue admires a large gypsum flower in an Unnamed Cave in the North Cumberland Plateau. Photo by Bob Biddix, February, 2011.

Geological Sequence for the Cumberland Plateau Escarpment in the Jamestown, TN Area

Name of Formation Age	Thickness
Rockcastle Conglomerate Pennsylvanian	200 +
Fentress Fm. Pennsylvanian	100-300
Pennington Fm. Mississippian	300
Bangor Ls. Mississippian	60-120
Hartselle Fm. Mississippian	30-60
Monteagle Ls. Mississippian	200
St. Louis Ls. Mississippian	90-120
Warsaw Ls. Mississippian	30 +

Figure 23.4. Geological Sequence for the Cumberland Plateau Escarpment in the Jamestown, TN area.

water, due to the impervious beds of shale in the Pennsylvanian formations, but tend to stay on, or close to the surface, and form surface streams which flow off the edge of the plateau and down the sides of the Cumberland Escarpment.

The underlying Mississippian formations make up the rest of the geologic column in the area. The Pennington Formation, which is the highest of the Mississippian Age formation contains sandstone, shales, and limestone and formed in a location close to shore. Caves can be found in the limestone of the Pennington Formation, but are rarely large. The Bangor Limestone is a thick limestone formation and was formed further from shore. Many large caves are formed in the Bangor limestone. The Hartselle Formation contains sandstones and shales and indicates near-shore

conditions. It prevents the movement of water downward from the Bangor limestone into the Monteagle Limestone. The Monteagle Limestone, which is located near the base of the Cumberland Escarpment is a very thick, cave-rich limestone. The Monteagle Limestone is the most important cave-bearing zone in Tennessee.

The sides of the Cumberland Plateau are relatively steep, and the thick Mississippian limestones are exposed, and this is where most of the caves covered in this book are located. If you look at Figure 23.1, the Cave Density Map of Tennessee, you will notice a distinct band of blue, yellow, and red running from Pickett County along the Tennessee border south-southwest to Franklin County along the Alabama border. This marks the western edge of the Cumberland Escarpment where the majority of Tennessee's caves are located.

Geological Sequence for the Cumberland Plateau Escarpment

This information is taken from the Geologic Map of the Jamestown Quadrangle, Tennessee, GM 115-NW. This map was prepared by Robert C. Milici and published by the Tennessee Division of Geology in 1992. This map is a good representation of the geological sequence of the entire area covered by this book (Fentress, Overton, and Pickett Counties). This sequence is given from the top down. The Rockcastle Conglomerate and the Fentress Formation are of Lower Pennsylvanian age. Everything beneath is Upper Mississippian.

The **Rockcastle Conglomerate** is 200 feet thick, or more in this area. It is "sandstone, fine- to coarse-grained to conglomeratic, with quartz pebbles up to 1/2-inch long. Commonly crossbedded or massively bedded, with some low-angle accretion beds. In places middle of formation contains 50 to 75 feet of medium dark- to dark-gray silty or sandy shale and Nemo coal bed."[1] But think: Massive sandstone and

1 Robert C. Milici, "Geologic Map of the Jamestown Quadrangle, Tennessee—GM 115-NW", TN Division of Geology, 1992.

Figure 23.5. Carol Lamers examines a large gypsum flower in an Unnamed Cave in the North Cumberland Plateau. Photo by Bob Biddix, February, 2011.

conglomerate. The cap-rock that holds up the top of the Cumberland Plateau. May form vertical cliffs at the top of the Escarpment. No caves here!

The **Fentress Formation** is anywhere from 100 to 300 feet thick in this area. It is "shale, silty, medium- to medium dark-gray and olive-gray, medium-gray to olive-gray sandy siltstone; and fine-grained light-gray sandstone, all lithologies commonly rippled and burrowed; contains lower Wilder and Wilder coal beds."[2] But think: Shales and sandstones with two layers of coal. No caves here!

The **Pennington Formation** is about 300 feet thick in this area. It is "mostly shale, greenish-gray, grayish-red to grayish-purple, with a few interbeds of medium-gray to very fine- to medium-grained fossiliferous limestone, medium gray siltstone and silty, light olive-gray to yellowish-gray microcrystalline to fine-grained dolomite."[3] But think: Mostly shale, not usually a cave-forming horizon.

The **Bangor Limestone** is about 60 to 120 feet thick in this area. It is "limestone, very fine- to coarse grained medium-to medium dark gray, some oolitic or bioclastic, some argillaceous, generally medium- to thick-bedded, some crossbedded, slightly cherty, with a few thin interbeds of medium-gray shale."[4] But think: Mostly good, cave-forming limestone.

The **Hartselle Formation** is about 30 to 60 feet thick in this area. It is "limestone, sandy to silty, fine- to medium-grained; weathers to yellowish-brown, crossbedded sandstone, in places grade into medium-gray to live-gray shale."[5] But think: The beds that divide the Bangor Limestone from the Monteagle Limestone and prevent the downward movement of groundwater.

The **Monteagle Limestone** is about 200 feet thick in this area. It is "limestone, very fine- to

coarse-grained, medium, light gray, some oolitic or bioclastic, with a few interbeds of yellowish-gray, very fine-grained dolomite, generally medium- to thick-bedded, some crossbedded, with spongy fossiliferous chert (Lost River Chert of Elrod) near base."[6] But think: Thick-bedded limestone ideal for cave development.

The **St. Louis Limestone** is about 90 to 120 feet thick in this area. It is "dolomite, fine-grained, light- to medium-gray and fine-grained, medium-gray limestone; black, nodular to ropey chert, medium- to thick-bedded, some with abundant *Lithostrotion*."[7] But think: Dolomitic limestone is also good for cave development.

The **Warsaw Limestone** is the lowest formation exposed in this area. It is 30 plus feet thick, but the bottom is not exposed. It is "limestone, and some dolomite, fine- to medium-grained, medium-gray, some bioclastic, silty or sandy, generally medium-bedded; weathers to yellowish-brown siltstone or very fine-grained sandstone."[8] But think: This would be a good cave horizon if it was better exposed.

THE OBEY RIVER KARST

Geologist John Hoffelt wrote the following excellent description of the Obey River Karst:

> The Obey River Karst is located along the East Fork of the Obey River. This is a north flowing tributary of the Cumberland River near the western edge of the Cumberland Plateau. The river has incised a deep gorge in the relatively flat-lying Mississippian limestone and a number of significantly large and long caves have formed adjacent to the bottom of the gorge.
>
> Major caves include Xanadu, Zarathustra, and Mountain Eye, with a combined length of more than 75 km. They have developed

2 Ibid.

3 Ibid.

4 Ibid.

5 Ibid.

6 Ibid.

7 Ibid.

8 Ibid.

at several levels, with the lowest still actively draining the plateau. What makes these caves unique is the large amount of sediment in their upper levels. Dating of the sediment with cosmogenic nuclides by Anthony and Granger (2004) indicates episodic incision pulses up the Obey River and Caney Fork and confirms ages of late Tertiary to Pleistocene for the upper-level cave passages. Xanadu has nearly 39 km of mapped passages. It is known for its large passages up to about 30 m high and wide and nearly filled with breakdown and sandy clay in several places. This requires much grueling climbing up and down steep slopes, over and over.

The local hydrology is typical for the Cumberland Plateau. Water collects on Pennsylvanian sandstones, shales and conglomerates, runs off, and sinks where it reaches the Bangor limestone. The water descends until it reaches the underlying Hartselle Sandstone, which restricts downward flow. During low flow the East Fork of the Obey River sinks into the massive Monteagle Limestone after breaching the Hartselle Sandstone. It flows underground, leaving a 10-km stretch of dry channel with the caves adjacent to it. This is one of the largest and longest dry rivers in the Appalachians. The river water resurges at the large Enchanted Spring with overflow at Dragons Breath Cave.

During large rain events the sink point overflows quickly, and the normally dry bed becomes active. Although the caves are now mainly dry, the lower level of Mountain Eye can rapidly flood because it carries at least some of the water from the underground Obey River. There must be an extensive flooded system that carries the river water

beneath the dry valley (Sasowsky, 1990).

From the study of the caves along the East Fork of the Obey River, Sasowsky and White (1994) developed a hypothesis that caves in the Cumberland Plateau tend to form master conduits at distinct levels downdip and subparallel to the overlying valleys. The caves are thought to form along geologically young stress-release fractures developed beneath the valley due to unloading as the valley deepens. As evidence they cite the concordance of the main cave passages in Xanadu and Zarathustra Caves with the topographic contours of the surface valleys. They cite other studies that show fractures strongly concordant with local topography and concentrated along the axes of valleys.[9]

Understanding the geology of this area will help you to appreciate both how the caves formed and where to look for new caves.

SUGGESTED READING

Without a doubt, the book "Caves and Karst of the USA," Edited by Arthur N. Palmer and Margaret V. Palmer and published by the National Speleological Society in 2009, is the best single guide to caves and karst in the United States. This book should be in every serious caver's library. On pages 85-94 you will find the section on "The Cumberland Plateau of Tennessee" by John Hoffelt. This book is still In-Print and available from the NSS Bookstore at the time this book went to press. The entire book in 445 pages long and is an incredibly useful reference book.

---

9 John Hoffelt, "The Obey River Karst" published in "Caves and Karst of the USA", Edited by Arthur N. Palmer and Margaret V. Palmer (2009), pp 89-90.

Figure 24.1. Erica Sughrue admires an incredibly long gypsum flower petal in a cave in the North Cumberland Plateau. Photo by Bob Biddix.

CHAPTER 24
Epilogue

The North Cumberland Plateau, specifically Fentress County, Overton County, and Pickett County as featured in this book are exceptionally beautiful both above and below ground. Compared to some other parts of Tennessee, they remain remarkably pristine. Many large, remarkable caves are found here, as you have seen in this book. But getting there, in this beautiful countryside is half the fun! There are wonderful above-ground places to visit, too.

Despite the relatively remote location of many of these caves, they were well-known during the time of saltpeter production, especially during the War of 1812. Much works remains to properly survey and document this mining activity before foot traffic through these caves slowly, but surely, obliterates it. Much more work remains to properly explore and map these caves. No doubt, many thrilling discoveries wait to be made.

Slowly, but surely, my goal of documenting the history of cave exploration in Tennessee is nearing completion. The remaining titles in this series of books will be "Caves of the Central Cumberland Plateau" and "Caves of the South Cumberland Plateau".

Happy caves to you, until we meet again!!!

APPENDIX A
Do You Want To Be A Caver?

The fact that you are reading this book and are interested in the caves of the North Cumberland Plateau is an indication that you may want to become a cave explorer. Exploring caves can be a lot of fun; but, unfortunately, it can also be dangerous if you are not properly trained and equipped. There is a national organization, the National Speleological Society (NSS), that can provide you with information on local chapters in your area and can put you in contact with local cave explorers. They can be reached easily by email at **NSS@CAVES.ORG**

If you are not a computer user, you can contact the NSS by mail or telephone.

> **The National Speleological Society**
> **6001 Pulaski Pike NW**
> **Huntsville, AL 95810-1122**
> **256-852-1300**

The NSS has a bookstore that sells books on caving and caving techniques. Several suppliers of caving equipment advertise on the NSS web site, and in NSS publications. The NSS web site is located at:

> **HTTP://WWW.CAVES.ORG**

If you decide to explore caves, please remember the NSS' motto:

> Take nothing but pictures
> Leave nothing but footprints
> Kill nothing but time

Tennessee is located in one of the most cave rich areas of the world. The NSS has active chapters (grottos) in Chattanooga, Cookeville, Knoxville, Livingston, Nashville, Oak Ridge, Pikeville, Sewanee, and Spencer, that you may wish to join, if you live in this area. The NSS web site can give you up-to-date information on how to contact a grotto in your area. Never go into a cave without proper training and proper equipment. Some commercial caves offer wild cave tours. These tours are an outstanding way to learn safe caving techniques from experts before you venture out into wild caves on your own.

> *Have fun and be safe.*

Figure A.1. This expert caver, Keith Filson, is ascending a rope in Robinson Cave. Can you identify all of the equipment he is using? Would you know how to safely rig this drop, as shown in this photo? If the answer is "NO", please seek instruction from qualified cavers before ever trying this on your own. Photo by Bob Biddix, November 8, 2014.

Figure B1. Alfred Crabtree stands by a stubby stalagmite in Wolf River Cave. Photo by Chuck Sutherland, July 7, 2012..

APPENDIX B
Glossary

A

Acetylene – A flammable gas (C_2H_2) formed by combining carbide and water.

Anastamoses – A very wavy, irregular, bedding plane between two beds of limestone.

Anthodite – A cave formation consisting of radiating or branching crystals of calcite or aragonite.

Anticline – An upward, convex fold in sedimentary rocks.

Aragonite – A mineral composed of calcium carbonate ($CaCO_3$), the same as calcite, but forming orthorhombic crystals instead of hexagonal crystals as calcite does.

Archaeologist – A scientist who studies human history and prehistory.

Archaeology – The science that studies the material remains of past human life.

Ascenders – Mechanical clamping devices for ropes with a ratcheting action that allows them to be raised easily, but to lock when weight is applied. They are placed on the rope then attached to the body and feet with slings.

B

Bacon Rind – A thin, banded, flowstone formation that resembles a strip of bacon.

Bat – A nocturnal, flying mammal of many different species. They frequently spend the daylight hours inside caves and some hibernate inside caves during the winter.

Bedding Plane – The contact between two layers of sedimentary rocks.

Belly Crawl – A crawlway so low that it can only be negotiated flat on your stomach.

Biology – The science that studies the living organisms of the Earth.

Blue Hole – A Blue Hole is a sinkhole that extends down beneath the water table. Frequently, cave passages lead off underwater from these features. Their name derives from their appearance when viewed from an airplane.

Bolt – A metal pin, usually about ¼ inch wide and 1 inch long, driven into a hole drilled into rock. Used to provide a point of support where no natural anchor is available.

Bolt Climb – To climb a vertical, or even overhanging, wall, by placing bolts progressively higher and using them to anchor the rope.

Borehole – A very large walking passage.

Breakdown – A pile of rocks in a cave room or passage, formed by the collapse of the cave roof.

Breakdown Block – An individual piece of rock in a pile of breakdown.

Breakdown Slope – A sloping surface inside a cave, composed of or covered by breakdown.

C

Cable Ladder – A flexible ladder consisting of two small steel cables with small, aluminum rungs. These are available commercially in 10-meter sections. They can be rolled into a small bundle for easy transport through a cave. Two, or more, sections can be connected to make longer lengths.

Calcite – A mineral composed of calcium carbonate ($CaCO_3$), which is the main component of limestone. Calcite is also the main component of most cave formations, such as stalactites and stalagmites.

Canyon – A cave passage that is several times as high as it is wide.

Carabiner – A metal snap link used in technical climbing, especially to rig ropes.

Carbide – A man-made chemical, calcium carbide (CaC_2). Reacts with water to form acetylene gas. $CaC_2 + H_2O = C_2H_2 + CaO$.

Carbide Lamp – A lamp, usually manufactured from brass, which combines carbide and water to produce acetylene gas, which burns with a very bright flame.

Cave – A naturally occurring cavity in the Earth's crust, which is large enough to permit human exploration.

Cave Cricket – A species of cricket specifically adapted for life in caves. During mild weather some species of cave crickets leave their cave at night to forage for food on the Earth's surface.

Cave System – A group of caves connected by exploration. Frequently used to describe a large cave with several entrances.

Caver – A person who explores caves. This is the term cave explorers use to describe themselves.

Cavern – A term used to denote a very large or extensive cave.

Chamber – A large, room-like portion of a cave.

Charcoal – A black, organic substance formed by burning wood in an oxygen poor environment, resulting in incomplete combustion. Charcoal is composed primarily of organic carbon.

Chert – A microscopically grained quartz mineral (SiO_2) of various colors that forms beds, lenses, and nodules in limestone. Frequently used by prehistoric peoples to make stone tools.

Chimney – n. A passage narrow enough that you can climb up or down by placing your hands and feet on the opposite walls.

v. To climb up or down by placing your hands and feet on the opposite walls of a cave passage. The back is also occasionally used as a point of contact.

Clay – A very small, microscopic grain of sediment or dirt, usually composed of hydrated aluminum silicates.

Climb – n. A vertical section of a cave that requires climbing skills to ascend or to descent.

v. To ascend or descend a vertical section of a cave.

Column – A cave formation that extends from the ceiling to the floor.

Commercial Cave – A cave that has all or part of its passages developed with walkways, steps, and lights and is open to the public for guided tours. A show cave.

Connection – A naturally occurring passage which, when discovered, connects two caves which were previously considered separate caves.

Conservation – The preservation and wise use of our natural resources.

Crawl – n. A horizontal section of cave that requires crawling on your hands and knees or stomach to negotiate, due to a very low ceiling height.

v. To move on your hands and knees or your stomach.

Crawlway – A cave passage that is so low that cave explorers must crawl on their hands and knees or stomachs.

Crystal – The solid form of a mineral, which displays symmetrically arranged plane surfaces. This external shape is determined by the internal atomic structure.

Curtain – A thin, wide, frequently wavy speleothem hanging from the ceiling or wall and resembling a curtain. Also called a drapery.

D

Dendrochronology – A method for dating wood by comparing the width of the growth rings.

Dome – A vertical passage extending upward from the ceiling of a cave passage or room.

Domepit – A vertical passage extending both upward and downward in a cave passage or room.

Drapery – A thin, wide, frequently wavy speleothem hanging from the ceiling or wall and resembling a drapery. Also called a curtain.

Dripstone – Cave formations composed of calcite or aragonite, formed when dripping water deposits dissolved limestone.

Drop – A pit or a cliff that must be rigged with rope or a ladder to descend.

E

Entrance – A point where a cave opens to the surface and is large enough to permit human passage.

Escarpment – A steep slope, usually with cliffs, that separates two relatively level areas of different elevations.

F

Fill – Secondary deposits of sediment in a cave passage, usually consisting of clay, silt, sand, gravel, or a combination of two or more of these.

Flint – A lustrous, microscopically grained quartz mineral (SiO_2), usually gray of black, which forms beds, lenses, and nodules in limestone.

Flowstone – A cave formation composed of calcite or aragonite, formed when flowing water deposits dissolved limestone.

Formation – A secondary mineral feature in a cave, such as stalactites, stalagmites, columns, helictites, soda straws, shields, bacon rind, and the like.

Fluorescein Dye – A fluorescent, organic dye frequently used in groundwater tracing studies.

It is a red powder in the pure state and a bright, yellow-green in the dissolved state.

Fossil – The remains or traces of animals and plants that lived in prehistoric times.

Fossil Trunk – A trunk passage that no longer carries water, even during flood events, and is now high and dry.

G

Geologist – A scientist who specializes in the study of geology.

Geology – The science that studies the structure, history, and origin of the Earth.

Gibbs Ascender – A brand of mechanical ascender. It will slide up the rope but not down, unless all weight is released.

Grotto – A term used to describe a single cave room. Also the term used for a chapter of the National Speleological Society.

Ground Water – Any water below the surface of the ground.

Guano – The accumulated excrement of cave-dwelling animals, especially bats.

Gypsum – A mineral composed of hydrous calcium sulphate ($CaSO_4$-H_2O), which forms colorless to white crusts and crystals in a variety of forms.

Gypsum Crust – A layer of fibrous or crystalline gypsum that can occur on cave walls and ceilings.

Gypsum Flower – A flower-like group of curved gypsum crystals.

H

Hand Hold – A projection, depression, or other irregularity in the rock that can be used by a climber to support himself with his hand.

Hard Hat – A protective helmet worn by cave explorers to protect their heads from bumping the ceiling in low passages, from falling rock dislodged by cavers climbing above them, and in case of a fall.

Helictite – A cave formation that grows in bizarre, twisting shapes apparently without regard to gravity.

Horror Hole – A cave that is tight, wet, muddy, and with multiple drops that is extremely difficult and dangerous to explore.

Hydrology – The scientific study of water and its distribution and movement.

I

Instant Cave – Explosives used to enlarge a tight spot in a cave so that it is large enough for human passage.

J

Joint – A fracture in sedimentary rocks, usually perpendicular to the bedding planes.

Jumar Ascender – A brand of mechanical ascender. It will slide up the rope, but not down, unless the release button is pushed.

K

Karst – A type of topography found in areas of limestone bedrock, characterized by caves, sinking streams, sinkholes, and other features.

Karst Window – A relatively large sinkhole, sometimes with vertical sides, that opens all the way down to the water table in an area of karst

L

Lapiez – A surface composed of weathered limestone.

Leach – To remove minerals by dissolving them in water.

Lead – An unexplored passage in a cave.

Ledge – A horizontal projection along the side of a wall.

Limestone – A sedimentary rock composed primarily of calcite.

Limestone Pavement – A relatively flat area where limestone is exposed at the surface.

Lower Level – A series of cave passages developed at a lower elevation than the rest of the cave.

M

Map – n. A two-dimensional representation of a cave, showing its horizontal extent that may include cross-sectional representation to also show the vertical extent.

v. To gather the data necessary to draw a map.

Moni-sized – A restriction in a cave passage that has been enlarged enough that even Gerald Moni can fit through.

N

National Speleological Society – An organization of cave explorers and speleologists, founded in 1941, to promote the exploration, preservation, and scientific study of caves. NSS.

Native Americans – This is the "politically correct" term for the people who lived in North America before the arrival of Europeans in 1492. These people prefer to be known as American Indians.

Nitrates – Chemical compounds that contain the NO_3^- ion. Nitrate minerals are highly soluble in water.

Nitrogen A colorless, odorless gas that makes up 78% of the Earth's atmosphere.

NSS – The National Speleological Society.

O

Onyx – A term use to describe lustrous, sometimes layered, flowstone.

P

Paleontologist – A scientist who studies fossils to learn about the history of life on Earth.

Paleontology – The science that studies the history of life on Earth.

Palette – A disk-shaped flowstone formation, usually growing from the wall of a cave. Also referred to as a shield.

Passage – A horizontal section of cave.

Phreatic – Refers to water below the water table. Also, cave passages that form beneath the water table.

Pit – A vertical passage extending downward from the surface, the floor of a cave passage, or the floor of a cave room.

Pitch – A vertical section of cave that requires difficult climbing or rope to negotiate.

Piton – A metal spike, pointed on one end and with a ring or opening on the other end. It is driven into a crack in the rock with a hammer and a carabiner is attached to the end to provide a point of attachment for a climbing rope.

Polje – A very large, flat-bottomed, closed depression in a karst landscape.

Popcorn – An irregular flowstone or gypsum formation with many rounded knob-like surfaces.

Prussik – To ascend a rope by any of a variety of methods.

Prussik Knot – A knot that will slide easily when there is no weight on it, but that will hold securely when weight is placed on it. By using two or three Prussik knots, a climber can ascend a standing rope.

R

Rappel – To descend a rope by any of a variety of methods.

Rhodamine WT Dye – An organic red dye used for tracing ground water flow.

Rig – To secure ropes or cable ladders so that a drop can be safely descended and ascended.

Rimstone – A raised flowstone edge surrounding a pool of water.

Rimstone Dam – A naturally formed flowstone dam occurring at the downstream edge of a cave pool.

Rimstone Pool – A pool of water surrounded by a raised edge of flowstone.

Rock – The solid material that forms the Earth's crust.

Rock Shelter – A rock overhang that resembles a cave entrance but does not open into an actual cave.

Room – A room-shaped opening in a cave.

S

Saltpeter – A naturally occurring mineral, calcium nitrate $Ca(NO_3)_2$, used in the manufacture of gunpowder.

Saltpeter Cave – A cave with enough saltpeter in the dirt to have been mined commercially.

Saltpetre – A spelling of saltpeter that was widely used in the 1800s.

Sandstone – A sedimentary rock composed primarily of cemented sand grains.

Scallops – Shallow, rounded pockets in a cave wall, formed when water was flowing in the cave passage.

Sedimentary Rock – A rock formed by the deposit of water-borne and/or wind-borne particles or by the accumulation of chemically or organically precipitated materials.

Selenite – A clear, colorless variety of gypsum, occurring in distinct, transparent, monoclinic crystals.

Shale – A sedimentary rock composed primarily of cemented clay particles.

Shield – A disk-shaped flowstone formation, usually growing from the wall of a cave. Also referred to as a palette.

Show Cave – A commercial cave.

Side Passage – A cave passage that leads off of another cave passage.

Silt – A small grain of sediment or dirt, approximately the size of a particle of flour. Larger than clay particles, but small than sand grains.

Sink – n. An abbreviated form of the term sinkhole.
> v. For a surface stream to disappear underground.

Sinkhole – A surface depression in an area of limestone rock formed either by solution as water drains underground or by the collapse of a cave passage or room.

Sinkhole Plain – An area of relatively flat topography with numerous sinkholes.

Sinking Stream – A surface stream that abruptly disappears and goes underground into a cave.

Siphon – A section of water-filled cave passage connecting two section of cave passage with air is frequently referred to as a siphon. However, true siphons rarely, if ever, occur in caves. The more proper name for these water-filled sections of cave passage is a *sump*.

Skylight – A natural opening to the surface in the ceiling of a cave passage or room.

Soda Straw – A thin, hollow stalactite, similar in size and shape to a drinking straw.

Soluble – Capable of being dissolved, usually referring to water.

Speleogenesis – The origin and development of caves.

Speleologist – A scientist who studies some aspect of caves, such as their biology, geology, meteorology, and the like.

Speleology – The scientific study of caves, their origins, and their features.

Speleothem – A secondary mineral deposit in a cave.

Spelunker – A person who explores caves. Cave explorers rarely use this term to describe themselves, preferring instead to call themselves cavers.

Spring – A place where water naturally flows out from underground onto the Earth's surface.

Squeeze – n. A section of cave passage so small that it is just barely possible to fit through.
> v. To move through a very small section of cave passage.

Squeezeway – A passage so small and tight that the explorers must squeeze to get through it.

Stalactite – An icicle-shaped cave formation that hangs down from the ceiling.

Stalagmite – A conical-shaped cave formation that grows upward from the floor.

Stoke Marks – Black marks left on the wall where Prehistoric Indians tapped their cane torches to remove excess embers from the end.

Stoopway – A cave passage that is too low to stand up completely, but not as low as a crawlway.

Suck – If air flows into the entrance of a cave, that cave is said to suck.

Suckhole – A cave that is miserable to explore and has few, if any, redeeming features.

Sump – A section of cave passage that is completely filled with water.

Survey – n. A map prepared by using an accurate compass, a measuring tape, a clinometer, and sketches.
> v. To prepare an accurate survey or map.

Survey Station – A point in the cave from which compass direction, inclination, and distance are measured to the next point.

V

Surveyed – A cave or cave passages that have been accurately mapped.

Swallet – An opening in a karst area where a surface stream disappears underground. Also known as a swallow hole.

T

Terminal Breakdown – A breakdown that completely blocks a cave passage.

Topographic Map – A map that represents the surface of the Earth by using lines to indicate points of equal elevation at selected intervals. These lines are referred to as contour lines.

Totem Pole – A tall, cylindrical stalagmite.

Trunk – A large, main passage in a cave that extends for a long distance compared to other passages.

Traverse – n. A difficult ledge or section of wall that must be crossed to continue exploring a cave.
    v. To move across a difficult ledge or to move laterally across a wall.

U

Unsurveyed – A cave or cave passages that have not been accurately mapped.

Upper Level – A series of cave passages developed at a higher level than the rest of the cave.

Vadose – Refers to cave passages that form above the water table.

Vandal – A person who vandalizes a cave.

Vandalism – Altering a cave, either accidentally or intentionally, by breaking formations, leaving trash, writing on walls, or otherwise changing the original appearance of the cave.

Vat – A container built to hold cave dirt to allow water to percolate through the dirt and remove the nitrate minerals.

Virgin Passage – Cave passage that has not been entered previously.

W

Walking Passage – A cave passage large enough to walk without stooping.

Walltites – An icicle-shaped cave formation that hangs down from the wall.

Water Table – The horizontal plane beneath which all open spaces in the Earth are filled with water.

Wild Cave – A cave that has not been developed for guided tours. Also, any portion of a commercial cave that has not been developed for guided tours.

Figure C1. Stephen and Anya Webb stand by a white stalagmite in the Enchanted Forest of Wolf River Cave. Photo by Chuck Sutherland, June 30, 2018.

APPENDIX C
Other Books By This Author

BIG BONE CAVE, 2006, National Speleological Society, Huntsville, Alabama, 220 pages. *ISBN 978-1-879961-24-1*

The fascinating story of America's largest saltpeter mine, located 50 miles north of Chattanooga. Also the site of the discovery of giant ground sloth skeletons, an Ice-Age jaguar skeleton, and several American Indian mummies. The book includes many photographs and maps.

BLUE SPRING CAVE, 2010, National Speleological Society, Huntsville, Alabama, 346 pages. Coauthored with Bill Walter. *ISBN 978-1-879961-36-4 (Soft Cover)* *ISBN 978-1-879961-37-1 (Hard Cover)*

Blue Spring Cave is Tennessee's longest mapped cave with over 35 miles of surveyed passages. Although its natural entrance has been known since prehistoric times, only 500 feet of cave had been explored as recently as 1989. In that year a group of cavers pushed a tight, blowing crawlway at the rear of the cave and discovered miles and miles of fantastic, virgin cave passages. This book is the complete story of that exploration. It is lavishly illustrated with photographs and maps.

CAVES OF CHATTANOOGA, 2007, National Speleological Society, Huntsville, Alabama, 198 pages. *ISBN 978-1-879961-27-2*

The exploration, use, and commercial development of nine Chattanooga-area caves. Learn how for 8,000 years, the caves were used by the Cherokees until their relocation in 1838; how settlers explored and used these caves; how the caves were mined for saltpeter, the main ingredient of gunpowder, during both the War of 1812 and the Civil War. Read never-before-published stories of fascinating discoveries deep inside Lookout Mountain. Be amazed by the Great Cave Hoax of 1927. Included are the complete stories of Lookout Mountain Cave, Mystery Falls Cave, Ruby Falls Cave, Raccoon Mountain Caverns, Nickajack Cave, Sequoyah Caverns, Mystic Caverns, Russell Cave, and Wonder Cave.

CAVES OF FALL CREEK FALLS, 2016, National Speleological Society, Huntsville, Alabama, 322 pages. *ISBN 978-1-68044-007-2*

The greater Fall Creek Falls area has the largest number of caves of any public land in Tennessee. The many large, interesting caves combined with the stunning wilderness area makes this a Caver's Paradise. The roughly 15 miles wide by 16 miles long area covered in this book contains 1,184 known caves, 12 of which are over a mile long.

Modern cave explorers have been unraveling the secrets of these caves since the early 1950s. Exploration, mapping, and dye tracing show two huge underground drainage systems: one in the valley of the Caney Fork River and the other in the valley of Cane Creek. This book describes those caves and their hydrological connections.

This book is not only about these caves, but also the cavers who explored them. There are tales of secrecy and mistrust as rival groups of cavers sought to hide their discoveries from others. There is also the story of the development of land adjacent to Fall Creek Falls State Park by greedy and unscrupulous developers who threatened to ruin the groundwater.

Come along for thrilling tales of exploration and adventure.

CAVES OF GRASSY COVE, 2014, National Speleological Society, Huntsville, Alabama, 286 pages.
ISBN 978-1-879961-49-4

Grassy Cove is the largest sinkhole in North America. It is 3 miles wide and 6 miles long. All of the precipitation falling into Grassy Cove and draining into Grassy Cove flows into Mill Cave and reappears 7 miles to the south to form the headwaters of the Sequatchie River. Dye traces show that water sinking underground in Haley Cove and Bat town Cove another 4 miles to the north also join into this system.

The erosional processes that formed Grassy Cove have created a vast, underground network of caves that is still being explored today. Cavers are still discovering new caves and new passageways. They all hope to be the one to find a way into the main Mill Cave Trunk, still mostly inaccessible at this time.

CAVES OF THE HIGHLAND RIM, 2019, National Speleological Society, Huntsville, Alabama, 290 pages.
ISBN 978-1-68044-01206

Nashville, Tennessee sits in a geographic basin known as the Nashville Basin. As you leave this basin, in any direction you go you rise nearly 300 feet onto a feature known as the Highland Rim.

The escarpment for this feature exposes several layers of thick-bedded limestone which are well-suited for the development of caves. Outstanding among these layers is the Bigby-Cannon Limestone.

This book describes several dozen of the larger and more interesting caves developed in this Highland Rim. Some of these caves were explored in prehistoric times by the Indians. Others were used by the early pioneers for the production of saltpeter, the main ingredient of gunpowder. Modern exploration began in earnest in the 1950s and continues today. This is the story of the exploration of these caves, told in the words of the original explorers and surveyors wherever possible.

Caves of the Highland Rim is lavishly illustrated with 265 maps and photographs. Come long for thrilling tales of exploration and adventure.

CAVES OF KNOXVILLE AND THE GREAT SMOKY MOUNTAINS, 2008, National Speleological Society, Huntsville, Alabama, 304 pages.
ISBN 978-1-879961-30-2

The history of the exploration, use, and commercial development of fourteen caves in the Knoxville/Great Smoky Mountains area. Learn how these caves were used by American Indians for 8,000 years, how Daniel Boone explored these caves and opened the first saltpeter mine west of the Appalachian Mountains, how settlers explored and used these caves, how caves were mined for saltpeter, the main ingredient of gunpowder, during both the War of 1812 and the Civil War.

Included are the complete stories of Cherokee Caverns, English Cave, Gap Cave, Indian Cave, Meredith Cave, New Mammoth Cave, Alum Cave, Forbidden Caverns, Gregorys Cave, The Lost Sea, Tuckaleechee Caverns, Appalachian Caverns, Bristol Caverns, and Morrill Cave.

CUMBERLAND CAVERNS, Third Edition, 2010, Greyhound Press, Bloomington, Indiana, 196 pages.
ISBN 978-0-9663547-5-1 (Soft Cover)
ISBN 978-0-9663547-6-8 (Hard Cover)

The story of how this cave, first discovered by Aaron Higgenbotham in 1810, has grown to become one of the world's largest and most famous caverns, including historical anecdotes from the 1800s and the modern exploration during the 1900s. Features fourteen full-page maps and numerous photographs, including fourteen in full color. The First Edition was published in 1989 by the National Speleological Society. The Second Edition was published in 2005 by Greyhound Press.

DESCRIPTIONS OF TENNESSEE CAVES, 1971, Tennessee Division of Geology, Nashville, Tennessee, 150 pages.

This book provides descriptions of 316 caves, along with numerous maps and photographs. There is a special section on the history of saltpeter mining in Tennessee during both the War of 1812 and the Civil War. Although this book was first published in 1971, it has been reprinted numerous times and is still in print.

DUNBAR CAVE: THE SHOWPLACE OF THE SOUTH, Second Edition, 2011. National Speleological Society, Huntsville, Alabama, 240 pages.
ISBN 978-1-879961-41-8

This is the fascinating story of how this cave, first explored by Native Americans 8,000 years ago, grew to become one of America's major caves. Includes the complete story, maps, and photographs as modern explorers add miles of passage to this former show cave that had been explored for the last 150 years. Featured are recently discovered Indian Glyphs, the Big Band Era (1931-1947), and the Roy Acuff Era (1948-1966). This cave is currently a Tennessee State Park and is open to the public.

SNAIL SHELL CAVE, 2012, National Speleological Society, Huntsville, Alabama, 246 pages. Co-authored with Bob Biddix.
ISBN 978-1-879961-44-9

This book describes the complete history of the exploration of Snail Shell Cave and the other caves that comprise the Snail Shell Cave System. This vast underground drainage system begins near Eagleville and flows northeast for 13 miles to emerge as a huge spring on the bank of the West Fork of the Stones River. Approximately one-fourth of Rutherford County Tennessee is drained by this complex, three-dimensional system. Serious exploration began in the 1950s by NSS members and continues today, with cave divers making startling new discoveries.

ORDERING INFORMATION

All of these books may be ordered directly from the National Speleological Society's Bookstore. The NSS web site is located at:

HTTP://WWW.CAVES.ORG

INDEX